DO OR DIE

The escort and prisoners get slowly under way. Schübler's brain is working feverishly. If he lets himself and his men be taken to the commissar, then in a few minutes the Russians will know they are Germans, and that they have put on Russian uniforms to infiltrate Soviet territory. If, on the other hand, they open fire, then they will not only be disobeying orders but possibly also betraying all their countrymen who are roaming behind the Demarcation Line this perilous night.

What was he to do for God's sake?

Then the Oberleutnant reaches for his machine pistol, as if adjusting the strap. His fingers are quicker than his brain. His lips become a thin gash of determination. He's a soldier not a murderer, but if he wants to survive he has no choice but to pull that trigger . . .

Also by Will Berthold in Sphere Books:

PRINCE—ALBRECHT—STRASSE
DEATH'S HEAD BRIGADE
EAGLES OF THE REICH
LEBENSBORN
BROTHERHOOD OF BLOOD
THE GOLDEN EAGLES
INFERNO I: BLITZKRIEG!

Inferno II: Bloody Turning Point

WILL BERTHOLD

Translated by Fred Taylor

SPHERE BOOKS LIMITED
London and Sydney

First published in Great Britain by
Sphere Books Ltd 1986
30–32 Gray's Inn Road, London WC1X 8JL
First published in Germany under the title
Inferno: Siege und Niederlagen

TRADE
MARK

Set in Plantin

Printed and bound in Great Britain by
Collins, Glasgow

The Sea Lion Who Didn't Like Water

The briefing meeting on the Contentin Peninsula, where fighter bases sit cheek by jowl during the Battle of Britain, is short and without much joy. Always the same crap: attached to the main force, nurse-maiding over the Channel and then back. The fighters are supposed to protect the big bombers, but their tanks only carry enough fuel to allow them twenty minutes over Churchill's Island, without allowing for combat manoeuvring. They have to turn back quickly, leaving their charges to their own devices, and hope they'll reach home on the last of their fuel. The neighbouring squadron lost four Me 109s yesterday – not because they were shot down by the enemy but because they plunged into the sea with empty tanks just before they reached the coast.

And when the bombers came back, the fighter boys were forced to listen to complaints about the lack of protection. The complaints were unfair. No one can fly further than his fuel will allow, and Reich Marshal Göring's order for the fastest to stick with their slower comrades, no matter what, is asking for trouble.

Squadron Leader Michalski, who's crazy and has a touch of real guts, has become famous throughout the entire Luftwaffe because in the officers' mess a few days before he bearded his C-in-C in public and told him that the Reich Marshal's new tactics were 'unnecessary, and about as much use as a eunuch at an orgy'.

The Oberleutnant is one of those experts they call fighter aces, and his men worship him – not just because he's got a whole lot of pretty medals. These 'collar-and-tie soldiers' – as they are known with bemused admiration by other branches of the Wehrmacht – have plenty of medals of their own, plus the smartest uniforms, the fastest promotion, the best rations – and they pay for those privileges with a casualty rate that's also the highest after the U-boat men.

'At least there are no Stukas,' says the pale, freckled Hinrichs after the briefing, and furtively scratches his groin with one hand. The others grin crookedly. Unteroffizier Hinrichs brought a souvenir back from his last outing to Abbéville: a dose of the crabs, also known as 'sailors around the mast'.

'See what that kind of thing does for you, mate,' leers Feldwebel Feugele, then switches to a fair imitation of Göring's voice. 'You're supposed to fly like a bird, not screw like a rabbit!'

'How do I know where I picked it up?' Hinrichs growls. 'Not where you think, anyway.'

'Yeah. Wherever,' Feugele goads him on. 'Just don't come too near us. Keep at least a couple of metres away,' he demands, and the others break up with laughter. 'Christ, you're really burning a hole in your underpants there...'

'Arsehole,' Hinrichs snaps back hotly. 'You'll get yours.'

Oberleutnant Michalski looks at his watch. He shakes his head, takes a slug from his mess-tin, half cognac and half coffee with a shot of pervitin for the nerves – the 'flier's cocktail' – then lights a cigarette and pricks up his ears as if he can hear the sound of aircraft engines already.

Then he casts an eye over his happy little band. Seven men left, with one packed in ice in the basement of the Luftwaffe hospital at Abbéville, waiting for a decent burial as soon as bad weather grounds his comrades – by which time there'll probably be a few more ready to join him.

The weather forecast for the next day predicts a depression approaching from the west, which means maybe soon there'll be a break.

'Attention!'

The men obey with a languid clicking of the heels.

'Once I had a comrade...'

Each time the chorus of the old song seems to get thinner. More and more members of the squadron are not there to sing, and the badly trained reinforcements that come from Germany week after week are not yet in full voice.

It's time. The Feldwebel signals, and his men clamber up into their 'crates'. The beefy Feldwebel, who never seems to be lost for words, comments on the entire procedure, 'Better a sore behind than a cold arse'.

Squadron Leader Michalski is the last to get into his aircraft. He waits until the Ju 88s they are due to escort have flown over the airfield. Field Marshal Eberhard Milch, Göring's deputy, had long talks during his last visit to the front line with the men who were forced to fly the 'miracle bomber'. He had been an understanding commander – listened to all their descriptions of the plane's faults and to their complaints. When he got back to Berlin he wrote in his report, 'The crews do not fear the enemy; they fear the Ju 88'. Then – at Göring's urging – he had the squadron disbanded and the crews transferred to other units. A typical case of Nazi psychology.

Michalski nods to his groundcrew. They remove the brake blocks from the wheels and release the cable that connects the Me 109 to its fuel tanker like an umbilical cord. The propeller begins to turn, throwing up a cloud of dust. The squadron leader guns the aircraft forward over the grass, faster and faster, picking up speed, hauling the joystick in towards him, and the Me climbs.

Beneath them, around Cape Griz Nez, Bavarian mountain troops are rehearsing the storming of the cliffs of Folkestone. They wave up at the vast fleet of aircraft, then give up counting how many planes are heading across the Channel to England today. The sappers and infantrymen concentrated around Calais can look with the naked eye and see the place where they will land on the enemy coast as part of 'Operation Sea Lion', just as soon as the Royal Air Force has been annihilated. According to Göring's initial estimate, this should have taken fourteen days. In the meantime, he has altered it to five weeks. During this period, the Navy will get together 1.2 million tons of shipping to carry whole armies in this 'glorified river crossing', but, as cheeky Möllner is fond of saying, 'Things don't always go the way Their Holinesses would like them to.'

Either Göring has made another disastrous mistake in his estimates of the enemy's strength, or the British are summoning pilots and planes out of thin air. Including the new Spitfires, which are in the process of shattering the Me 109s' command of the skies. The fighter ace Galland, once graciously asked by Göring what his heart most desired, answered coolly, 'Spitfires, Herr Reich Marshal'.

It is a question of opinion whether the Spitfire or the Me is the better plane; but the one thing is true, and it is that the plane with the better pilot wins.

'If experience with the Hurricane had led German pilots to become careless,' wrote American author Martin Caidin in his book *The Me 109*, 'then any who thought they could dismiss the Spitfire in the same way came in for a lethal surprise.'

The early missions against English targets revealed a disadvantage of the Me 109 very clearly – a range that was far too limited for the demands of the task at hand. Even while the Wehrmacht was still fighting in Europe, it had been forced to move the airfields forward very swiftly to keep up with the front line and stay within range of enemy targets. The Messerschmitts kept their reputation because of outstanding organisation on the ground – a fragile basis for success.

More flying time and a greater range would have made impossible logistical demands, and, surprisingly, the Germans made no use of disposable auxiliary tanks, which could have been jettisoned before the planes came into contact with the enemy.

Of course, the Germans recognised the need for giving the Me 109 a greater operational range. Most targets in Britain were outside its scope, which meant the bombers arrived at their destinations without fighter escort, just when they were most vulnerable, and it is beyond dispute that the limited range of the Me 109 – never improved during the Battle of Britain – was one of the main reasons for the Luftwaffe's disastrous defeat, a defeat that can be seen as one of the turning points of the war. The Me 109s never had a period of more than twenty minutes during which they were able to afford protection to their bombers. If they had been given thirty minutes more flying time, the battle would have been a much more close-run thing.

The squadron crosses the Channel in a cloudless sky without sign of the enemy, but just before they reach the coast, they are ambushed by a mixed force of Spitfires and Hurricanes. Since the pilots of Fighter Command pay no attention to any of Göring's rules, the main German force, involved in a crazy battle for existence, ignores them too, and most manage to reach their target.

In the confusion, Michalski pulls a trick that is his own and pretty hard to copy: he goes into a dive, full throttle, takes the Me 109 right down, then pulls up again and comes from below to attack instead of from above. He catches an RAF pilot, who has been taught: 'Think of your Hun coming out of the sun'.

A short burst of tracer.

Michalski watches the burning Spitfire cartwheeling down towards the ground.

He gets into radio contact and orders his men to break off their dogfights and get back to their embattled bomber charges.

Beneath him are old Norman churches, idyllic streams, villages with thatched houses; keeping to 12,000 feet, the Oberleutnant flies over a cathedral whose spire is pointing upwards to a heaven that has been turned into hell. For hours now, waves of bombers have been attacking Southern England, dropping their bombs or being downed, hitting their targets or just jettisoning their loads aimlessly around the countryside. The earth below is pockmarked like a diseased skin.

Shortly before Michalski's squadron turns and leaves the Ju 88s to their own devices, they hit a flak trap. The first of the Jus explodes. Feldwebel Sack, manoeuvring wildly, tries to escape the deadly concentration of fire. He loses his left wing. Finished. No one is clear whether he manages to bale out before his aircraft hits the ground. The escort fighters have to turn back now, while the group of Ju 88s suffers a fate that has become typical of its missions over Southern England. 'At 12,000 feet, the situation was still manageable, though difficult. At 6,000, the enemy had all the advantages,' writes Wolfgang Dierich in his book *Combat Squadron 51*. 'More and more of our comrades were downed by fighters or flak. Thirteen crews never came back. A Hurricane from 213 Squadron shot down our commander. Oberst Fsicher was killed, while his navigator, Oberleutnant Lüderitz, and Leutnant Schad were seriously wounded and taken prisoner.

'First Group lost four crews, Second Group two and Third Group six. Few of these survived to reach the English prisoner-of-war camps.

'As the group turns, Spitfires, Hurricanes and Defiants are onto them like hawks. Apart from the thirteen losses, almost every plane is damaged by tracer and cannon fire. Major Marienfeld, commander of Third Group, and Oberleutnant Lange of 9 Squadron each manage to shoot down a Spitfire. Leutnant Unrau's crew are chased across the Channel by three Hurricanes. His radio operator, Feldwebel Winter, shoots down a Hurricane. After one of the engines had been shot up, the Ju was able with difficulty to reach the French coast and – when the second engine stalled – to make a skilled bellyflop landing right on the top of some cliffs. When they got out, uninjured, they counted 180 direct hits on the fuselage of their plane.'

In the skies over Dunkirk, the triumphant Luftwaffe had lost a tooth or two; now, over Southern England, it was threatening to lose its bite altogether. The returning fighters now had to realise that they had to make their own way home, and that Fighter Command still attacked them even when they were short of fuel and couldn't afford to undertake costly manoeuvres. The Spits and Hurris were waiting in strength, coming firing out of the sun and shooting down anything that came within range of their eight wing-mounted machine guns.

The Battle of Britain had begun on August 13th 1940. Operation Sea Lion was supposed to take German land forces onto the island by mid-September. The Luftwaffe gave all it had: swarms of bombers, fighters, fighter-bombers and Stukas headed westward from their bases on the coast. Every clear day witnessed an incredible slaughter among the clouds. Again and again, Fighter Command's squadrons cut a deadly swathe through the formations of bombers before their Messerschmitt escorts could even begin to intervene. At times the German crews could have believed that they were fighting apparitions, not men.

'They are always in the right place. They never miss us,' writes Cajus Becker in his book *Eyes through Night and Fog*. 'When we shoot one down, two more appear in its place. They seem to know exactly the path our bombers are flying, and they even seem to know our numbers in advance.

'How do they do it? How do they achieve this amazing certainty? What mysterious power allows them to recognise the flight path of the German formations, time after time?

'In headquarters buildings in France, the commanders of the German bomber forces puzzle over this increasingly urgent question. Because the losses are high, much too high. Sometimes 20% or even 30% of the planes fail to return. Others only manage to reach French soil after suffering fearful structural damage. But the material losses can be made up. Only the experienced, highly-trained crews are irreplaceable.

'They had reckoned that this battle would be hard, that this would be no easy number, victory without tears. But they had not counted on the enemy's invisible, inexplicable superiority, this constant ability to be in the right place at the right time.'

There is the usual gathering of fighters over the Channel, the head count. Each pilot is concerned with his own business, usually staring fixedly at the red light that shows a low fuel level. For now Steinhoff's group, respectfully dubbed 'the Abbéville boys' by the English, is all together. They are creeping back to their home bases. Strict radio silence is in operation, so that the English will not be able to get a fix on any latecomers who have not watched their time or their fuel gauges.

Hinrichs, the crab-catcher, got left behind and panicked. 'I'm on my own, completely on my own,' he howled into his radio, utterly against orders.

'Shut your face, you stupid bastard,' growled one of his comrades who was on his way home. 'You're not alone. You've got a Spitfire up your arse!'

Möllner crashes into the sea 200 metres from the French coast and is rescued. Then they realise that Feugele is missing. They silently start to cross him off their list, but then he phones from a neighbouring airfield. Had to crash-land because he ran out of fuel. Within a short while, the Feldwebel appears in a Kübelwagen, home again.

'What was the hurry?' asks Hinrichs after congratulating him. He looks up, sees clouds gathering in the sky; that means tomorrow they'll be grounded for the first time in a long while.

Towards midday they drive into Abbéville. In the meantime, little Fritzmann has succumbed to his burns and has been booked in for burial along with the others in the heroes' cemetery, and Feugele is asking himself whether it isn't a bit of a waste to put Hauptmann Feuerbach in a proper coffin when all they managed to get of him out of his shattered aircraft could just about have filled a paper bag.

Other squadrons from the area have also got their dead out of ice. They stand to attention as five fighter pilots are given up to the earth. They put on their respectful faces, hoping that it will all be over quickly and that they won't be the ones in the coffins next time.

Then they sing 'Once I had a Comrade . . .' Today they had five: they've had five hundred, and they'll have millions by the time this war is over – not all of them comrades, but all of them very, very dead.

Hinrichs is pale, collapsed, sobbing snot and tears. Feugele snaps at him to pull himself together, but his own eyes are moist.

The losses are appalling, and they are due to accidents as much as enemy action. Some of the resulting scenes are too much even for the most cold-blooded Luftwaffe men. The writer and Stuka pilot Valentin Mikula tells of one comrade who crashed, 'After fifteen minutes, the pilot was loaded into an ambulance. His mortal remains bore little resemblance to a human being. The mouth had been sliced open from ear to ear, the teeth hung randomly from the jawbone, he was scalped, his rib cage deformed, and not one bone was still intact. His left arm had been torn out of its socket, the right crushed into the body. His right leg had been torn off at the knee, with only a few hanging shreds of flesh to show that there had once been a continuation. The left knee cap had been neatly sliced off and couldn't be found anywhere. His behind was burned beyond recognition. But this lump of flesh was still alive. The doctor pumped morphine into him, so that his senses were dulled. Neverthless, the monster continued to breathe, no matter what he did, as if it had only just learned how to do it. It cursed its bad luck and peered at the others out of its good eye, trying to read the full tragedy of its fate in their faces. The rest of the young fliers, who had just arrived at the scene, had a chance to see what a man looked like after a bad crash landing. The monster cursed in rich Low German dialect in a semi-delirium as they loaded it into the ambulance and finally gave up the ghost only just before it arrived at the Luftwaffe hospital... A normal soldier dies when his time comes, but a Stuka pilot has to have someone help him a little...'

After the burials, they head straight for the nearest pick-up bars. They have passes until midnight, with an extra two hours' extension because the weather's lousy. Oberleutnant Michalski went back to base straight after, to churn out the letters to the next of kin. Even though the procedure has become automatic and the letters are always pretty much the same, he finds the writing difficult, and falls into fantasising about who will write a letter to his mother, and when. He has no father; Michalski senior was killed in the First World War.

As for the rest, they sit themselves down in some tacky French bar and find themselves some even tackier French girls, and they drink themselves into an optimistic frame of mind, and they stroke their own highly-decorated chests, and they don't give a damn about the hangovers they'll have in the morning. In any case, tomorrow there'll be no flying – not that they care whether they start out with a fuzzy head or not. It's always the same shit, and no one really thinks they're going to clear the skies over England this day or the next.

'I reckon the sea lion's got sea sick,' says Feugele.

'You'd be better off thinking about that redhead over there, before the others snap her up,' says Hinrichs.

The waiters know them and serve them with a smile. As Frenchmen they don't, of course, have much time for the German military, but for them the Luftwaffe crews are the best of a bad lot, because they blow their combat allowances on booze and tip heavily. From time to time, a waiter will ask after this or that pilot whose name they have been given, and then there are usually long faces all round, which mean: he's had it. Or, as Güssregen insists on putting it, 'Fighter pilots have happy lives, but by Christ they're short.'

'*In the middle of the water, swims a naked farmer's daughter . . .*'

Möllner raises his glass to continue the drinking song, '*On her tits, just for good measure, a bunch of frogs are taking pleasure . . .*' The rest of them laugh and join in in chorus, '*And in her pussy, how does it feel to see a fat and squirming eel? And in her arse there's weed, my dears . . .*' Some of them are choking with laughter now. 'Cheers!'

On July 19th 1940, the capital of the Reich was one big sea of flags. The streets were packed with cheering crowds. Hitler drove to the Kroll Opera House to address the Reichstag and celebrate his victory over France. 'At this hour, I feel myself duty bound to make one more appeal to England,' he said to thunderous applause. 'I believe that I am able to do this with real sincerity because I am not the vanquished, begging for a favour, but a victor appealing to reason.'

The British rejected his offer. They had no intention of making peace, just as Hitler had never really considered making war against England. An ambiguous statement by the Luftwaffe general, Hans Jeschonnek, led to rumours that Hitler had deliberately halted his Panzers at the gates of Dunkirk, thus allowing the English to escape. There was no question of this being true, but it was clear that as Germany's self-styled Supreme Commander prepared the invasion of England, he seemed oddly half-hearted.

'The German generals were well aware of the risks that their troops would face in crossing the water,' writes Liddell Hart. 'They harboured doubts that the Navy and the Luftwaffe could secure the army's passage, and they demanded that any landing be on a broad enough front (from Ramsgate to Lyme Bay) to disperse and stretch the British defence forces. The German Admirals were even more chary of what might happen if the British fleet appeared in the Channel. They had little or no confidence in their own ability to ward off any such intervention. They therefore took the opposite view from the generals, arguing that it would be impossible to offer cover for a broad-front assault and that it would be better to concentrate on a relatively narrow strip of coast, using small land forces at first – a view that deepened the Army commanders' doubts. Admiral Raeder was particularly insistent that air superiority in the invasion zone was an absolute priority.

'After a meeting with Raeder on July 31st, Hitler accepted the Navy's advice that an invasion was impossible before the middle of September. Then "Sea Lion" was postponed to 1941, since Göring assured him that the Luftwaffe would be able to prevent intervention by the British Navy and also to clear the RAF from the skies...'

In the meantime, three air fleets had been established by the Germans to support Operation Sea Lion. They were to begin their operation with a thunderbolt. The Luftwaffe had at its disposal 1000 bombers, 870 fighters, 330 Stukas and 270 fighter-bombers. The Ju 87s, like the Messerschmitts, were based on airfields right on the Channel coast of France. The Ju 88s were to fly from Southern Norway against English targets. The actual date was dependent on the weather. Ideally, they would approach under cloud cover but have blazing sunshine for the actual attack. The codename for the order that would make the Luftwaffe operational: 'Eagle Day'.

The first formations were spotted at 5.30 on August 13th over Amiens, a second group near Dieppe and a third over Cherbourg. The weather was perfect, but as soon as the formations left the cloud cover, the Hurricanes and Spitfires were on to them, and the battle was joined. While the fighters fought it out with the English defenders, the main force was unprotected. Göring threw his squadrons into battle ruthlessly, round the clock, but it was only rarely that they succeeded in doing real damage to their targets in South-East England.

Interceptor fighters hit the second wave before they even reached the bombing zone. And the third. A bloody and merciless aerial battle raged all day. Heinkel IIIs exploded in mid-air. Crews of Ju 88s parachuted into captivity. And the wretched Ju 87 was often caught on its way back across the Channel. On that one day, the Germans lost 55 aircraft and the British 13. The shine had begun to go from the Luftwaffe's reputation.

And 'Eagle Day' was beginning to look more like the Day of the Vulture.

Right from the start, it was clear that the Battle of Britain was going to be a struggle decided by the laws of attrition. Werner Mölders, fighter ace, popular idol and first Commander of Fighters, later admitted, 'I went through a hundred nightmares. By the time the battle was over, I had become an old man . . .'

There was worse to come. On August 14th, bad weather prevented large-scale operations, but on the day they called 'Bloody Thursday', everything that could fly was on its way to England. The formations crossed the Channel, left the white cliffs of Dover behind them, flew purposefully on across the 'Garden of England' – the county of Kent. They encountered no enemy aircraft as they flew over feudal manor houses, ruined castles, mediaeval cathedrals and huge fruit orchards. The countryside was pretty and appeared peaceful, without a stormcloud in sight – but the idyll was deceptive and treacherous.

Shortly before they reached London, which Hitler had put out of bounds to all German aircraft, the Messerschmitts turned tail and began to head back towards the continent. Still no sign of any English fighters in the target area. Fighter Command had pulled its fighter squadrons back from the Channel and was using its auxiliary coastal airfields for refuelling and emergency landings.

Over the Channel, the returning fighters met the first Stuka squadrons beginning their long attacking runs on the English air fields. At a stroke, the paradise that was South-East England was transformed into a fiery hell. Barrage balloons attached to rockets were suddenly fired into the air, reaching heights of up to 6000 feet, to protect the airfields and armaments centres from the dive bombers. The British flak began firing, steadily and accurately. And suddenly the Spits and Hurris were among them, mercilessly picking off their victims from the lumbering bomber formations, knocking them out before they could release their loads, moving on into frantic one-to-one fights with the German Messerschmitts. The Ju 87s of Dive Bomber Squadron 1, the vanguard of the attacking force, were given no alternative but to fly right through the midst of the British fighters. The slow bombers manoeuvred skilfully. Their pursuers shot past them like hounds put off the scent by a wily, larger beast, but they came back for more.

Or they looked for other victims. Formations of anything between 80 and 150 aircraft were in permanent action over England. Three entire air fleets were using every aircraft they had, making the greatest number of planes ever to attack England on one day during the course of the entire Second World War. For the German command, 1786 aircraft was such an overwhelming advantage that it had to be sufficient to annihilate the RAF to such a degree that any Channel crossing by the Army with Luftwaffe support would be a picnic.

The battle never seemed to stay in one area for long, but the British were uncanny. Each formation was intercepted as it approached its target and engaged by the British fighters. Wherever bombers appeared, be it over Middle Wallop, West Malling, or Martelsham, Spitfires were ready on the spot to give them a hot reception. They seemed to be able to work out the targets in advance; it was as if they had attended the German briefings. It was like the story of the hare and the tortoise, where the hare flogs himself to death because his opponent is always there first.

The English held two powerful trumps, unknown to their German opponents. In France a commando team had captured the 'Enigma' encoding machine used by the German General Staff and transported it to England; it was re-assembled at Bletchley Park. British scientists succeeded in putting this electronic Cassandra to use very quickly. Thus the British, by intercepting and then decoding the Luftwaffe orders for missions over England, would know in advance where the German bombers were heading and could make their arrangements. 'Enigma' remained one of the best-kept secrets of the Second World War, and was publicly revealed only a few years ago.

The second secret weapon was known to Göring, for the Germans had a similar - though still rather less well-developed - technology that they called *Funkmesse* or 'radio measurement'. What Luftwaffe bomber crews thought of as witchcraft was, in fact, a form of electronic magic called radar. The entire English coast was covered by a chain of radar stations. The radio masts of 'Chain Home', some as much as 250 feet high, were unmistakable, and at the beginning were targets for the Germans, though attacks were not very successful.

'Even while we were assembling over the Pas de Calais, our formations were under surveillance from radar's all-seeing eye,' wrote German fighter commander Adolf Galland in his autobiography *The First and the Last*. 'Every move we made was recorded on the virtually all-embracing situation charts at the British fighter bases, giving Fighter Command the advantage of using its forces at the most opportune time and exactly where they were needed.

'In the same struggle, we had to fall back on our all-too-human naked eye. The British fighters could depend on a much more wide-ranging and accurate electronic 'eye'. Our orders were some three hours old when we came into contact with the enemy, while the British ones dated from as many seconds as it took them to gauge the situation from the latest radar readings and to transmit it via the fighter bases to the pilots in the air.'

One further advantage for the English was obvious. They were 'playing at home'. If one of their pilots was shot down and bailed out, he could be back in a replacement machine an hour later. A German pilot, on the other hand, would be taken prisoner and lost to the Luftwaffe for the rest of the war. And the new British Munitions Minister, the press tycoon Lord Beaverbrook, was an inspired choice. He pushed up production so quickly that soon the British were building more than twice as many planes as their opponents.

And Fighter Command was superbly organised and led. Air Chief Marshal Sir Hugh Dowding, a weak-looking man with a bony face and slightly staring eyes, was an eccentric, a mystic who believed that he could communicate with his dead pilots. Raymond Cartier called him 'the most colourless and cold personality in the British Air Force'. His own people nicknamed him 'Stuffy'. He had an aversion to uniforms, which did not prevent him from building up Fighter Command to a total of 53 squadrons by the outbreak of war and forcing through the development of the Spitfire. His headquarters was a girls' school.

From Bentley Priory, Dowding directed the Battle of Britain, which was above all a struggle of fighters against fighters. He could also rely on French and Polish pilots who had volunteered for the defence of Britain. Both sides soon had their air heroes, and the Mölders and the Gallands on the British side were called Sergeant James H. Lacey or Squadron Leader Douglas Bader; like their counterparts, they notched up one victory after another.

Bader, who had had both legs amputated after a prewar flying accident, was known in England as the 'legless wonder'. He commanded 242 Squadron. And today they had scrambled after two German formations, each of thirty aircraft, had been spotted. Bader flew on a south-easterly course. The bombers were over the North Weald. The six Hurricanes banked, came out of the sun. The Group Captain had told them to fly straight into the formation, to drive the Germans apart. Their engines screamed. The silhouette outlines of the enemy planes loomed large, larger. Bader hit the third wave.

'As he and his two accompanying planes approached, he opened fire, then suddenly plunged between the bombers and dropped off away,' writes Edward H. Sims in his book *Fighter Pilot*. 'Experiencing him shooting through their formation so quickly and unexpectedly, the terrified Dornier 17 and Me 110 pilots scatter in all directions. The second trio whizzes through the dispersing formation and shoots to kill; Bader comes out of his dive and climbs again – looking for one of the now-scattered enemy planes. As he comes up, with McKnight to his left and Crowley-Miller behind him and to his right, he sees three Me 110s above, banking hard. He sets his sights on the last one in the formation and guns his Hurricane towards it. After a 10,000 foot dive, at full speed, he now has a taste for action. Bader watches the shape of the Me 110 growing in his sights. The enemy pilot climbs and banks sharply to the right. Bader follows him. The shape grows. He starts to catch up . . . closer . . . closer still. Now he's there . . . within range!

'His thumbs press down, and the eight Browning machine

guns chatter maniacally. The Hurricane shakes from the recoil. Bader is so close that the concentrated burst tears into the Me 110 with tremendous force. Flames burst from the wing tanks. Bader practically saws against the fuselage of the enemy plane with his own wings and takes his thumbs from the firing button. The twin-engined Messerschmitt falls off to the right. The route of its plunge is marked by thick, billowing black smoke . . .'

Until now, the aerial battle had meant victories and losses for the British as well as the Germans. Both sides had consistently lied in their teeth about their kills. But it was becoming hard to ignore the fact that the British were heading for air superiority, making 'Operation Sea Lion' an impossibility.

Previously the German chain of command had been scattered, unco-ordinated, irregular. During the second phase of the attack on England, a new tactic was tried: small formations with strong fighter protection attacking carefully chosen targets, principally the 'Sector Stations', the Fighter Command bases ringing London: Kenley, Biggin Hill, Hornchurch and North Weald. If Fighter Command pulled these bases back, it would lose the advantage of having forward airfields; and if the German attacks continued to be mounted with such ruthlessness, the Luftwaffe could well regain the mastery of the sky within a week.

Churchill recognised the fact.

A short while previously, the US Secret Service had informed him that Hitler had reacted with exceptional anger to the effects of a rather ludicrous bombing raid by the RAF on targets in Germany.

During the night of August 25th, a few German bombs had been dropped on London in error. Göring threatened to court martial the crews. Churchill, never one to miss an opportunity, now saw his justification for a retaliatory raid: he assembled 81 Wellington and Hampden bombers for an attack on Berlin. No one could say how they would handle the 2000 kilometre journey. But Churchill's judgement was that Hitler's hysterical character would lead him to order attacks on London as soon as a British bomb fell on Berlin, thus easing the pressure on the Fighter Command bases.

August 25th, a Sunday, was quite cloudy, so that navigation, pretty rough and ready at the best of times, was made even more difficult. Only 29 English aircraft even got as far as the general area of Berlin: even fewer flew over the city and dropped a total of 22 tons of bombs on the northern suburbs.

The next day, the sirens screamed again.

This time there were twelve dead and 28 injured.

Hitler jumped straight into Churchill's trap: he ordered his bombers to change their target to London.

The invasion army for Britain, the island where no foreign army had set foot since William the Conqueror in 1066, is standing ready. Despite its doubts, the Navy has got together the necessary shipping. In Calais a certain Herr Dix is already acting out his role as the future SS and Police Chief of Britain. He is carrying around a list of more than two thousand Englishmen and Englishwomen who are to be arrested when London has been taken. Thousands of posters printed in English call upon the population to give their allegiance to the German military authorities, with the threat of punishment if they disobey. All that is missing is fine weather and Göring's repeatedly promised air cover, the umbrella under which Sea Lion will launch its perilous crossing of the English Channel.

'The plans and preparations continued, and the besieged English had to watch as Hitler's Europe armed for the great test,' writes the American author Hanson W. Baldwin in his book *Great Battles of the Second World War*. 'By the beginning of September 1940, the German Navy had collected together 168 transport ships totalling 700,000 tons, plus 1910 barges, 419 tugs and trawlers and 1600 motor boats, and had already begun to concentrate this fleet in the Channel ports, from Rotterdam in the north to Le Havre in the south. After many disagreements and violent arguments between the various branches of the Wehrmacht, Hitler came up with a compromise plan which would put 90,000 shock troops ashore on a broad front between Folkestone and Bognor. The 16th, 9th and 6th Armies – 13 divisions for the assault, 12 in reserve – were to cross the Channel, storm the beaches and conquer England.'

The British recognised the danger.

'The RAF bombed the crowded ports of Flushing, Ostend, Dunkirk, Calais and Boulogne,' writes Janusz Piekalkiewicz, 'where more than 1000 barges were waiting for the beginning of "Sea Lion" and another 600 were ready around Antwerp.

On the night of September 13th alone, 80 ships were sunk in the port of Ostend. During the nights of the 14th and 15th, the RAF staged repeated raids against shipping concentrations in the ports between Boulogne and Antwerp. The transport fleets for "Sea Lion" suffered severe losses, particularly in Antwerp.'

The British Secret Service realised from the German troop concentrations and the predicted moonlight and tides that the invasion would be unleashed during the second week of September. And there was a further indication: Reich Marshal Göring, Commander-in-Chief of the Luftwaffe, had arrived on the Channel coast. He left his mahogany-lined dining car, bombastic, vain and boastful, his colossal bulk squeezed into a self-designed creation in white; he acknowledged the guard of honour solemnly with his raised Marshal's baton. The man whom the fighter ace Johannes Steinhoff (later head of the postwar Luftwaffe) called 'fat, idle, and corrupt', has already been dubbed 'Hermann Meier' by the public – the name he said he would assume if just one enemy aircraft crossed the German border*.

Oberleutnant Michalski of Fighter Squadron 27, ordered to a reception for the Reich Marshal along with a group of other officers, sees the red satin boots worn by the 'iron man' of the Luftwaffe and digs his neighbour in the ribs. 'See what happens when you marry an actress,' he growls.

Until recently, the relationship between the C-in-C and his fighter pilots had been one of complete trust. It was the first thing to go overboard during the Battle of Britain. The next thing to go was the famous – or notorious – Stukas. They had to be withdrawn because the RAF were bringing them down like ripe fruit. The Me 110 came next: instead of acting as long-distance fighter escort for the big bombers, the cumbersome fighter-bombers proved so slow and vulnerable that they had to call on the protection of the Me 109s themselves.

The German bombers had no chance of victory at any time during the months-long battle. The twin-engined bombers could only reach a tenth of the island: they were now realising the consequences of rejecting General Walther Wever's idea of a four-engined bomber that could 'reach the Urals'.

*'My name is Meier . . .' The equivalent of 'then I'm a Dutchman.'

This time, Göring is not so eager to get back to his amusements; he prowls the Luftwaffe bases, threatening, jovial, ridiculous and very dangerous, a man who could 'cry like a woman over the losses suffered in futile missions' (Herbert Malloy Mason). Göring appears in surprising places, without announcing himself. At the command post of the fighter commander Oberst Theo Osterkamp, he finds a post with the scrawled message: 'Who do the English need to lead them if they want to lose the war?'

'Osterkamp, that's aimed at me,' the Reich Marshal snaps at him. 'Take it down immediately!'

The low morale at the airfields is impossible for him to ignore. He had issued orders for the Luftwaffe commanders to move their headquarters so close to the coast that they can see the Channel. As Göring treks around the heights of Cape Blanc Nez, he hears Oberst Werner Junck complain, 'I'll set up my new headquarters in mid-Channel. It'll mean I'll be up to neck at high tide, up to my arse at low, but at least I'll be looking the enemy in the eye!'

In his book *Eagle Day*, the author Richard Collier writes about Hauptmann Heinz Bär, a headstrong Saxon who was shot down by a Spitfire right in front of the Reich Marshal's eyes. 'A patrol boat fished Bär out of the Channel. He was dragged ashore to meet Göring, soaking wet and frozen to the marrow. When the Reich Marshal asked him with the kindly smile of a favourite uncle what he had thought of while he was in the water, the Saxon answered grumpily, "About your speech, Herr Reich Marshal – the one that said England's not an island any more."'

As dawn approaches on the morning of September 7th, there is a sense on the Luftwaffe airfields of Northern France of the calm before the storm. Though the planes have been ready for take-off for hours, the ground crews are still fiddling with them. The crews themselves know that the concentrated attack will not happen until the afternoon, but they are already out of their tents, barrack huts and farmhouse billets and listening to the word on what's going to happen.

The attack is against 'Loge'.

There is no such place on any map. 'Loge' is the codename for London. The raid on the British metropolis is in retaliation for the bombs that fell on Berlin, and will also serve the purpose of dealing a final blow against the depleted fighter forces of the RAF, which are expected to defend the British capital to the bitter end.

'On September 6th a message reached Squadron HQ,' writes Karl Gundelach in his book *Bomber Squadron 4*. '"The squadron is to be brought to full combat readiness by the evening of the 7.9." While the groundcrews worked feverishly, a COs' conference took place at Divisional HQ the following morning to discuss the mission. The raid was to be against London. All formations of Air Fleets 2 and 3 were to combine for a massive attack on the English capital.'

As always, Bletchley Park has warned the English ground defences, and as always the radar stations have picked up the approaching Luftwaffe forces well before the English coast. Fighter Command assumes that the enemy is intending one final knockout blow against the battered bases of the South-East and it scrambles its Spits and Hurris – a serious, though understandable mistake.

Flying in close formation, tight waves of bombers follow the line of the Thames. They shun the sorely damaged airfields of Kent and Essex and continue in the direction of London, take aim as they move around the big bend in the Thames, the bend that will become known as the 'Bend of Fear'.

The seven million people of London hear their sirens howl; they have howled before, often, and it has always been a false alarm. The people on the streets stay where they are, while the customers in the pubs continue to drink their beer. The ground batteries don't dare fire at first, for fear of hurting civilians through shrapnel. Finally, as the first sticks of bombs tumble down on the docks and Woolwich Arsenal, they flee to the underground stations.

The ground defences seem weak. London is almost defenceless. By the time the Hurricanes and Spitfires are redirected to defend the capital, they have to waste precious time by landing to refuel.

In the east of the city, a huge column of smoke shoots skywards. Dozens of fires are threatening to combine into a vast sea of flame. New formations of German bombers appear with strong fighter escorts. Death rains through their bomb doors. The formations veer off back in the direction of the Channel and encounter new waves of bombers. Some of the escort fighters have so little to do that they play games shooting down barrage balloons on the way back, like hunters amusing themselves by killing helpless hedgehogs.

The Thames is crowned with a huge, fiery rainbow that lights the attackers' paths. On the BBC Radio, a hysterical fire officer screams again and again: 'Send us all the pumps you can find! the whole world's in flames here! All your pumps, do you hear me?'

The vehicles on the streets stream eastwards towards the docks, like an endless dragon's tail, or a stream of lemmings. The column halts, and bombs explode among the cars and trucks. The heat becomes unbearable. In places, the tarmac cooks. Anyone who treads on it can lose a foot, a limb, or life itself. Death stalks the streets right through London. The tongues of fire eat their way through to the famous City.

The wooden building materials stored at the Surrey Docks burn brightly. The fire spreads to the warehouses; paints and varnishes fuel the wave of destruction. Soon afterwards, hundreds of barrels of rum go up. The alcohol burns beautifully. The flames spread to a warehouse full of pepper. Anyone within miles who isn't finished by the smoke stands a good chance of succumbing to the searing sharpness of the spice.

Most of the bombs land in the centre and east of London. The City is in flames, too. The waves keep coming for eight hours. 625 bombers, escorted by 648 fighters and fighter-bombers, drop 300 tons of high-explosive bombs and 13,000 incendiary charges. 'By the time the aircraft, which are each carrying 1800 kilograms of 1 SC 'Satan' incendiaries, begin their approach shortly before midnight, the fires over London are visible from 200 kilometres away,' writes Karl Gundelach, describing the 'General Wever' Squadron's part in the raid. 'The docks are belts of flame to the north and south of the Thames. Streets have been turned into fire-traps. Dead and living alike are being pulled out of cellars. For the first time, the ghostly sound of buried human beings knocking is heard in London. It is the first of eighty-six nights of bombing that London will have to suffer.'

The 'Blitz' has begun. In the first two nights of bombing, 842 human beings lose their lives and 2347 are injured.

At 20.53, the British General Staff reached agreement that the bombing was the signal for the invasion of England. They issued the codeword 'Cromwell – Invasion Imminent', bringing all forces and Home Guard troops onto full alert to await the invasion.

Suddenly, the church bells sounded. Crossroads were barricaded, bridges blown up. Military vehicles jostled for position on the roads. The chain of command proved rickety.

The Home Guard, many of them armed with broomsticks, mobilised. Rumours ran from village to village that German parachutists had already landed. None of the amateur warriors had the slightest idea of what was really happening.

In Dover, people are told that Dungeness has already been taken by the Germans, and in Dungeness people shake their heads over the tragic conquest of Dover by the Huns. And it is true to say that the rumours that are spreading through the countryside are just as wild and terrifying as they must have been in the dark ages. There are constant reports of landings by German parachutists, but all the sounds that the night can provide are harsh commands, curses, church bells. And the engines of more German bombers.

At points on the main roads that lead inland to Canterbury, Maidstone and Horsham, troops stand ready by three-metre high tanks, each holding 2500 litres. They are ready 'to inundate the advancing Germans with a mixture of petrol and diesel oil – a glutinous stream of 120 litres per minute that burns at a temperature of almost 300°C.' (Richard Collier).

The Home Guard is on alert right through the night. It has been assembled for the first time in 900 years – and its members come up with the most bizarre collection of weapons, from African assegais to four dozen rusty rifles of 1902 vintage, relics of a long-forgotten play at London's Drury Lane Theatre. Around Southampton, troops of the 4th Division sleep fully clothed, all bundled into buses as best they can.

The cause of this confusion is not so much fear and terror but the itchiness of local commanders. Churchill, who happens to be at his country home, Chequers, at the time, has no idea that his troops are fighting ghostly actions against invisible 'parachutists' all over the country. He sleeps deeply, and has given instructions that he is only to be awoken if the USA enters the war.

The chaos in Southern England continues into the daytime. Rumours race across the countryside. Thomas Goodman, a London fireman temporarily transferred to Dover, hears that there has been a landing at Sandwich, and that the seas are black with the floating corpses of Germans.

While Göring, surrounded by his officers, performs undignified little dances at his command post on the Channel coast and calls up his wife to announce excitedly, 'All London is burning!', the inhabitants of the South of England breathe a sigh of relief and realise that the events of the night were a false alarm.

The Sea Lion never launched himself. And neither will he, even on September 15th 1940. 'Operation Sea Lion' won't go near the water. Just at that point, when the battle against England is reaching its climax, Hitler reveals to his close associates that he intends to attack the Soviet Union at the earliest opportunity.

September 15th is nevertheless a day when both sides are looking for a decisive blow: 200 German bombers, escorted by 600 fighters, fly towards London.

'On this day, the skies over England witness the most bitter, the craziest and most widespread air combat of the entire battle – it is 'Stuffy' Dowding's fighter pilots' big day,' writes Hanson W. Baldwin. 'By all their reports, they achieve the highest kill ratio ever: 185 enemy aircraft are destroyed. The Germans admitted losing 43 of their own, and in fact lost 60. Their bombing raids were useless; even Göring's insistence on 'five fighters for each bomber' could not nullify the Hurris and the Spits.'

That evening, London is alight with rumours of victory. It is true that the 'kill' statistics are wildly exaggerated once more, but it is clear that all Göring's efforts to bomb the island to its knees have been in vain. He tries the ruse of strapping 250 kilo bombs under the tails of Me 109s – the pilots contemptuously refer to them as 'dodos' eggs' – and turns his fighters into camouflaged bombers, but the British are only fooled by this once and in future raids have to be mounted at night.

London is permanently in a German bomb sight. 'Business as usual', the British say mockingly, or 'London can take it'.

When darkness falls, thousands of families move with their mattresses, blankets and thermos flasks from the slums of the East End to the West, because they believe that the walls in the wealthy districts will withstand bombing better. Thousands more pour into the underground stations for protection, including women and children with their cats and dogs, calmly and almost in silence. The calls to evacuate the city fall, for the most part, on deaf ears. No one has any intention of fleeing from the 'lousy Jerries'. Even the royal family stays in Buckingham Palace, which is promptly hit by a bomb. Bombs rain down on the Tower, the wax figures melt in Madame Tussaud's exhibition, and all the city's stations are damaged. The Old Bailey and the Guildhall are in ruins, and Fleet Street is burnt out. The massive dome of St Paul's Cathedral looms high above the city. Scarcely a stone stays intact in Dockland.

The aerial battle over England will drag on well into 1941; its intensity will lessen, even though men on both sides will show a genius for survival. One RAF pilot is shot down seventeen times and survives. Another leaps naked from his bathtub into his 'Spit', is shot down by an Me 109 and parachutes down over the East End, where he lands in the ruins to be greeted by a horde of angry, homeless women who try to beat him to death with various items of household equipment. Only when he explodes into a stream of cockney oaths do they realise that the pilot in his birthday suit is one of their own.

At Buckhurst in Sussex on the estate of the Earl de la Ware, the butler announces, 'An officer of the German Air Force is waiting in the drawing room and would like to speak to you, M'lord.' At Cadborough Farm near Rye, a farm worker discovers a hole in the roof of an outside privy and inside it a German pilot, well and truly stuck. As the sturdy Brit takes him prisoner, the German says in faultless English, 'It looks like I got out of one load of shit into another.'

The Luftwaffe loses 467 fighters in 23 days. Leutnant Erich Hohagen maintains, 'The Channel is a bloodsucker, constantly draining our strength'. Oberleutnant Hans von Hahn, leader of the first group of fighter wing 3, reports, 'There are very few of us who haven't had the experience of crashlanding in the Channel with our machine shot to pieces or without a propeller.'

Hauptmann Helmut Wick, the most successful German fighter pilot for some time to come, could no longer take solid food and lived solely on black coffee and English cigarettes. Unteroffizier Delfs engaged one of his own aircraft in furious battle, then baled out by parachute and got himself entangled in the sleepers of a mineral railway near Calais. His commander, Squadron Leader Priller, launched a frontal attack on a train that was threatening to squash Delfs, wing-mounted guns blazing.

Hardly any pilots were managing to get any sleep. Oberleutnant Schäfer, a fighter-bomber pilot, went endlessly circling over his airfield and waited for someone to turn on the marker lights; in his tense, exhausted state he had forgotten to take off his sun glasses. Oberleutnant Ludwig Franzisket drank a small bottle of rum before every mission and Eduard Neumann, who had already flown as a pilot in the First War, led his formation 300 kilometres in the wrong direction without noticing that his compass was not working.

The new fighter chiefs were all under thirty and had already become legends: their names were Werner Mölders, Adolf Galland, Hannes Trautloft, Wolfgang Schellmann or Günter 'Franzl' Lützow. In the case of Hermann Wick, a twenty-five-year-old made his way from squadron leader to wing commander in three months. He downed his 56th opponent over the Isle of Wight. Minutes later, he was shot down by the English Flight Lieutenant John Dundas - fourteen kills - who was almost immediately caught by Wick's sidekick, Rudolf Lanz - who later was killed over Abbéville.

This was the fate of the fighter pilot: they fought across a battlefield that was already lost, died for a place that their Führer had already written off in favour of bleaker, crueller battlefields. The transfer of the air war to the night meant that the daylight fighters were virtually unemployed. It was now the bombers' turn to pay the blood price.

The German public knows nothing of the poor communications, the constant changes of targets, the looming débâcle that faces the Luftwaffe in the skies over England. Again and again, the fanfares announce 'special reports' on the radio, and the announcers talk excitedly of 'bombs on England'. The Propaganda Ministry is still insisting that the surrender of the island fortress is imminent, and in the Reich capital, according to the American agency 'United Press', books have been opened on when precisely the British will give in. Wehrmacht officers plump for the beginning of October, while the international press, slightly more cautious, gives Churchill another two weeks.

And at just this time, on October 12th, 'Operation Sea Lion' is postponed by Hitler for an indefinite period - which in practical terms means forever. While the dictator transfers his attentions to the East, the futile air offensive over Southern England rolls on.

'Beginning on November 1st 1940, the Luftwaffe undertook its last major change of tactic,' Franz Kurowski writes in his book *The Air War over Germany*. 'From this time on, all the large, important industrial areas and ports within range of the bombers were to become targets for night attacks. That meant that bombers would have to fly two, sometimes three missions in one night.'

It also meant, however, that the Second World War had now crossed a barrier into the final level of total war against civilian populations. It was doubtful whether it was possible to select military targets even by daylight, and by night it was obviously impossible to confine bombs to war installations. Anyone who carried out massed bomb raids against industrial suburbs – particularly with navigation at the primitive level of autumn 1940 – was waging war on women and children in a way expressly forbidden by the Washington Conference in 1922.

A year previously, the belligerent powers had still kept within this consensus. Then accidental raids had been greeted with retaliatory measures. The rate of escalation had been dictated not by ethical considerations – either on the German or the British side – but merely by practical possibilities. And in plain language that meant: the side that had the planes at its disposal was the one that took 'revenge', while the other side presented itself as the helpless victim of an atrocity. It was a bloody charade in which the roles of victim and perpetrator changes constantly.

And there were no 'guilty' countries – only guilty human beings.

'A war consists almost entirely of actions that in peacetime would be classified as criminal,' says the British author Alastair Revie, who took part in the Second World War as an officer. 'As a consequence, the entire assumption that it is possible to avoid crime in war, or even to reduce it, was an absolute non-starter. New definitions of what constitutes a war crime had to be found as the years went on. As late as 1940, international committees and neutral statesmen were still trying to establish criteria . . . Once, however, attack had succeeded counter-attack a few times and it had been recognised that the process of dropping bombs from a great altitude and at night on targets such as factories, marshalling yards, docks and suchlike was far less certain a business than had been thought, then it became accepted that 'carpet bombing' or 'terror raids' were a more or less unavoidable phenomenon. And gradually both sides ceased to make moral justifications for mass bombing raids. It was the cue for the destruction of Coventry and the mass raid on Mannheim . . .'

Night after night, London was turned into an inferno – between 100 and 300 Luftwaffe aircraft came each time, and each time fewer returned. The German raids became less effective as the skill of the defenders increased. Experts have reckoned that Göring would have needed twenty times the number of aircraft actually available to him in order to have 'annihilated' London as he had promised.

'The target was, to put it simply, too big, and the quantity of bombs, which averaged a ton per aircraft, was too small, cynical as it may sound,' wrote the British authors John W.R. Taylor and Philip J.R. Moyes.

Even cities such as Birmingham, Leeds and Sheffield became targets. Quite often, the Luftwaffe dropped its bombs in artificially created forest fires set up by the British to represent 'burning cities'. The British radar network functioned almost perfectly. They started to use Blenheims as night fighters, even though the pilots were dependent on moonlight or the probing beams of searchlights for their navigation, and even though the probability of being brought down by their own anti-aircraft guns was greater than their chance of hitting a German plane.

But the attackers were not just psychologically under threat. England's big trump was still the Enigma machine. At Bletchley Park, usually hours before the actual raid, the British would have worked out the target and thus prepared their defences in advance.

Enigma – the British called it 'Ultra' – was an indispensable weapon for Churchill. On November 14th 1940, however, the necessity for secrecy led the Prime Minister into a decision that was militarily necessary but impossible from a humanitarian viewpoint. At three that afternoon, the decoding team at Bletchley Park learned that a huge German raid on the English industrial town of Coventry was to be mounted that night. For the first time, Göring's fliers were to use the *Knickebein* technique, an improved navigation aid. The weather conditions were extremely favourable for bombers. It was a full moon and there was no wind. Given these circumstances, it was probable that once the two squadrons of Kampfgruppe 100, who were acting as pathfinders, reached the town and dropped their marker flares, the civilian population of Coventry would be faced with catastrophe.

There was still time to warn the people of Coventry.

At first, the Prime Minister could not be reached, and then he decided to reinforce the defences around the city but not, however, to warn the civilian population, in order to protect the Enigma secret. At eight that evening, the sirens howled in the city for the first time. The population made its way without haste or panic into the shelters, never guessing that the raid would last until 5.30 the following morning and would destroy whole residential areas along with the aircraft factories, precious old buildings and the famous cathedral.

The sea of flame was visible for more than 100 miles, and acted as a marker for the next waves of German bombers. 'We came closer and closer,' said an eyewitness report published by the Wehrmacht High Command. 'The beautiful and yet horrific scene came so near it was tangible. Thick smoke billowed over the rooftops of the city and way out into the countryside. We could see great columns of flame shooting into the sky. One particularly extensive area of burning close to a lot of smaller fires showed that a vital industrial installation must have been hit. We were above the target. The British anti-aircraft guns blazed desperately away at us, and all around were the flashes of exploding shells. We could see the heart of the fire. At that moment, we let loose our bombs. The aircraft shook. Beneath us, a patchwork of new explosions erupted. We were the first plane of a group of German aircraft; others had been there before us, more would follow – until the light of the new day revealed the devastation that had once been Coventry.'

Associated Press reported from London: 'German bombers mounted a raid that began in the twilight of the evening and ended at dawn, which transformed parts of the city into infernos and cost at least a thousand dead and injured as it destroyed the heart of this once peaceful city in the middle of England. Coventry's beautiful sandstone cathedral, once famous throughout Europe, is now a smouldering heap of ruins... The whole night through, the narrow streets through which once Lady Godiva rode a thousand years ago echoed and shook with the impact of bombs and the roar of anti-aircraft fire.'

A more precise report a few days later declared that the 'revenge' raid had killed 551 people and seriously injured 865. The damage was so total that the night of 14th/15th November was reckoned to be the high point of the night attacks on England. And, in fact, there were direct hits on twelve aircraft factories, causing English plane production to be reduced by one fifth during the immediate aftermath.

Göring made sure that the raid was trumpeted as a great victory. Goebbels introduced a new word to the German language: to 'coventrify'. And the city's name became a symbol through the world for the new, ruthless aerial war that had become part of humanity's experience – and one that the British and the Americans would soon be waging with far greater efficiency against Germany.

The very next day, the British announced raids on Hamburg, Bremen and the Reich capital. 'The raid on Berlin began in the early hours of the morning and continued for several hours,' the communiqué from Bomber Command announced with some exaggeration. 'It caused a series of large fires that were visible from some 30 miles away.'

Such reports were still more propaganda than actual terror, but soon the extent of the terror would make propaganda superfluous.

And the long-lost German bomber offensive rolled on like a headless chicken. The crews that unleashed hell over the fortress island had to fly through hell to get there and back, often several times in one night. They were so battle-weary and exhausted that as time went on, untrained groundcrew personnel and even medical officers flew along with them to give the gunners a few hours sleep.

What it was like to fly back from England in those days is only too vividly described by Oberleutnant Küchle, an officer of Bomber Squadron 51, who took part on the attack on Portsmouth on the night of 10th/11th 1941, was hit twice by British night fighters, and held back to circle over the French base to avoid endangering his comrades when he had to make his inevitable crashlanding. 'During the course of the raid, my aircraft was hit 38 times. The right wheel had been shot to pieces. The presence of eight to ten large holes in the fuselage led to the assumption that the British had used explosive shells or wing-mounted cannon. I observed three guns on each wing of the fighters. Perhaps there was a cannon among them. The night fighter fired green tracers. The armoured cockpit roof (made by Opel) had received several hits, which had not penetrated the armour. The right propeller had been hit twice. Likewise, the electrical connections were damaged by fire.'

If Oberleutnant Küchle survived that mission with no more than a fright to remember, one raid on England ended for a particular Ju 88 crew in a much grimmer fashion. Ack-ack fire and the attentions of night fighters had wreaked grave damage on the bomber commanded by Oberleutnant von Claer of the *Edelweiss* squadron. Two of his crew lay dead in the aircraft, which was still just manoeuvrable. But as he limped across the Channel, his luck ran out. He was forced to go down and ditch the plane in the Channel.

There was no way he could save the Ju 88, but Oberleutnant Claer and Feldwebel Märte were able to launch the dinghy and put on their life jackets. They got out of the wreck before it sunk. They paddled through the stormy seas in the leaky dinghy. 'With difficulty, they retained enough control not to be at the mercy of the sea,' wrote Wolfgang Dierich in his chronicle of Bomber Squadron 51. 'Hours went by. As night fell, their heavy fliers' clothes had long since soaked through with salt water and were threatening to drag them down into the depths, despite their lifesavers . . .

'The two men realised even in their battered, exhausted state that the life jackets could not keep them afloat. They struggled to keep alive, but their strength was fading fast. Nevertheless, they were alert enough to see that one could survive if he had the other's life jacket to add to his own. The Feldwebel was married with two children, while his commander was a bachelor. The Oberleutant stripped off his lifesaver and gave it to Märte at the certain cost of his own life. Märte could only find the heart to put it one when he was sure that the Oberleutnant had drowned. He continued to hold Claer's corpse. 'A German U-boat found the pair of them the next morning, Märte unconscious and suffering from salt water burns all over his body. It took them on board and back to base,' Dierich concludes his account.

The invasion that never was, the Sea Lion that was afraid of water, cost the German Luftwaffe 3363 dead, 2117 wounded, and 2265 aircraft. 2641 aircrew were posted either missing or captured. The German Luftwaffe lost a quarter of its fighters and 35% of its bombers.

'The Battle of Britain was not simply a turning point of the war,' says General Johannes Steinhoff, 'it was a victory for the British. The very young German Luftwaffe – it was only six years old, after all – lost so much of its irreplaceable reserve of skill, experience and courage, that it could never again fulfil its chief task, which was the defence of the Reich from destruction by Allied bombers.'

And the battle continued. In the course of April 1941, the

British claimed 6131 dead and 6900 wounded on their side, mostly civilians. The last raid took place on the night of 11th May over London. 507 German aircraft, most of them already earmarked for transfer to the Russian front, dropped another 711 tons of high-explosive bombs and 2393 incendiaries, causing 2000 fires and 1212 deaths.

During the Battle of Britain, 30,000 civilians died, 50,000 were injured, and 100,000 homes were destroyed – horrific figures that would soon be far exceeded by the Anglo-American attacks on the Reich.

Goebbels' propaganda machine said not a word about the end of the bombing offensive. No order of the day explained to the Luftwaffe's survivors why they had lost so many of their comrades. 'In Germany, the end of the offensive against England ended with an almost eerie quiet,' said Adolf Galland. 'The Sea Lion . . . died as it had lived, in the archives of the Wehrmacht General Staff.'

Damned Atlantic!

Suddenly the warning sirens howl on the ship, loud and ugly. The crew of the *Admiral Scheer* rush to their stations. Their sea boots echo over the steel floors, and above on the deck they sound like a herd of rampaging elephants. The bolts shake in their plates. The siren howls on.

'Shit on it!' curses Petty Officer Dünnbier, slamming his cards down on the table. A half-played hand of trumps in threes at skat, and now has to be the moment for a combat alert.

His mates put on their combat gear – gas masks, hammers, and life jackets rolled into a bag – but Dünnbier takes his time. He has been detailed to the prize crew, which gives him a kind of passenger status at this point. He is also under orders to report to the dressing station on the middle deck for duties as an auxiliary medical orderly, but there's no hurry, because until the shooting starts there'll be no wounded to attend to.

The next thing the petty officer does is to butter himself a piece of bread, nice and thick. He has only been at sea a year, but he already knows that there's not nearly as much hurry at this stage as everyone likes to pretend. He has his head screwed on – which is why he's made it to petty officer while his brother Franz, who joined up at the same time, is still greasing away as an ordinary sailor on the cruiser *Thor*.

It is true that the *Admiral Scheer* is packed to the gunwales with provisions, but the captain is notoriously mean with his rations, because he never knows how many guests he's liable to have. The more successful the ship is in its piratical tasks, the more prisoners are liable to end up on board, and then they'll have to count every portion of food.

It is November 5th 1940. Late afternoon. The sea is quite rough, the sky clear. A spotter plane has reported a convoy of eight British steamships in grid square A K 85. Heading east, 90 miles from the *Admiral Scheer*, which is stalking them like the witch after Hansel and Gretel.

'Attacking course!' orders Captain Krancke. The 10,000

ton ship, with its thin armouring – it is a product of the Treaty of Versailles, and its advantage lies in its speed of 27 knots – turns about.

'A cruiser, Captain,' the officer of the watch reports.

'Distance?'

'Distance 170 hectometres.'

The commander pauses for a moment.

'Heavy artillery – fire at will!' he bawls then.

Six 28-centimetre guns spit death from their barrels. The *Admiral Scheer* shifts to lee. She is engaged in battle with the British auxiliary cruiser *Jervis Bay*. The weaker enemy ship, commanded by Captain Fegen, defends herself bravely but without prospect of victory. Her superstructure collapses like a house of cards.

Pillars of flame shoot from her stern.

The British cruiser is drawing the Germans' fire to protect the convoy. She shows the red ensign, takes hit after hit. But after the twentieth direct hit she goes onto her side and sinks, still blazing.

'Go for the merchantmen!' Krancke orders.

The *Admiral Scheer* turns and heads straight amongst the near-defenceless, fleeing freighters, like a fox in a chicken-yard. Every shell a direct hit. Every direct hit sowing death and destruction.

One after another, the tanker *San Demitrio* (8703 GRT), the steamers *Trewellard* (5201 GRT), *Maidan* (7908 GRT), the *Kenbane Head* (5201 GRT) and the cargo boat *Frisno* are shot to pieces. Other ships from the convoy manage to steam away, despite the grave damage, but are rapidly hauled in and taken as prizes.

From now on, the *Admiral Scheer* is naval enemy number one for the British. They put battleships and destroyers on her trail, but in the meantime the German vessel is able to refuel from the tanker *Eurofeld* and take on ammunition and provisions from the supply ship *Nordmark*, enabling her to continue roving the seas in search of booty, even though three separate fleets have been sent after her by the British Admiralty.

The *Admiral Scheer* continues to litter the seabed with wrecks of various sizes. Conditions on board are still extremely crowded because of the numbers of prisoners, and on December 18th she spots a really fine, fat freighter, sitting there like a Christmas feast in her sights, too bulky to move.

This time it is Dünnbier's turn for some action. He is a member of the prize crew put aboard the captured refrigerator ship *Duquesa* (8651 GRT).

'Nice ship,' says the petty officer as he boards her. 'All respect!' And he's not even aware yet that she is carrying 3339 tons of frozen meat and 720 tons of fresh eggs for England – 15 million eggs.

The Christmas table has been well laid for him.

The successful conclusion of the war in Western Europe offered the German Navy, which had been severely weakened by the Norwegian campaign, unheardof opportunities. Its area of operations in the trade war being waged at sea now extended from the North Pole to the Pyrenees. U-boats, cruisers and other surface combat units had easy access from the French Atlantic ports and no longer needed to fear the British blockade on the northern sea routes, to play tricks or shoot their way into the sea lanes.

'The first to appear was the heavy cruiser *Admiral Scheer* in November 1940. It was one of the two surviving 'pocket' vessels, and its arrival in the Atlantic took everyone by surprise,' writes Cajus Becker. 'It hit a poorly defended convoy, sank several ships and caused unholy chaos in the Allied convoy system. After this success, she made her way south at first, so as to appear later somewhere else, mount a lightning raid and then disappear again. This hit-and-run system caused serious problems to the British, despite their overwhelming numerical superiority; they could not be everywhere at once to protect their ships against these ambush attacks.'

An even more serious problem for the British were German cruisers, which – as they had in the First World War – acted as wolves in the fold, appearing from nowhere to slice through British convoys, sinking ships and taking them as prizes. The most successful was the *Atlantis* commanded by Captain Rogge; the former freighter *Goldenfels* converted into a warship, had operated in the Indian Ocean during the first winter of the war and had completed the longest active service cruise of any warship in history, steaming 100,000 sea miles in 622 days. During this time, she sank 22 merchant ships totalling 145,000 tons.

By November 1941, her end had come; she had no chance

against the British cruiser *Devonshire*. The crew was rescued by the submarine U 126 and put aboard the supply ship *Python*. The British got the *Python* too, and the former crew of the *Atlantis* was rescued a second time by a German U boat – which finally brought an end to this remarkable odyssey.

These cruisers – the 'German corsairs' (Raymond Cartier) – waged a lonely war on the seven seas, cut off from their bases, always mindful of their pursuers, without mail from home for months on end. The *Atlantis* was followed by the cruisers *Wider*, *Thor*, *Pinguin* and *Komet*. They sailed under false colours and only showed their guns when they were up close to enemy shipping. They often had hundreds of prisoners on board, and feeding and clothing them was their number one problem.

The cruisers waiting in the 'dead' area of Andalusia (South Atlantic) found it hard to believe their radio operators when they were told they would be receiving thousands of eggs and crates of steaks.

At first they thought that the enemy had cracked their code and was trying to lure them into a trap, but then the story about the *Admiral Scheer*'s haul spread from ship to ship.

The floating goodies basket that the *Scheer* had snapped up could not be taken into port because of shortage of coal. Leutnant Götsch, the commander of the prize crew, ordered the coal to be used exclusively for keeping the refrigerated compartments functioning. Once that was used up, the freighter would be scuttled and the prize crew would board another German vessel – provided that the British didn't turn up first.

On Christmas Eve 1940, the self-service trade reached its highpoint. Ship after ship anchored alongside the *Duquesa*. Eggs festooned the marines' Christmas tree. At a point 15 degrees south and 18 degrees west, the party began, beginning with the *Eurofeld* and then the *Nordmark*.

Petty Officer Dünnbier, temporarily in charge of the rations, distributed the eggs with such a look of pride as if he had laid them himself. 'Blimey, fifty thousand of 'em,' he said to the boys from the *Nordmark*. 'What you going to do with them?' He added a few half-pigs. 'Just don't spoil yourselves, lads,' he added with a chuckle.

There seemed to be no end to the stuff. In naval circles, the

Duquesa became known as 'Provisions Store Wilhelmshaven-South'. And the slow provisions ship was also being used as a prison. For the moment, more than a hundred seamen from all over the world were being held on board.

And then comes Petty Officer Dünnbier's personal Christmas gift: the *Thor* turns up, which means a chance to see his brother again.

The ship moves closer, slow and painful. She had been lurking near the mouth of the River Plate and had been engaged in murderous combat by the British cruiser *Caernarvon*.

Petty Officer Dünnbier stands at the railing and looks at the approaching jollyboat. He is looking forward to seeing his twin brother, his other self.

'You can have what you want!' he calls out to the new arrivals, generous in his pleasure. 'I'll even play you a Christmas chorus!' He puts on the record.

'*The bells never rang more sweetly*...' the loudspeakers intone.

The men from the *Thor* come aboard. And then something strange happens: when they see Petty Officer Dünnbier, they literally shrink from him.

'What's up?' says the petty officer, who looks identical to his brother except for the uniform. 'Am I a ghost or something? Do I stink?'

'Oh, shit,' says one of the men from the jollyboat, then shrugs and sneaks away.

Dünnbier turns to the next one.

'We had a dust-up,' says the man, staring at the floor as if he was trying to learn the pattern of the bolts off by heart.

'And?'

'Thirty-seven casualties. More than eighty wounded.

'Is something wrong with my brother?' Dünnbier asks, suddenly fearful.

'He was one of them,' the sailor answers with a gulp. 'I mean, among the dead...'

'*At christmas time* –' The choir on the record ploughs on to the chorus: '*The bells never rang more sweetly*...'

'Shut up!' yells Dünnbier, unable to hold himself back. He grabs the nearest crate of eggs, smashes it against the gramophone, and no one has the heart to bawl him out for it.

An hour later, the jollyboat returns, this time with the few belongings of the dead man. They are handed over to his brother: a watch, a few books, two letters and some photographs.

Petty Officer Dünnbier stares at a picture that could be of himself. He sits crouched in the corner, reading letters that he knows by heart now, saying nothing, asking nothing, eating nothing – and no one calls him into line.

When on February 18th the *Duquesa* – cleared of its cargo as if a horde of locusts had been through it – is finally scuttled, Dünnbier is brought on board the replacement ship only with the aid of some force.

The branch that benefited most from the short access to the Atlantic was the U-boats. The advantage served to outweigh to some extent the fact that their commander, Admiral Dönitz, could call on no more U-boats at the end of 1940 than he had possessed on the outbreak of war. Production had only just kept up with losses, which to be precise meant that twenty-eight vessels had been lost during the first year of the war and twenty-eight new ones built.

Since June 1940, however, Dönitz had been enforcing the 'wolf pack' tactic rigorously, which meant operating up to nineteen U-boats in the same area at once. During the first month alone, 63 ships weighing 355,431 GRT were sunk with the aid of this tactic. The U-boats and the convoys had been locked ever since in a war to the death that seemed unending. If the grey wolves succeeded in sinking more tonnage than the British could replace, the food situation on the fortress island would become critical. But it could only succeed if the commanders of the U-boat branch managed to build more vessels – and particularly vessels that were of ocean-going size.

The tactic had been refined: the U-boats' commanders risked more than ever before, and often extremely successfully. One U-boat would stalk the convoy and call the other when the time came. Then the fun would start. Experience told, however, that the defensive capacity of the convoys tended to increase at about the same rate as the effectiveness of the U-boats.

The first crisis of confidence among the U-boat crews had nothing, however, to do with deficiencies in quantity of armament – which never reached their planned extent – but came from the disastrous experience with the torpedoes they called 'Weserübung'. The returning crews told their commander-in-chief that they would have sunk an extra 150,000 GRT at least if the torpedoes – fired at great risk to the U-boat men from close quarters – had not proved to be duds down to the last one.

'You can't expect me to fight with a wooden rifle,' said Günther Prien, the commander who got inside Scapa Flow to sink the *Royal Oak* and who later sank more tonnage than any other man in the war.

On April 20th 1940, Grand Admiral Raeder had set up a committee to look into the reasons why these torpedoes, which operated with magnetic and remote control fuses, had gone right under enemy ships' keels, or even failed to reach their targets at all. There were demotions and courts martial, but the reasons were never adequately explained, and the big clean-up fizzled out.

Meanwhile, the fuses had been improved. Dönitz sent one of his most trusted officers, Kapitänleutnant Victor Oehrn, commander of the just-completed new U-37, to try out the improved torpedo on active service. For the other U-boats, the order was still to use three ordinary torpedoes and then one with a magnetic fuse – Russian roulette à la Dönitz.

U-37, operated to the north of Ireland, used its deck guns to sink the Swedish ship *Erik Firsell* (5066 GRT); two days later in the Bay of Biscay the British *Dunster Grange*, a 10,000 ton monster, and then the *Sheaf Mead* (5000 GRT) and the *Uruguay* (3425 GRT). On the French coast, Oehrn bagged the French ship *Brazza* (10,387 GRT), the *Julien* (a fishing smack of 177 tons) and the *Marie-Jose* (2477 GRT). In all, the U-37 sank nine ships with a total displacement of 41,207 GRT.

And then came the full report: out of five magnetic-operated torpedoes, two had exploded prematurely and two had – probably – not exploded at all. The commander-in-chief of U-boats promptly forbade all use of the new torpedoes, even the improved version. From now on, the commanders used only the old-style torpedoes, with continued success.

The British were now routing their convoys over the northern passage and were thus presenting a concentrated target for the enemy. 'The apparent advantage of the German position was, in fact, based on a misunderstanding of the overall position,' wrote Herbert Michaelis. 'The failure of the

German air offensive in the summer and autumn of 1940, followed by Hitler's cancellation of 'Sea Lion', had also hit the navy hard. The destroyers that had been kept in the Channel to ward off the invasion now became available for anti-sumbarine duties. The British were further reinforced when on September 2nd 1940 the USA handed over 50 aging destroyers to strengthen the convoy protection fleet...'

Despite all this, the second winter of the war was a grim, gloomy period, the worst time of the war. The endless sinkings by U-boats began to affect the food situation. Though even in England the reports tended to be prettified, there was no hiding the fact that losses were high: Convoy SC 26, attacked by seven U-boats, lost six ships, and when Convoy HX 126 met ten U-boats, ten ships were sunk.

'The life of merchant seamen, especially tanker crews, was a nightmare,' writes Cartier. After victory, Churchill would confess, 'The only thing that really worried me during the war was the U-boat threat'.

'The first U-boat to use the new ports was U-30 under Fritz-Julius Lemp,' wrote the French author Lëonce Peillard in his book *The Battle of the Atlantic*. 'On July 7th 1940, he took on fuel and torpedoes for a tour along the Portuguese coast.

'On August 29th 1940, Dönitz left Sengwarden for ever. He took up quarters in Paris on the Boulevard Suchet until his new headquarters at Kernevel was ready.

'There he hastened to have plans made for new bases along the French Atlantic coast. First Lorient and La Pallice, then Brest and Bordeaux. On October 25th 1940, just after he had met with Franco, Hitler summoned Dönitz to him...'

The conversation between Hitler and his admiral concerned the task of protecting the new U-boat bases against British bombers, for the RAF was mounting day-and-night raids against their deadliest enemy. The new bases could only be useful if the U-boats could be protected from bombing while they were being armed and repaired.

'"I shall give you all you need," said Hitler. "You need do nothing."

'A few days later, Reich Minister Dr Todt visited the U-boat staff and together they worked out a plan for U-boat bunkers - including which terrain was suitable, where the bunkers and the cells would be, and how thick the concrete needed to be. Engineer Dorsch of the Todt Organisation fetched German, Italian, Hungarian and Czech workers to France, then added French workers, and at the base at Kernevel (Lorient), the pace of work was feverish. No fewer than 15,000 men were at work building the vast bunker.

'At the end of 1941, 12 U-boats could dock in La Pallice and 40 in Lorient, the largest German base on the Atlantic – completely safe from bombing.'

The great convoy battles continued. The war at sea became more ruthless by the day. 'In a single night during October – they called it "the night of the long knives" – the wolf pack notched up 31 ships sunk, totalling 173,000 tons,' writes Gerald S. Snyder. 'During the following night, seventeen more were added to the tally, and only thirteen from that convoy reached British ports unscathed. It was no longer unusual for a U-boat to use up all its torpedoes and return home with 50,000 GRT of shipping sunk to its credit.'

The effectiveness of the U-boat fleet would have been considerably increased if Dönitz had been given his own air arm for long-distance reconnaissance duties, but the jealous Göring had put a spanner in his works with the words, 'Everything that flies is mine.'

In January and February 1941, the Luftwaffe put several aircraft of the type FW 200 ('Condor') at Dönitz' disposal, to aid the U-boats in hunting down convoys. For a while the co-operation was successful, and then it came to misunderstandings between the U-boat commanders and the Luftwaffe observers. Finally Göring withdrew his aircraft again and the grey wolves – whose misfortune was their bad eyesight – were forced back on their own resources again. This meant that sometimes a convoy would pass-by unharmed, only a few sea miles over the horizon.

The British Navy, still the most powerful in the world, did all it could to loosen the U-boats' grip. Convoy escorts were strengthened, radar improved, permanent air patrols were instituted, and in March 1941 there was some light at the end of the tunnel for the hard-pressed islanders. Within the space of nine days, they rid themselves of the three most experienced and successful German U-boat commanders and their crews.

The first victim was Günther Prien. On March 6th, he and his U-47 had come across a convoy just south of Iceland and had attacked immediately. Then he encountered a Sunderland flying boat. Prien dived, followed the convoy, attacked again the following morning, but then found himself being chased by two destroyers.

The *Wolverine*, under Captain Rowland, pursued U-47 all day. Prien was an old fox, familiar with all the ruses and tricks of the trade; time and again, he succeeded in throwing the destroyer off the scent. But Rowland had served in submarines, and he knew a thing or two. The duel continued until dark. Shortly after midnight, the British captain bagged the German submarine on his Asdic screen again.

The battle continued. The *Wolverine* lost contact again. But at 5.18 the following morning, she spotted the swell from a U-boat zig-zagging on the surface of the water. Rowland followed at full power. 'Prepare to ram!' he ordered.

Immediately before collision point, the U-boat slipped away, down a depth of about 130 feet. 'I could see her bilges under the water, see the places where the water spilled out,' said the Englishman, who was determined to pursue his quarry to the last drop of fuel and the last depth charge.

'It was not even necessary to score a direct hit with the depth charges,' Gerald S. Snyder writes. 'Water cannot be compressed, and so the waves that ensued after an explosion were very powerful in their effect. Often just one charge was sufficient to puncture the skin of a U-boat, for the explosion alone exercised a pressure of hundreds of tons. If it exploded under the vessel, it would shoot upwards like a rocket, and if it exploded to the side, it could roll the U-boat over, tearing out the rivets or buckling the armour plating, so that the boat began to leak. Or the charges would push the U-boat down to the sea bed. And if just one bomb exploded within 15 metres of the vessel, it could put the propeller and rudder out of action. It would go completely out of control and sink almost immediately.'

For days Wilhelmshaven radioed Prien's boat in vain, 'U-47, report your position, report your position . . .'

U-47 never reported in again. Ever.

It was another ten weeks before the Wehrmacht communiqué announced: 'The U-boat commanded by Captain Günther Prien did not return from its last active service mission.'

Next it was the turn of U-100, commanded by Joachim Schepke. On March 17th, the commander had attacked a convoy off Canada and had been forced to surface by depth charges. Schepke clambered up into his conning tower just in time to see a British destroyer heading straight for him to ram his boat. He was crushed in the collision and all his men died. A bare 30 minutes later, the destroyer *Walker* rammed U-99 under Captain Otto Kretschmer. The commander and most of this crew ended up prisoners of the British.

Just as success seemed within grasp, there came a turning point in the fortunes of the U-boat war. If three of the most experienced and successful commanders could all meet their dooms in such a short time, how would it be for the hastily trained crews that were now replacing the veterans?

The relatively weak submarine branch could not carry on its war against such an overwhelmingly superior enemy alone. The success of the surface raiders was a matter of luck. If the British were to tighten up their defences, the likes of the *Atlantis* would soon be neutralised - added to which, in December Hitler had declared war on the USA, apparently without any idea of the implications for the battle of the Atlantic.

Grand Admiral Raeder, however, saw yet another chance to bring into action the heavy surface vessels that had always been his obsession, and which the pessimists in the Wehrmacht had long since written off. As early as July 1940 he had stated in a memorandum: 'The leadership of the sea war is convinced that the course of the war makes it possible to talk about a virtual rebirth of the battleship.'

The first attempt with the *Admiral Scheer* had gone well. The *Admiral Hipper* was sent into action next. She engaged a strongly defended troop convoy, was forced to withdraw and head for the safety of the nearest German-occupied port at Brest.

At the beginning of 1941, the *Admiral Hipper* fought her way out into the Atlantic again and attacked a convoy near the Azores. Simultaneously, Admiral Günther Lütjens had sneaked through into the North Atlantic with the *Gneisenau* and the *Scharnhorst* to mount raids on shipping. For the moment, four heavy surface vessels were in competition with the U-boats for prizes. Just as Dönitz had achieved a great coup for the U-boat branch with the Scapa Flow sinking, so Raeder wanted his big surface vessels to achieve a clearcut success that would prove their worth.

Raeder was not a flexible man. His nature was authoritarian, and he insisted on his orders being carried out to the letter, even if the officers who had to carry them out were convinced of their foolishness. His two fleet commanders, Admiral Hermann Boehm and Admiral Wilhelm Marschall, could not fall in with his ideas and were sacked. Admiral Günther Lütjens was appointed to succeed them; he had no intention, he said, of becoming the third fleet commander to be sent into the wilderness, and from the outset he left no doubt that he would obey all Raeder's orders implicitly.

What was to happen, however, when orders issued in offices in Berlin turned out to be wildly impractical? One order of Raeder's stated that combat with enemy warships was to be avoided. Since, however, all convoys were accompanied by warships by this time – often by quite strong naval contingents, in fact – the order was quite unrealistic. It was a matter of battle to the death or no battle at all.

The military commanders, however, wanted their big success – but they didn't want to run any risks.

It was within this strange framework that the first voyage of the newly-commissioned battleship *Bismarck* began – only to culminate in one of the greatest tragedies in the history of naval warfare.

The Admiral boards his ship that afternoon, which means no more shore leave. The situation is starting to get serious. There are many signs that the *Bismarck* is preparing for her first active service voyage. The crew eat their pea soup and swap filthy stories, to cover up their nerves.

No one knows what's happening – though everyone's got their own firmly-held theory about it.

The *Bismarck* is still at anchor in Gotenhafen*. Then, half an hour later, she's at sea, heading for the Great Belt and the Skaggerak. The huge engine turbines are turning. The war at sea's bloodiest drama has begun with a quiet slipping of anchor under the simple codename 'Rheinübung'.

The crew are stood down. The auxiliary watch are told to get some sleep, to conserve their strength for the rigours to come. But the youngsters among them, who have not yet experienced war, are much too excited.

'Gentlemen,' says Admiral Günther Lütjens as he greets his officers, Captain Lindemann at their head, in the

*Now Gdynia in Poland.

Admiral's suite to formally issue their orders. 'Tonight our sister ship, the *Tirpitz*, will be dropping anchor here to camouflage our departure. We shall reach Norwegian waters tomorrow morning, swiftly fill our bunkers in Bergen, and then join with the *Prinz Eugen*. A joint operation: Raiding duties in the Atlantic.'

The admiral reels off his speech as if he knows it by heart. 'On the orders of the Commander-in-Chief of the Navy, combat with enemy vessels is to be avoided where possible.' The Admiral looks briefly up from his charts. His face is smooth, expressionless, and a Knight's Cross sits between the slightly over-wide collar of his uniform shirt. 'I assume that the British will realise that the *Bismarck* is moving into an active role by the time we leave Norway. We shall sail out of Bergen with a dummy convoy. All available German U-boats have been ordered into the area of operations. The Luftwaffe is to strengthen its presence there. Any questions?'

'No, Admiral,' says Captain Lindemann.

'I have no doubt,' the Admiral continues, 'that the enemy is aware of the *Bismarck*'s fire power and operational range. He will throw all he has right at us.' He pauses. 'It is a matter of victory or –'

He dismisses the officers with a laconic gesture. Lütjens looks right through them, as if they were made of glass. He is not the kind of man they have affection for and many of his orders are incomprehensible to them. But no one argues: orders are orders. And an officer of what used to be the Imperial Navy carries out his orders, whether he likes them or not.

The ratings have no problem with their attitude. They have dubbed the Admiral 'the black devil'.

The captain is still in charge of his ship, the largest and proudest ship of the German Navy. It took five years to build, has a displacement of 41,700 tons; 89 guns, including four turrets each with two 38-cm guns; a crew of 2403; 190,000 shells in stores; 175,000 horsepower engines; a coating of modern chrome and nickel armour that makes the giant ship immune to torpedoes.

The crew feels a proprietorial pride towards the ship. Almost all of them are volunteers, flocking to join the crew of the flagship. Like all the others, she had been dubbed 'lucky' when she was launched – even though plenty others given the same baptism are sitting on the bottom of the sea. Of course, none of them were any where near as good as the *Bismarck* and her sister ship, the *Tirpitz*.

The navy's most modern ship is a tremendous technological achievement, no one doubts that.

The first combat mission of the flagship of the German fleet will show whether the massive investment in labour, skill, money and time has paid off.

The ship is reckoned unsinkable. The sea trials confirmed that again, even though they were curtailed by two months to bluff the English into thinking that the *Bismarck* was not yet ready.

The *Bismarck* is a floating fortress, and also a floating town, with neighbours who know each other, and passers-by who have never seen each other. There are streets, squares, barber shops, laundries, shoemakers' shops and tailors' workshops. There are even civilians on board, who are subject to military discipline as auxiliary medical orderlies only during formal combat situations.

The ship is 246 metres long and 36 metres wide. A city of men only. The only women are stuck on the bulkheads as pinups, common property of the crew and a major source of conversation.

'Yeah, but what good is it when the flesh is only on paper?' growls Private Lauchs.

The young soldier belongs to the Second Technical Half-Division. They have been excused guard duties for the past two hours, and their adventures so far have been modest: Burger had stomach pains and they have cut out his appendix on the hospital deck. Mössmer was found smoking and has been sent off to do a couple of rounds of the upper deck as punishment. He ran a hundred metres, hopped through a port hole and disappeared. Hengst was ordered to see the Kapitänleutnant and spent three hours looking for him. By the time he found him, the officer had forgotten what he wanted. The private escaped with a mild telling off.

'Do you want any schnaps?' asks Lauchs.

'Cretin!' answers Mössmer and does an exaggerated imitation of his mate's voice. 'Want to go to a whorehouse? Want a blonde or a brunette? Maybe a redhead?'

Hengst makes an obscene gesture.

'Piss off,' says Lauchs. 'What's to eat?'

'Pea soup,' Mössmer grins. 'Little green bastards.'

'Schnaps,' Lauchs persists. 'Five bottles. I saw a civilian

steward stashing it in his locker. Friends,' he says, raising his voice, 'that is contrary to orders.'

'And we'll make sure that orders are observed,' Hengst chips in.

Mössmer frowns. 'Pinching from a comrade,' he says.

'French cognac, three star,' Lauchs continues. 'And male civilian stewards are only half-comrades.'

The others move closer, curious and thirsty. No big fuss. A few of them stand guard while an ex-locksmith among them cracks the crude lock.

Lauchs clasps three bottles to him tenderly. 'I've left him two,' he says. 'See what a decent mate I am.'

There is only the usual ship's noise, a quiet, even hum and growl of engines. The decks are steam-heated. The temperature is regulated by air conditioning. The men are packed tight together in the ratings' quarters. Two officers share each sleeping compartment. Only the Commander, the Admiral and the First Officer have their own cabins.

Their first active service voyage begins with a schnaps orgy so far as the boys of the Second Technical Half-Division are concerned. Petty Officer Lindenberg has a sensitive nose; he can smell alcohol through the thick steel plating. The crew make friends with the drunken petty officer. They booze and banter, and time after time they drink the health of Corporal Link. He's getting married in five days, the ship's first proxy wedding, and so they decide to celebrate in advance.

'What's her name?' asks Lindenberg.

'Else.'

'Got a photo?'

Link supplies a picture willingly.

'Nice face,' says Mössmer with the air of a man who knows class. 'What are her legs like?'

'Terrific.'

'Good tits?'

'Everything a young seaman could want,' murmurs Link with a stupid grin.

'Good in bed?'

'Mind your own damned business,' growls Link, reddening. He decides to put a stop to the conversation, and heads to the other deck to the toilet.

Death makes no distinctions, but toilets are divided according to rank. Whether it's the schnaps, or simply because it's too far to go, Link sneaks into the officers' toilets

– and is promptly spotted on his way out.

'Hey, you!' a young leutnant bawls at him. 'What are you doing here?'

'Nothing, Herr Leutnant.'

'Don't talk rubbish,' says the officer. 'And shit in your own place next time!'

Link snaps to attention. 'Very good, Herr Leutnant!' he roars, and salutes the officer. He is aware that this one is no sailor, it shows a mile off. One of the envied and despised 'passengers', a member of the prize crew of the five pilots on board, a skinny, toffee-nosed type, more of a boy than a man.

'Do you know where the Second Technical Half-Division are?'

'Yes, Herr Leutnant,' Link roars again, and inside he's thinking, 'You beginner, you amateur, you goddammned landlubber!'

'Then take me there, man!'

Shit, Link thinks. If I clear off, I'm in trouble. If he finds we've been boozing, we'll end up in the brig. And if we're in the brig, we're likely to spend the entire jolly sea war staring at the ceiling.

He stops, comes to attention again. Leutnant Ernst Fischer, temporarily transferred to the navy as a pilot, steps onto the deck.

'Attention!' bawls the senior man present.

'Carry on!' the leutnant says, almost in a kind of dazed terror.

There is a half-empty bottle of cognac on the mess table. A corporal tries to hide it.

'Leave it be,' says Ernst Fischer. He grabs a mug and fills it. 'Boozing means the brig,' he says, and swallows it down in one gulp.

The others stand around in astonished silence as the officer and Lindenberg throw their arms round each other like schoolgirls. They don't know that the young flier is engaged to Lore, Petty Officer Lindenberg's younger sister.

'The air's better upstairs,' says Fischer with a laugh. 'But the schnaps is hundred proof down here.'

Suddenly everyone's back in the swing of things. When Corporal Link feels confident enough to come in, to give his mates a belated warning, he sees the officer in the middle of the crowd, engaged in some kind of celebration with Lindenberg. Good fun, war, he thinks. Like travelling by sleeping car. Another cognac, waiter! Petty officers are fantastic. This leutnant from the Luftwaffe is a good bloke, too. The officers in general are great – always asleep or turning a blind eye. Great ship altogether...

They toast everyone and everything in turn. They have no idea that the ship is going about. In the eternal night of the lower deck, they lack any sense of time. They don't see that the flagship of the German fleet is under clear blue skies and has long since anchored in the port of Bergen.

'Operation Rheinübung' has been painstakingly prepared. The Commander-in-Chief North has transferred infantry units to Bergen and is massing armoured units in the port. Dummy convoys are steaming up and down the coast. Pioneer boats are busy. The navy has ships guarding the approaches right up to the Arctic Circle.

These measures are intended to confuse the enemy. He is not to know whether the *Bismarck* is supporting a German invasion of Iceland, escorting a mammoth convoy, or breaking out to raid the Atlantic sea lanes.

Slowly and easily, she slips out of Bergen Fjord, closely followed by the heavy cruiser *Prinz Eugen*, a 14,400 ton ship with a crew of 1600. Once at sea, they form up with two barrage breakers forward and five destroyers providing protection on the flanks for the big ships.

Captain Lindemann has surrendered his command to the Admiral. Course 260°. Sea: 2 to 3. Wind: force 4 to 5. Visibility: 8 sea miles. Speed: 22 knots.

The escort ships are dismissed.

Prinz Eugen and *Bismarck* take a new course. Admiral Lütjens decides on the more dangerous Danish route.

Before the schnaps runs out, the warning sirens howl.

The men of the Second Technical Half-Division sober up very quickly as they stumble towards their action stations...

At the Admiralty in London, they are working at disentangling the threads that point to the Germans' true intentions. Very confusing threads. They have a report from an agent in Bergen that a big German warship has arrived in the port. So far as the British are concerned, a ship without a name.

The *Bismarck* has a legendary name, one that inspires fear even in the most hardbitten English seadog, but they believe that she is still undergoing sea trials in the Baltic.

British Admiral Sir John Tovey has to know whether, and if so in what strength, the German naval force has left Bergen. Any answer could only really come from aerial observation. But on this day, May 21st 1941, the weather is so bad that the entire RAF had been grounded on orders from on high.

After long debates behind closed doors, a volunteer is given permission to take off on a reconnaissance mission: a Captain Rotherham. He has so many combat missions behind him that he had been excused further active service.

He attempts the impossible, using a flying boat of the old-fashioned 'Maryland' type. If he flies too high, he won't be able to see anything, while if he goes too low, he will come within range of the newly-established German radar installations.

He decides to fly beneath the radar. Rotherham powers just above the surface of the fjord at less than 200 feet, flies over the port, penetrates the cloud cover and establishes that the harbour is empty of German warships.

He must make sure. He does one more suicide glide, under lethal fire from the German anti-aircraft positions, before weaving his way out and sending a radio message to England that will resound like a thunderclap: enemy ships weighed anchor!

After landing in England, the pilot runs to a telephone, still in his flying suit. Sir John Tovey hesitates to take countermeasures before discussing the details with Rotherham. Only once he has subjected the captain and his crew to something approaching the 'third degree' does he decide to believe their story and issue a general alert to the British Home Fleet.

The *Bismarck* and the *Prinz Eugen* have an advantage of something like six hours.

The British Admiralty dispatches the heavy cruisers *Suffolk* and *Norfolk* to check the Denmark Strait. The *Hood*, the biggest battleship in the world, the *Prince of Wales* and six destroyers head for the area of the Hvalfjord. The cruisers *Birmingham* and *Manchester* go on patrol west of Ireland. In the west of Scotland, the cruiser *Arethusa* stands ready with five destroyers. The hunt is led by Tovey's flagship, the *George V*, accompanied by the aircraft carrier *Victorious*, seven cruisers and six destroyers. Five more British cruisers lie in wait off the Faroes.

The *Bismarck* is hunter and hunted.

Maybe she is a lucky ship.

She is certainly a lonely one.

The weather is bad. Thick curtains of fog obscure the shapes of the ships. Twelve below zero.

The British cruiser *Suffolk* possesses a modern radar setup. But she manages to locate everything but the *Bismarck*. The first time, it is pack ice, the next time the *Norfolk*. In both cases, she sends premature reports to London that she has found the *Bismarck*.

The *Hood*, commanded by Vice-Admiral Holland, and the *Prince of Wales*, along with six destroyers, change course.

A mistaken report takes them in the right direction, as it happens.

Then the *Suffolk* makes contact for a third time. She knows that this time she has found the *Bismarck* because this time the shells start to fly from the Germans' gun turrets. The *Norfolk* is also engaged by the German flagship.

Both ships retreat at full speed and hide in the fog. Only just in time. Sir John Tovey realises that the *Bismarck* can fire 'blind' by using electronic target-finders.

The English retreat, but they keep contact, if at a respectful distance. *Suffolk* and *Norfolk* seem like nothing so much as little dogs stalking a huge animal from a distance, never daring to come too close.

The *Bismarck* has now nothing to fear from them – though she has reason to beware of the reinforcements that they will have summoned.

Admiral Lütjens is well aware that the order to avoid combat is already a dead letter. The seas are getting rougher, and the waters are icy cold, as friend and foe brace themselves for the last, great classic sea battle.

On May 24th 1941 at 5.05 a.m., after 36 hours and five minutes of active service, the *Bismarck* and the *Prinz Eugen* have made contact with enemy vessels at a point 0.5° north by 38° west. Their observers report: 'Battleship, approx. 46,000 tons. Four turrets with two guns each, calibre 40.6.' There is no doubt that this is the *Hood*, the largest battleship in the world. With a crew of 2400. With radar. With the new anti-aircraft guns.

The two groups of ships have a bare half an hour to ready

themselves for battle. The *Hood* is older, the *Bismarck* ultra-modern. They are now twenty sea miles apart: coming within range.

'Ready for action!' come the orders on both sides. Once in German, once in English. On both sides there are men who have wives, children and mothers. Men who under other circumstances would be accountants, craftsmen, farmers, leading peaceful, useful lives. And whom war has called onto these steel giants. And some of whom will triumph and some die. For such is war.

The alarm sirens scream through the decks of the *Bismarck*. The nerve endings of the men at combat stations shudder in rhythm with thousands of sea boots trampling over the steel floors.

'Can't someone turn that damned thing off?' moans Private Lauchs, clapping his hands over his ears to shut out the din from the siren.

The readiness reports from the artillery, the engine room and the main deck all flood into the ship's nerve-centre, the bridge. The First Officer reports the ship's battle-readiness to her commander. The information is passed on to the Admiral. Men hastily buckle on their combat gear: gas masks, hammers and rolled-up life jackets. The *Bismarck* is heading into battle for the first time, with the *Prinz Eugen* steaming alongside her.

Her opponent behind the thin veil of fog is the *Hood*, the pride of the British fleet. A national symbol. More than twenty years old. Always the centre of attention when the king reviews the fleet. Pictures of her are in children's schoolbooks and hang in offices and private homes.

The *Hood* has one Achilles' heel: her munitions stores. The deck armour is too thin. The British Admiralty has known this for years and has tried repeatedly to do something. But there was always either a shortage of funds, or the *Hood* was off showing the flag somewhere.

Bismarck hoists her battle flags. The *Prinz Eugen* follows suit.

The *Bismarck* opens fire. Her guns vomit death. A 22-second pause between each salvo.

'Covering fire!' bawls the gunnery officer into his mike.

The *Hood* is returning fire, but Vice-Admiral Holland has made a mistake: he has mixed the *Prinz Eugen* up with the *Bismarck*, and is concentrating his fire on the closer – but less lethal – of the two warships. His position is unfortunate. His ships are sailing keel forward towards the enemy vessels and cannot bring their big guns into operation.

But their fire is accurate. The third salvo finds the range. The sea erupts. An inferno of smoke, steel and fire.

'What's that?' Mössmer asks, terrified. 'Us or them?'

'You'll know when you start getting wet feet,' says Petty Officer Lindenberg.

'This is a trap!' moans Lauchs. 'One direct hit in the engine room here, and we'll drown like rats.'

'Shut your face!' Link snaps.

'Your trou-sers full . . . The cheeks of your arse wide o-pen . . .' chants Hengst, to the tune of the Horst Wessel Song, the Nazi anthem.

Lights are burning below deck, but the men are blind so far as the progress of the battle going on above deck is concerned. They feel the exchanges of fire as gentle blows to the back of the head.

Leutnant Fischer is also on combat alert. Senseless. There is nothing for him to do. He's going crazy. He can feel the gentle pain in the stomach that is the frontline soldier's barometer of fear. In his squadron on the Western Front he was reckoned to be an ambitious type. Four kills in combat. But now he's standing around like an idiot with nothing to do.

The *Hood* is moving round into a better combat position. Late – too late.

The *Bismarck*'s next salvo roars from her gun barrels. Her officers peer anxiously through their binoculars.

No sign of impact! What's wrong? No hit? Duds?

Suddenly a hug pillar of flame shoots skywards.

A direct hit. One explosion. 46,000 tons of steel goes up. So quickly that it can't be glimpsed with the naked eye. Red-hot steel is spread over a huge area of sea. 2397 human beings are incinerated.

The *Hood* has been blown to pieces.

Only three men survived. All the other members of her crew died at the moment that the magazine of the *Hood* was hit.

The horrified commander of the *Prince of Wales*, which has already suffered severe damage, watches the battleship sink. He has no choice but to run for it. The two German ships immediately change their direction of fire and both begin to aim for him.

As the English Vice-Admiral Walker sends his laconic report to London, 'The *Hood* has blown up', the decks of the *Bismarck* have erupted into a fever of celebration. Everyone is running around, yelling. Men are in each other's arms, screaming themselves hoarse, punching each other in the ribs.

'Christ, did you see that?' bellows Hengst.

'Why? Did you?' Pfeifer retorts.

'What a war!' Link shouts. 'What a war!'

'Calm down, sailors,' Petty Officer Lindenberg soothes them.

Some are singing, others dancing. Others are turning cartwheels. Everyone is telling everyone else exactly how it happened. The story is going from man to man, getting more colourful as it goes further, even though none of them actually saw the sinking of the *Hood*. Only a handful witnessed it from the bridge and the upper mess deck. A few individuals – and a British film camera.

Then the Admiral's voice comes over the p.a. to restore calm.

'This is the Admiral of the Fleet speaking,' the voice resounds through all decks. 'Men, we have won a magnificent victory . . . We have destroyed the enemy's greatest battleship. The enemy will be bent on revenge. We shall have to reckon with his ruthless attention, the power of an enemy who outnumbers us ten, perhaps twenty to one. We shall meet him with the same courage with which we met and vanquished the *Hood*.' Lütjen's voice remains matter-of-fact. 'At this moment we can have only one watchword,' he concludes. 'Victory or death!'

All at once, there is a stillness among the men of the Second Technical-Half Division. 'Yeah, well,' growls Petty Officer Lindenberg. 'He's a mad bastard.'

'I hope he's not too far gone, that's all,' retorts Lauchs.

It's gone quiet on the other decks as well. Many men are writing letters, others having a smoke, and now the loudspeakers are pouring out soft music, especially the current big hit and the song most requested by the crew: 'Come Back'.

But the 2403 men on board the steel colossus know that whether or not they return depends on the British. Without anyone saying it openly, there is a quiet, unspoken question haunting the ship: what is the enemy doing?

The *Hood* has been blown apart and the *Prince of Wales* has been seriously damaged. The *Bismarck* has been damaged, but only to an extent that is repairable with equipment carried on board. According to the classic rules of naval warfare, the way cadets learn them at the academy, the tactic now is simple: attack, destroy and disappear.

The *Prince of Wales* is so badly damaged that she can scarcely defend herself. Captain Lindemann suggests to his chief that they deliver the *coup de grâce* and then disappear into the vastness of the Atlantic as quickly as possible.

'No,' Lütjens replies, without reason or explanation. It is not his decision, however, but is in line with orders from on high from the inflexible Admiral Raeder, whose word was: no combat unless absolutely unavoidable. He had been forced to fight the *Hood*; it is possible to avoid combat with her crippled companion. It is senseless, but orders are orders – and his career is his career.

His companion ship, the *Prinz Eugen* remains on their old course for some three hours. At about 18.20, the Admiral dismisses the ship and she sails off in a south-westerly direction.

On this Saturday, the 24th May 1941, the devil seems to have got it in for the British Navy. Around midday, the weather takes a turn for the worse. Sleet and rain storms. Fat, black clouds in the sky.

At the Admiralty in London's Whitehall, the officers on duty have hardly got out of their clothes for days. The same question, over and over: where is the *Bismarck*? What is her course? Will the flagship of the German fleet duck back to port or continue raiding operations in the Atlantic? At the time that Admiral Sir John Tovey, the Commander of the Home Fleet, received the bad news about the *Hood*, his flotilla, led by his own flagship, the *King George V*, was 550 miles from the site of the sinking. He did not know that the *Bismarck* had been hit several times during the course of the battle. And again one of those incredible coincidences intervened. The Sunderland flying boat Z 201, circling over the scene of the carnage shortly afterwards, radioed in: losing oil. The decoders assumed that the plane was referring to its own engines and did not pass the message on to Admiral Tovey. Thus instead of exploiting the chance to press home his pursuit of the German flagship, he spent time gathering a huge armada together.

The forces drafted into the hunt for the *Bismarck* on the English side totalled: 8 battleships and battlecruisers, 2 aircraft carriers, 4 heavy cruisers, 7 light cruisers, 21 destroyers and 6 submarines, along with a host of aircraft. While his huge fleet gathers, covering an area of 8000 square sea miles and representing a crushing superiority in fire power and numbers, the Admiral lies down for a few hours. Sir John Tovey is a tall, easygoing man who spreads confidence like a radiance among his staff. When the latest piece of bad news comes in, his officers hesitate to wake him. Towards four in the morning, the responsibility becomes too much for them. They shake him awake with the news, 'the *Bismarck* has disappeared.'

This time, however, fortune favours the British. As they flounder around in the thick fog, Admiral Lütjens betrays himself by breaking his radio silence. Wrongly believing that enemy ships are close by, he makes radio contact with Group West.

The English track him down, but the dawning of the following day reveals another shock, giving the German battleship a seven-hour advantage. The location was correct, the position was perfectly calculated, but the ship is not where the British believe her to be.

442 minutes later, it turns out that the grid squares of the English chart were the wrong size. Sir John Tovey has presided over a costly blunder. He is now some 100 sea miles from the *Bismarck* and desperately searching for her new position. The Admiral has only one hope now: the planes aboard the *Ark Royal*, which has been ordered to the area from its base at Gibraltar, are approaching to within range.

On May 26th at 10.30 in the morning, a Catalina out of Northern Ireland spots a battleship. Position: 49° 33′ north, 21° 50′ west. Course 150. Speed of the ship: approximately 20 knots. The Catalina reports the sighting immediately. Soon the British communications system is buzzing, and the entire fleet knows it: the *Bismarck* has been found.

From now on, things really begin to hot up – and the ships that feel the heat are mostly English.

15 Torpedo-launching aircraft of the 'Swordfish' type take off from the *Ark Royal*. They approach at a medium altitude, find their ship, identify it as the *Bismarck*, then dive and fire their deadly steel fish. It does not occur to the young pilots – most of them still in the middle of their training – to ask

themselves why the 'enemy' is not defending himself. It is not until the last three are making their approaches that someone realises that they are not attacking the *Bismarck* but their own ship, the *Sheffield*. After an initial wave of panic, Admiral Tovey is forced to ask himself why, despite numerous direct hits, the Swordfish pilots failed to sink their brother ship.

There is only one explanation: the modern magnetic fuse fitted to the torpedoes must have failed. The English commander issues orders for the torpedoes to be fitted with old-style fuses. And the Swordfish are ready to set off for a second time. The deck of the aircraft carrier lurches and heaves in the seas as the aircraft are fuelled and loaded with the new torpedoes. It is 19.00. The clouds are hanging low over the sea at no more than 600 feet. A strong wind is blasting them across the sky. The crew are crowded onto the flight deck in a kind of anxious celebration, strong and fit young men burning to wipe out the blemish of their mistake on the *Sheffield*.

Their propellers begin to turn. The engines roar into action. Slowly, almost reluctantly, the planes rise from the deck, then gain altitude quickly, take a direct course for the German battleship.

The alarm siren sounds on board the *Bismarck*. Her guns position themselves in an iron band around the ship.

The first Swordfish explodes in mid-air. Her burning wreckage plunges into the sea. But the next is coming on. Very close behind. For a few moments it seems as if she is standing to attention in the air.

Then she releases her torpedo.

A torpedo that bounces and settles in the water!

Heading for starboard.

The German guns blaze at the speeding metal eel. A shell scores a direct hit. An explosion. A great pillar of water.

But the British keep coming from every direction.

The brave, almost foolhardy, British pilots weave their way inside the Germans' defences. The *Bismarck* responds by zig-zagging at full speed. She avoids three, four torpedoes.

Then a Swordfish dives from astern. The torpedo slices through the water with a low hiss. The two-cm German guns fail to find their range quickly enough. At first short. Then too far right, left. A shudder goes through the fo'csle. The *Bismarck*'s stern lifts, she is thrown round and ends up steaming in a circle.

A lucky hit on the rudder.

The Swordfishes turn away. Their crews don't yet realise that they have crippled the pride of the German fleet. But the Germans realise it only too well. They can no longer steer the ship. Technical personnel are hurried to the stern. Divers go down to inspect the damage. They work like madmen. Then the message starts to spread through the ship: 'Rudder damaged. Repairs in operation. Every hope of correcting the situation.'

But the exhausted divers who arrive back on deck know far better. There is no question that the damage is repairable at sea. They tell the officers. The officers order them to keep their mouths shut in front of other crew members.

At 21.05 Admiral Lütjens reports to Group West that he is 47° 40′ north, 14° 50′ west. Direct hit by torpedo in his stern.

Group West promises to send U-boats to help. It sticks to its promise. The big battleship trails round in a weary half-circle, heading for its inevitable execution. The crew has one night to prepare for death.

Right to the last, the crew resists the ghastly guest that is haunting the decks: death itself. Men in overheated rooms tremble as if they were caught in a frost, while men on the frozen upper decks find themselves sweating.

In the grey light of dawn, Leutnant Fischer is summoned to the commander's quarters to receive his orders. He is to fly the war diary of the ship to safety.

'We're shortening the voyage,' says Captain Lindemann sardonically. He offers the young flier his hand. 'Break a leg!'

Conditions are wretched. Dressed in fur-lined suits, the Leutnant and his co-pilot, a Luftwaffe Feldwebel, begin to make themselves ready to be catapaulted off the ship.

Men throng around the plane and the two pilots, forcing pieces of paper and letters onto them - agonised, hastily scribbled last words to parents, wives, children.

'Ready!' says a technician.

Just as Fischer is about to climb into the cockpit, his future brother-in-law, Petty Officer Lindenberg, comes up to him. He had been on his way to the dressing station to have a minor wound treated when he learned that Ernst was about to take off.

'Good luck,' he says, and can't meet the man's eye. His voice is steady, maybe a little too steady. 'Say hello to my parents,' and now his voice is breaking slightly. 'And take good care of Lore.'

'Come on, you'll be back a bit later,' says the Leutnant, and stares down at the dirty floor of the deck.

'Yeah. Sure,' Lindenberg answers. 'See you,' he adds, and walks off without turning round. Then Leutnant Fischer disappears into his Arado 196 Seaplane.

'The rats are leaving the sinking ship,' says a seaman as he watched them climb.

'Shut up,' says another.

'Reckon they'll make it?'

'Well, I'd say they've sure as hell got better chances than we have.'

'Chance. I like that.'

'When they have the next war, I'm going to volunteer for the Luftwaffe,' says a petty officer with a laugh. 'When there's nothing doing, they spend all their time playing cards, and when things get hot, they simply piss off.'

The sailors' gazes are fixed on the little aircraft, hungrily and with a kind of terrible longing.

The propeller is in motion. The engine has been warmed up. The Leutnant looks up from his controls and nods. The technician in charge of the catapult pulls his lever.

The Arado will be launched by air pressure from the deck.

The leutnant shrugs off his despondency – and his embarrassment at the fact that he, of all people, has been chosen to be saved. Now, however, he is no longer on the swaying deck of the ship; he is already aloft and in his element. His engines are screaming, straining to go.

They are ready for the catapult to fire. A last wave. The throttle is fully opened. Full on the accelerator.

'Shit. What's up?'

The catapult's not working. They'll have to get out.

'Don't worry,' the technician calls out. 'The compressed air hose has got tangled!'

Then another attempt. Futile. Leutnant Fischer clambers out, sweating. All the letters and papers are still crackling in his pocket. Those last greetings. He marches off to his cabin. His Feldwebel follows, watches with astonishment as the pilot hauls a pistol out of his pocket. Puts it to his temple.

'It's all shit,' he moans, and blows a bullet through his head.

None of the 1600 ratings and officers of the heavy cruiser *Prinz Eugen* will ever forget this sinister, endless night. They won't forget the heat, or the cold, the dawning horror.

Breakers the height of houses are washing over the upper decks. The wind is whipping the sea into a frenzy, tearing holes in the milky curtains of fog, sending the men on watch crazy and summoning up ghost ships, spitting salt water in their eyes and mouths.

The sailors talk quietly. They have had the need for silence drummed into them by their officers. No one on the upper deck is allowed to smoke. The enemy has not yet realised that the *Prinz Eugen* has split away from the *Bismarck*. Half of the crew has been excused watch, but most of the men are too tired to sleep. Men's minds are never excused watch, nor is their fear.

The huge engines rumble monotonously. The heavy seas hurl the cruiser from side to side as if she were a tin can. Barrels are floating in the water. German U-boats found and decimated an enemy convoy in the vicinity. Messages chase across the radio waves. A few transmissions from the *Bismarck* are picked up and decoded. No one can make much sense of the babble of radio messages. The English are going absolutely berserk in the transmissions.

The heavy cruiser, 210 metres long, 22 metres wide, has eight 20.3cm guns in four double turrets, two on the fo'csle and two on the quarter deck, plus more than a dozen 10.5cm twin anti-aircraft guns, as many 3.7cm flaks, and a few machine guns. She can steam at 32 knots and is therefore exactly as fast as the *Bismarck*. She took four years to build and has a displacement of 10,000 tons – strictly in accordance with the Washington Agreement of 1921, which does not include fuel, reserves of drinking water and so on. With these extras, the ship weighs in at a total of 19,800 tons.

New watch. Report to the officer of the watch. Instructions over the loudspeaker system. Then a slow waltz: 'I'll dance with you to heaven'. Suddenly the music stops. An uncanny silence. The food congeals in the men's stomachs. Herrings with mashed potatoes. Many of them throw up. Tablets are simply ineffective against this level of seasickness. Plus the terrible thirst. The men pour coffee down their throats, throw up, then fill their 'searchlights' – their mess tins – again and throw up again.

Eight men from the Third Marine Division are on duty at their combat station. Bosun Schwarz is making his inspection. He stops and stares at the pale, contorted face of

Seaman Marx. 'Good God. What's up with you?'
'Feel bad, Bosun.'
'Then sick it up, man!'
'Can't, Bosun.'
'Use your fingers!'
'That doesn't work either!'
'Wouldn't mind a schnaps,' says Gnuschke.
'You'd like that, eh? Schnaps and a woman with nice big tits,' Schwarz leers.
'I prefer slim ladies,' Gnuschke answers.
'You'll take what you damned well get,' Weinberger chips in.
'Well, you can forget the whole tribe of women until we get home,' says Bosun Schwarz.
Some of the men aren't sure where their nerves have gone, while others don't know where they got them from. With each minute of this weird, silent voyage, the *Prinz Eugen* is distancing itself more from the *Bismarck*.
Now they are alone. Alone in the middle of the hostile Atlantic. And they're learning to deal with something that no sea trials can teach: fear. Those futile hand movements, those dumb questions to keep the mind occupied, and the terse answers. Each man aware of both the coward and the hero in his own personality.
Their commander, Captain Brinkmann, has been on his bridge all night. He is of medium height, stocky, and if he put on a civilian suit you would hardly spot him for a naval officer. Right when he first took over the ship, he found the right words to describe what it was that he wanted to create on the *Prinz Eugen*. With pride and firmness he announced over the loudspeaker, 'We are a happy ship.'
At this point, at four in the morning and with the sea infested with British hunters, there was not much time for jollity. The *Prinz Eugen*'s escape seemed to have succeeded. The cruiser's newly-installed radar showed no enemy vessels in the vicinity. Radio messages were instantly laid before the commander. From them he learns that the *Bismarck* was torpedoed by a Swordfish shortly before the *Prinz Eugen*'s departure. But Admiral Lütjens tells Group West that the hit was not important.
Some British messages are also picked up and decoded. Captain Brinkmann knows now that the *Bismarck*'s speed is limited, and that she is losing oil. But she is still ahead of the

enemy. So long as Admiral Lütjens does the right things, he will get away.

Perhaps the *Prinz Eugen* will succeed in drawing some of the enemy's attention from the flagship. The cruiser is fully operational and ready for combat, fast and manoeuvrable, fitted out with all the most advanced marine technology. She has no need to fear the enemy so long as she doesn't have to face an overwhelming superiority.

Brinkmann's orders are to act as a long-distance raider. A dangerous command. Without escort, without air support, without proper planning or preparation, without destroyers or U boats – the *Prinz Eugen* will have to operate alone, left entirely to her own devices.

It is now four in the morning, and the wind has suddenly dropped. A dim, colourless daylight is beginning to penetrate through the drifting clouds.

If the weather continues to improve, the British will attack with aircraft. And it is inevitable that the *Prinz Eugen* will be spotted sooner or later.

Time passes with tortuous slowness and plays cat and mouse with the men's nerves. Nothing dramatic has happened since the sinking of the *Hood.*

Then the hideous scream of the alarm bell rips through the decks of the *Prinz Eugen*. Enemy aircraft in sight! Hundreds of pairs of sea boots trample over the decks. A Sunderland flying boat is circling over the cruiser. A reconnaissance plane. Now, twelve hours after the German ship had started her dash for freedom, the British have learned that the two prides of Hitler's fleet are no longer together.

'Nothing we can do,' bellows the First Artillery Officer, Lieutenant-Commander Paulus, to the man by his side. 'The bastards are flying high.'

'I'd do the same,' says the petty officer.

'Of course.' Paulus stares up at the tiny dot circling in the sky 25,000 feet above them. 'Let's wait and see.'

Paulus's face – and his jokes – are known throughout the ship's company. He is the most popular officer aboard the *Prinz Eugen*. He always has a pack of cards in his tunic pocket, and when there's nothing much happening he's liable to whip them out and do a trick for his men. He is actually a professional magician as well as an artillery officer. And his life story is about as exotic and varied as it could be for a man just turned forty.

He left school at sixteen, not entirely of his own free will, got himself to occupied Belgium, turned up on the doorstep of his father, an Admiral, made confession of some of his sins, and in 1917, under the reluctant protection of his father, he joined up to entertain the troops. It was there that he had learned his first tricks.

Then came the end of the war. Now Paulus joined an Italian travelling circus and developed a useful act.

'Ladies and gentlemen, here you see the greatest magician of the century. I shall perform for you attractions that no other artiste in the world has mastered. Thank you.'

And he would make rotten eggs disappear, saw girls in half, conjure up swans with two necks, swallow fire and breathe water.

When he got sick of all that, he sat down quietly and got his school leaving examination through an adult education institute, volunteered for the navy, and got his commission, despite a hundred days spent in the brig. He soon became known as one of the navy's most able gunnery officers.

But here, matched against a very high-flying Sunderland that appeared, disappeared, came back, disappeared again, and returned half an hour later, even a master magician could feel pretty helpless. Tense hours passed without anything happening. Why not? the men asked themselves. When was the enemy actually going to come?

Hours of uncertainty turned into days. Nothing happened. At least not on the *Prinz Eugen*. Nothing at all. Nothing on May 26th, nothing on May 27th, except for radio interceptions from the *Bismarck*, which gradually became more desperate, more frantic. Now everyone knew the scale of the tragedy and the slaughter that was being played out a few hundred sea miles from the *Prinz Eugen*. Now everyone knew that the flagship of the German fleet, disabled by a British torpedo, was waiting for death.

The men stood silent and bitter at their combat stations. They left their food untouched, refused to talk about the situation, even found they didn't want their cigarettes or want to hear jokes; they stared blankly past each other, obeyed orders mechanically, felt like hammering with their bare fists against the sharp steel bulkheads, screaming, cursing, crying, praying, or weeping, despairing.

For the first time, they had realised that they were surrounded, like the *Bismarck* by the British fleet, at bay and with not much more chance than the flagship's doomed crew.

Admiral Lütjens, the highest-ranking 'passenger' on board the *Bismarck* and operational commander of the disastrous *Rheinübung*, has sent his final radio message. One of them said: 'Ship incapable of manoeuvre. We shall fight to the last shell. Long live the Führer. Commander of the Fleet.'

The *Bismarck* is past saving, without even any chance of damaging the enemy. The sick battleship can only drag itself painfully, slowly and directionlessly across the ocean, preparing itself for a death-struggle, with about as much chance as an animal prepared for slaughter in the arena. But an animal is an animal. On board the *Bismarck* are 2300 human beings, most of them less than 30 years old. They have mothers, wives, girlfriends and sisters, and they would also have - in a sane world - the right to go home.

The *Graf Spee* found herself in a similar situation at the mouth of the River Plate in December 1939. Her commander, Captain Hans Langsdoff, was personally ordered by the Führer to fight to the death and to go under in an orgy of blood, death and twilight of the gods drama. Langsdorff was an officer, and an officer's job is to obey. Langsdorff was, however, also a human being. He sank the *Graf Spee*, saved the lives of his crew, and then shot himself afterwards to prove that he had not acted out of a cowardly instinct of self-preservation.

Admiral Lütjens is also an officer, and certainly also a human being. But he will not behave humanely; instead he will subject himself and his ship to the Führer's wish for perverse, sadistic death drama, an insane act of self-destruction that will do no harm to England and will serve Germany not at all.

The other side is preparing for the last act. On board the *King George V*, the crew are being fed encouragement and benzedrine. Letters are being written, jokes made, experiences recounted, speculations being made about the future, and tea with rum drunk.

At 8.43, the ship reaches a point less than 12 miles from the *Bismarck*.

Admiral John Tovey gives the order to open fire.

The first salvo spews out of the guns. On the *Rodney* too, the 40.6 centimetre turrets open up.

The *Bismarck* remains silent.

Not until two minutes have passed does she return fire.

'Fifty-five seconds to impact,' reports a British gunnery officer.

The crippled German giant opens fire on the *Rodney* first. Her first salvo falls short. But the third is on target.

The *Rodney* turns about and concentrates all her guns on the *Bismarck*.

The *Norfolk* intervenes from the north-east.

The heavens darken over with the bilious smoke of the explosions. Day becomes night, and the night is filled with flashes, with shrapnel and tearing impacts of high-explosive on metal, until the artificial night is a merciful veil over thousands of men's deaths.

The *Bismarck*'s defensive capacity is weakening by the moment.

Turret 'Anton' is knocked out of action. Turret 'Caesar' has only one gun left in operation. On the so-called Hindenburg Square, on the upper deck, the piles of corpses are turning into mountains. The flags on the mast are burning. Marines trapped by fires scream hideously for help that will never come. The flagship of the German fleet is turning into a wreck.

The crew of the *Bismarck* is involved in a struggle to the death. The wounded are tended to in the middle of exploding shells, and men driven from their stations by fires and damage report to the collection points like clockwork; everyone pulls their weight, hauling boxes of ammunition, cooling the red-hot gun barrels with fire extinguishers, rescuing trapped comrades.

Admiral Lütjens is killed on his bridge. A direct hit blows the First Officer's head clean off. The giant ship is an inferno above the waterline, but below everything is still intact and functioning, with the lights burning, the turbines turning, cigarettes burning, rumours spreading, conversations going on. The explosions of the shells seem like distant drums, scarcely distinguishable from the *Bismarck*'s own fire.

'You can say what you like,' says Private Lauchs. 'It's downright cosy down here.'

'Yeah. Just like an air-raid shelter,' Mössmer agrees.

'And she's still keeping her end up,' Link says. 'Those Tommies can blast away until their teeth drop out.'

The divisional officer enters the engine room.

'How are things, sir?' comes the urgent question from all over the engine room.

'Terrific . . . are you worried?'

'No,' says Lauchs. 'Not exactly worried. Just bored.'

The telephone buzzes. The officer picks up the receiver. The men stare at him through the short conversation.

'Okay,' the officer says then. 'Who feels drawn up to deck?'

'Everyone,' says Lauchs.

'And who's had some first aid experience?'

'All of us.'

The officer gives the problem some brief thought, then asks the petty officer, 'How many men can you spare. At the most?'

'Three.'

The officer looks from one man to another. 'I'm not enjoying this. All right: come on Lauchs, Mössmer and Link. Get ready.'

The three hesitate for a moment.

'Gentlemen, we don't have time for long farewells . . . we'll all see each other again.'

The gangways are still lit, the passages are free and there is no panic. Then the three see their first wounded. They climb through a buckled hatchway, accustom themselves to the smoke, the stench – and the experience of climbing over the bodies of the dead.

Finally they reach the emergency dressing station. Lauchs goes up to Staff Medic Thiele.

'Where are we supposed to report?' he asks.

'You can report where you like,' the officer snaps. He is working in his shirtsleeves. His hair is hanging over his face. He is panting with the exertion. He is cursing. When he talks to wounded men, however, his voice changes dramatically, becomes soft, almost tender. The three newcomers stand around in bemused silence, unable to look away however much they try.

'I can't do this,' says Link. 'I can't go another step. Stop it! Just stop this crap!'

'Pull yourself together!' Mössmer bellows at him.

'I can't go on,' moans Link.

The British guns resume their fire. A man is fumbling with a pocket lamp.

'We'll have the emergency lighting on again in a moment,' calls a Feldwebel.

'How much morphine do we have left?' a medic asks. 'Leave him. He's dead. Go on, don't stand there like idiots,'

he bawls at Mössmer the next moment. 'Carry him out!'
'Where?'
'Anywhere there's room!'
Link has had enough. Mössmer shouts at him, but he doesn't react. Then the emergency lighting flickers into life. The private mutters something to himself. He doesn't even seem to realise that he's praying, and it could just as well be that he's cursing. Who prays with his teeth clenched? Link repeats the words until they acquire some sort of meaning, draws back in fear of his own voice. He feels ashamed and struggles to rise above his own shame. 'Our father,' he begins. 'Our father . . .'
'No!' a wounded man screams. 'You can't cut my leg off! You're crazy . . . !'
'Who art in heaven – '
'Shut up!' Mössmer roars at Link. 'For God's sake, shut your mouth, or I'll punch your face in . . .'
'Hallowed be Thy name – Give us this day our daily bread –'
'He'll drive us all crazy!' Mössmer screams. 'Just stop it! Give us a hand and stop that crap!'
'And forgive us our trespasses,' Link continued, as if he hadn't heard him. 'As we forgive those who trespass against us –'
For a moment, all was still. Even the shells seemed to be giving way to the power of that prayer. Cynicism, fear, shame and hysteria had all disappeared. The wounded men whimpered softly. Then, suddenly, there was the sound of barked commands echoing through the gangways. Nevertheless, in that moment, despite everything, that hell of an emergency dressing station had been transformed into a place of worship.
Then came the next salvo.
A direct hit. Link will fall silent. For ever. Lauchs puts an arm around him. Mössmer helps carry him. 'Amen,' he says as he sets him down.
'Water,' one of the four men in the corner begs. A piece of shrapnel has torn his stomach open.
'In a moment,' says Thiele, and motions to an orderly.
'But we can't do that,' the man answers.
'Dammit,' Thiele roars. 'Do what I say!'
Most of the wounded have already been carried up onto the deck and thrown into the water. Many have made desperate

attempts to prevent it. But it is their only chance of surviving – if there is any chance at all.

Petty Officer Häuser is brought in. Both his legs have been blown off. The MO bends over him. 'Listen, I don't have time to bandage you up. Do you understand that?'

'Yes.'

'The cold water may stop the bleeding. There's a chance. But you'll have to be damned strong and be really clear that you intend to survive. Got that?'

'Yes, sir.'

'Take him out.'

And now, in the midst of all this misery and death, on board this burning wreck of a proud ship, an incredible miracle will occur. They will throw Petty Officer Häuser overboard, as carefully as they can, and the man will have an iron will. He will struggle for hours against unconsciousness. He will find an uncanny energy to combat death. He will withstand unimaginable pain. The sea will carry him way over to the other side, towards the *Dorsetshire*, the enemy cruiser lurking beyond range. British seamen will spot the wounded men floating in the water. Häuser will somehow find the strength to grab the rope thrown out by the enemy crew. Dozens of other German sailors, for whom these few moments are a matter of life and death, will hold back to allow this maimed comrade to be hauled up. He will be taken aboard the British vessel, given emergency surgery, and he will survive.

The medical team work with awesome efficiency during these last few minutes before the *Bismarck* goes down. A thousand hands work busily, even though the wreck is due to disintegrate any moment. Even after the direct hit, dozens of wounded are got up to the upper deck. Many of them try to prevent it, lash out, scream and moan. Their reactions become the most extreme when they are on deck and just about to be put overboard. Some of the team return below, denying their fear and their awareness that they may not have time to get on deck before the disaster. What's the use of throwing these people overboard? What's the use of trying to do anything for anyone on the *Bismarck*?

'Leave them,' says Thiele. 'Give me some morphine – all we've got. No, don't worry about sterilising the needles. Just get out of here, Weber. You'll miss out . . .'

'But what about these men, sir? What will happen to them?' asks the orderly.

Thiele shakes his head grimly. 'I'll give you three guesses.'

Then he is alone with the moaning and whimpering of the wounded.

Until now, Thiele has had no time to think of himself, or of what lies ahead for him. Or of his home and family. But now, in these final, terrible moments, the feeling of fear, of anger, of futility and waste pours in on him, just as, while the ship goes down, the water is pouring in on the hundreds trapped below... Suddenly, Thiele allows himself to feel death. He is consumed by an urge to go up onto the deck. There is still just time. He has done his duty, and more...

One of the wounded men is still moving. The young navy doctor makes a decision, goes over to him and gives him an injection. Then it is his own turn. He rolls up his sleeve, puts the needle in under the skin, then administers the injection, very gently and carefully, just as he would to one of his patients.

He lies down next to the wounded man. The man is smiling his thanks, even in that sleep from which he will never awake.

Medical Officer Thiele will also sleep for ever.

Only one gun turret is still firing. On the flight deck of the *Ark Royal*, a Swordfish has succeeded in taking off under the most difficult circumstances. Two others have followed. They circle over the burning wreck of the German battleship. In his book *Hunting the Bismarck* C.S. Forester reproduces their eyewitness accounts:

'The smoke was pouring from the battered, almost shapeless hull of the *Bismarck*, stripped of her upper works, mast, funnels, bridge and all. Yet under the smoke, plainly in the dull grey light, he could see a forest – a small grove, rather – of tall red flames roaring upward from within the hull. But it was not the smoke nor the flames that held the eye, strangely enough, but the ceaseless dance of tall jets of water above her. Two battleships were flinging shells at her both from their main and from their secondary armaments; and from the cruisers, twenty-eight-inch guns were joining in. There was never a moment when she was not ringed in by the splashes of near misses, but when the leader forced his eye to ignore the distraction of the wild water dance, he saw something else; from bow to stern along the tortured hull he could see a continual coming and going of shell bursts, volcanoes of flame and smoke. From that low height as the Swordfish closed in he could see everything. He could see the two fore-turrets useless, one of them with the roof blown clean off and the guns pointing over the side at extreme elevation, the other with the guns fore and aft drooping at extreme depression. Yet the aftermost turret was still in action; even as he watched he saw one of the guns fling out a jet of smoke towards the shadowy form of the *King George V*; down there in the steel turret nestling among the flames some heroes were still contriving to load and train and fire. And he saw something else at the last moment of his approach. There were a few tiny foreshortened figures visible here and there scrambling over the wreckage incredibly alive amid the flames and the explosions, leaping down from the fiery hull into the boiling sea . . .'

The *Bismarck* has a strong list to starboard. She is out of ammunition. At last - much too late - the formal order to abandon ship is issued. Explosive charges are prepared in the engine room. Senior Engineer Fischer ignites the fuses by hand, thus sacrificing his own life. The first men to leave jump from the wrong side and are dashed against the bilge keel.

The ship's commander refuses to abandon the *Bismarck*; he stands on deck, fully visible to all, and salutes the men treading water in the sea.

The *Bismarck* goes over to starboard. Very slowly, very gradually, as if she wants to give the men crowded aft as much time as possible to make their plunge into the waters. Then everything speeds up. Her keel goes into the air, and then her stern goes down. Her propellers are still turning. They are the last thing to disappear. Then it is over. The world's most modern warship has sunk. Survivors claim that she was sunk by her own crew, while the English claim her as a victim of their air-launched torpedoes. Whichever is true, it makes no difference to the actual event.

Hundreds of survivors are treading water in the Atlantic. The sea is getting rougher all the time. The first twenty or thirty are close to the stern of the *Dorsetshire*. The British throw down lines, haul the Germans up. It is Petty Officer Lindenberg's turn. He is helping a wounded comrade.

And then something terrible happens.

The English sight a German U-boat.

The sirens wail.

The lifesaving operation is called off. Because the survivors are not letting go of the ropes but are trying to haul themselves up with the last of their strength, the lines are cut – leaving the men in the water to face death for the last time with a tiny length of safety still clutched in their hands.

Of the 2403 crew members and passengers on the *Bismarck*, 83 are taken aboard the *Dorsetshire* and 30 aboard the *Maori*. About a half of them are close to death. The English do what they can. When a German dies, they drop their flags to half mast.

At 13.00 on May 27th 1941, the Reuter Agency reports: '*Bismarck* sunk.'

At 13.22, Group West asks for a report from the Commander of the Fleet.

But there is no reply from the *Bismarck*.

It is at about this time that the survivors begin to realise slowly that they have lived through the débâcle. A trained German surgeon placed himself at the disposal of the British on board the *Dorsetshire* as they worked to save the lives of the shipwrecked Germans. He hung his uniform jacket on a hook in the ante-room of the hospital deck, put on a borrowed white gown, and acted as interpreter, helped with operations, said comforting words to men as they came out of the anaesthetic.

The battle to save men's lives went on for hours. When the German medical officer came to himself again, he looked for his jacket and found that all the buttons had been cut off by British souvenir-hunters. For a moment he was furious, until exhaustion overcame him.

The captain of the *Dorsetshire* learned of the incident. He had a notice posted up to the effect that the stealing of the buttons from a British seaman's uniform would be considered unworthy and demanding that his men show the same consideration by returning the buttons in a box provided for the purpose. By the same evening, the German was able to take possession of every one of the stolen buttons.

It was all so close together: life and death, greatness and pettiness, tragedy and destruction, banality and horror, and a dash of humanity, during that man-made apocalypse in the Atlantic.

Aboard the *Prinz Eugen*, May 27th saw the morale of the crew sink to rock bottom. The *Bismarck* was out of radio contact. Messages to Group West remained unanswered. The ocean all around the *Prinz Eugen* seemed empty of all life. It was then that the captain received the horrifying report he had feared for hours.

Seaman Heinz Tröger is working on a buoy. He is big, strong, pale and unsteady. He is noticeably clumsy. Petty Officer Döhring is standing behind him.

'I'm having you taken off this job, Tröger,' says the petty officer.

'No, petty officer. I don't want to. I... I can't go.' Suddenly he jumps up and screams as loud as he can, 'I'm going crazy! I'm going crazy! Leave me here! Leave me here, or I'll jump overboard, or shoot myself! Shit all of you! I can't stand it!' His voice drops suddenly. Panting and stammering, he forces out the words, 'I'm scared... I'm so scared I can't stand it any more.'

'Pull yourself together, Tröger. I know this business is shit. Just lie down...'

'I don't want to!' Tröger bellows.

Everyone knows the face of Seaman Heinz Tröger. Just as everyone knows Fritz Tröger. Two brothers, so alike they can't be told apart, and with only a year between them. Their father was killed in the First World War, and they went to the same school, kissed the same girls at the same dancing classes, both volunteered for the navy, joined the same unit, swapped leave passes because none of their superiors could tell them apart, travelled on leave together, had a good time.

Their mother is in poor health. But she is good at 'pulling herself together'. Whenever her sons come home, she never shows how sick she is. It is only when the time for parting comes close that she finds it hard to keep the façade up, and she becomes paler, quieter, stops eating, has eyes red from crying, asks no questions, gives no answers. She raised them both on a miserable pension that was the Fatherland's thanks for what she lost in the First War; her husband had never come back from Verdun. His photograph still hangs above his desk, and the flowers on the table are changed daily.

And her sons grew up. They had to be as strong, as decent and as hardworking as their father had been before a shell blew his head off.

And then came another war. And then they took her sons away from her, as they had her husband twenty-five years before. They laughed as they left her; they were young and optimistic, and, of course, they were staying together.

Until a week previously. An hour before the *Bismarck* weighed anchor, both brothers were called to the orderly room. They were not too worried. They had had a few drinks together. They had spent a while in the brig on the *Prinz Eugen* on bread and water. Maybe they were due for some more of the same.

The Leutnant was very friendly. 'Right, you two,' he said. 'Have you been up to your tricks again?'

'No, Herr Leutnant,' they said together.

'Well, we can't have you staying together,' the officer said, pacing up and down the cabin. 'I'm sorry. But my brother's on another ship as well, you know.'

Fritz Tröger stood to attention and said between gritted teeth, 'Is there some regulation that says my brother and I can't serve on the same ship?'

'I'm afraid there is. And here are your transfer papers. But you're in luck: you're off to the *Bismarck*. Be happy!'

Orders are orders. No argument. A brief farewell. By the time they really have time to think about the separation, 'Operation Rheinüburg' is under way. Seaman Fritz Tröger is aboard the *Bismarck*, Seaman Heinz Tröger is aboard the *Prinz Eugen* – listening to the merciless voice of the loudspeaker that is cutting through the silence as he works now.

All parts of the ship become aware of it at the same time. In the engine rooms, in the workshops, in the gun emplacements, in the communications centre, in the galley, in the dressing station, in the living quarters, in the munitions stores, astern, aft, up in the crow's nests, down in the depths, 'The *Bismarck* has been sunk.'

Finished. Over. Blown to kingdom come. Sent to the bottom. After an hours-long death agony.

All those who can still pray, pray. Those who can still cry, cry. Those who can't do either, just sit in a corner and let their thoughts be, feeling the emptiness.

The despairing, crazed howl that comes from Seaman Tröger is heard and understood even by those of his comrades who don't know him. This man, who has lost his brother and will have to face his mother if he ever comes home, starts hammering against the wall with his fists, comes close to drawing blood with the force he uses against the steel bulkheads, and when he's had enough of that, starts to lash out wildly all around him. A few mates get hold of him, drag him off to the hospital on the quarterdeck.

Assistant Medical Officer Dr Schmidt, the man they call the 'double doctor' because he has two degrees, gives him a sedative injection. The morphine buys a few hours' relief for Heinz Tröger.

After the sinking of the *Bismarck*, the British Navy sets to work to destroy her companion ship, the *Prinz Eugen*. German ships have no bases in the Atlantic. They have to operate from supply ships, linking up somewhere on the high seas to stock up on fuel. The *Prinz Eugen* can only keep going for 6800 miles, even when fully tanked.

The British concentrate on tracking down these supply ships. Somewhere, they know, must be the tankers that are waiting for the *Prinz Eugen*, unprotected and virtually defenceless. For days they will have to wait, have patience, until they are directed to the rendezvous point. British vessels comb the Atlantic day and night. There is a permanent patrol by aircraft, each of which have their own grid squares of ocean to search and are in constant radio contact with their bases.

The long death-struggle with the *Bismarck* had tied down most of the enemy's ships while it lasted. It was the only reason that the *Prinz Eugen* was able to escape. The British also had to tank up their ships with oil before they could take up the pursuit.

Six supply ships are making their way across the Atlantic, independently of each other. Six risky missions, whose only chance lies in the poor visibility at sea this May week.

The first to go is the *Esso Hamburg*. Direct hit from a torpedo. Then the *Egerland* is blown to bits. The *Gonzenheim* and the *Friedrich Breme* are cornered and scuttle themselves. But somewhere the *Kota Pinang* and the *Ermland* and the newly-sent *Spichern* are waiting for the *Prinz Eugen*.

Huge clouds of black smoke mark the graves of the German tankers.

The situation aboard the *Prinz Eugen* is desperate. Even by the most favourable estimates, the heavy cruiser has no more than 200 tons of oil left in her tanks. Enough for half a day's sailing. If she fails to refuel, she will simply float around aimlessly in the middle of the Atlantic and do the same as the *Bismarck*. Despite the danger of betraying his position,

Captain Brinkmann sends the pre-arranged signal to the supply ships. Just two letters in morse code.

No answer

Another radio message.

Another.

It's over. The *Prinz Eugen* will perish for lack of fuel.

Then the radio operator picks up an answer. Another. The pre-arranged signal. There must be a supply ship in the vicinity. Brinkmann decides to forget about the enemy, to agree on a rendezvous point and make for it as quickly as possible.

160 tons of oil left. Half speed. Captain Brinkmann begins to really worry for the first time. Only the officers know the real situation of the *Prinz Eugen*.

Then there is smoke from a funnel!

The men in the crow's nest stare intently at the horizon.

'Identify!' the captain demands.

It is the *Spichern*. A dramatic, last-minute rescue, so long as the heavy cruiser is not caught by enemy bombers or submarines during the refuelling process.

Spichern steams ahead and pulls the *Prinz Eugen* towards it on a steel hawser before snaking out the oil pipe, which is pulled in and fed into its tanks by the *Prinz Eugen*. The tanker can deliver almost 300 cubic metres of oil.

Now that the lifesaving oil is pouring into his tanks, the captain does something very unusual. He turns to the officers close to him and says, 'So, gentlemen . . . And now I intend to go to my cabin and give myself a stiff one!' And he does, though he is back on his bridge within minutes.

Two hours later, the *Prinz Eugen* sets course for the north-west to make contact with the *Gonzenheim*, which together with the *Kota Pinang* was to act as escort and lookout to the *Bismarck*'s 'little sister' as she roamed the Atlantic.

The *Prinz Eugen* has three aircraft, Arado 196s, aboard, waiting for better weather in order to launch. Leutnant Hane is the youngest observer. To the astonishment and mockery of his brother officers, he sits in the galley every morning and eats his way through a plate of fried eggs. The pilots receive special rations: the First Officer makes sure that the sizes of the portions are rigorously adhered to. At the beginning of the voyage he had had all auxiliary galleys closed. The men were to be clear that the Officers had no special privileges as far as rations went.

'If I understand you rightly, Hane,' says Lieutenant-

Commander Paulus affably, 'your duties here consist principally of eating fried eggs, playing skat and drinking beer.'

The leutnant smiles, but his heart is not in it. Once the *Prinz Eugen* gets back to port, he will be given special leave in order to get married. The whole thing had already been agreed by the time 'Rheinübung' started and the marriage had had to be postponed. The young leutnant takes a perverse pride in showing everyone the worthless leave pass.

Hane goes to his cabin. Always the same jokes. Always those damned fried eggs. Always the First Officer's question, 'Have you eaten your fried eggs yet?'

Hane sits down at his table and broods. He met Ingrid a year ago. He had been an officer cadet and just back from the campaign in France. Then he had been promoted to leutnant.

He called Ingrid up. She had forgotten who he was. They had only been introduced fleetingly. So he had had fourteen days to win her. He had done everything wrong – and that had been exactly the right thing to do. A man who had been shot down once already, who was one of only three survivors from his squadron, had lacked the courage when the moment to pose a quite natural question had finally come.

She had come to the station with him. The train was already drawing into the platform when she said, 'But you wanted to ask me something?'

'Yes,' he had said. 'I'll write to you about it.'

And so they were engaged, so to speak, by postcard.

She visited him in Gotenhafen once, just as he was transferred to the *Prinz Eugen*. He was still shy. They had hardly held each other in their arms, and here they were talking about marriage. His parents had agreed. The Luftwaffe had issued a marriage permit without delays. The relatives were saving their ration coupons. And Ingrid was having a white bridal gown made, as if to fly in the face of war.

Leutnant Kling walks into his cabin. 'Now we're in trouble,' he oaths.

'What's up?' asks Hane.

'Your wedded bliss is up the creek again,' Kling says. 'Real shit. Engine trouble.'

The ship slows right down. No one knows what's wrong. The chief engineer is working like a madman. The ship is full of rumours, and some ripe language as well. One thing's obvious, whatever else may not be: the *Prinz Eugen* is no longer fully combatworthy.

The wind has started to blow away the cloud cover. The sun is shining. Glorious flying weather. And suddenly a British reconnaissance plane appears on the horizon. Despite his misgivings, the captain raises the speed again, steers an opposite course. God, if the enemy realises that we're crippled!

Every crew member is at action stations. Their eyes are strained, their palms damp with sweat.

The sky hangs almost preternaturally blue over the calm sea. A high-pressure area has caught them all by surprise, a punishment for all the meteorologists' false promises, giving perfect visibility for the first time since the beginning of 'Rheinübung'. Somewhere beyond that horizon, where the shimmering sea meets the sky, a vicious sea war is raging, and German U-boats are stalking Allied convoys and bombers are diving out of the sun onto shipping. The sun is heating up the decks. Off-duty crew members have made their way up from the lower decks to the air, to take in the breeze and the sun, to smoke a cigarette and swap those jokes that make the fear go away for a moment.

The heavy cruiser *Prinz Eugen* has been steaming at 28 knots on a north-westerly course since leaving the supply ship *Spichern*, searching for its would-be escorts, the *Kota Pinang* and the *Gonzenheim*. Its bow slices easily through the calm water. For God's sake, where are the British? Where are the Sunderlands, Liberators and Lancasters? The covers have been removed from the anti-aircraft guns. The observers are peering skywards until their eyes smart like sores.

The chief engineer reports from the engine room.

'For God's sake, what's wrong?' the captain bellows into his mouthpiece.

'Noises in the starboard engine, captain.'

'Well?'

'I reckon some kind of malfunction in the main bearing of the low-pressure turbine.'

'How long are you going to need for repairs?'

'I don't think we can repair it, captain.'

'Try!'

'Very well, captain!'

'And how fast can we sail?'

'Under the most favourable circumstances, five knots under maximum.'

The captain nods and summons his officers to a conference in the cabin on the bridge. He has a tough decision to make.

The lives of 1600 men and the fate of Germany's largest war cruiser depend on him.

'Well, we're right in it, gentlemen,' Captain Brinkmann begins. 'Our radio observation service is functioning beautifully. Please convey my heartiest congratulations to your people,' he says turning to the First Officer. 'And 104 enemy vessels are in the vicinity, while we sit here with our starboard engine finished.' The captain shrugs, continues in that quiet, calm voice of his. 'Damned bad luck, gentlemen. I intend to abandon the mission and attempt to make our way through to the French ports.'

The radio room buzzes through. The First Officer answers.

'Message for the captain,' says Commander Stooss.

'Put it through,' says Brinkmann.

Group West to captain of the 'Prinz Eugen', the message reads. *Recommend abandonment of the operation. No attacks on convoys. Advise retreat southwards. Approach to French coast cleared. Good wishes.*

'Funnel in sight!' bawls the man in the crow's nest at that moment.

'Action stations!'

Shortly afterwards, the observation service corrects the report. 'One of our own tankers. Could be the *Esso Hamburg*. Asking if she should prepare to refuel us.'

The captain considers for a moment. The fuel on board should do for the return trip, but then one can never have too much on board. 'Of course,' he says.

He looks at his wristwatch, thinks of this weather, 'fliers' weather' as they call it, and swallows back an oath.

'I'm off to breakfast now,' says the First Gunnery Officer, unmoved by everything. 'This kind of excitement always gets me an appetite.'

No one says much to that.

The ship is bursting with oaths and curses. Rumour succeeds rumour, wearing away at the crew's courage, peace of mind and nerves, inhibiting conversation. Everyone knows that the starboard engine is threatening to pack up, is overheating, affecting the ship's speed badly. Everyone below deck knows by hearsay that the sun is shining, that the enemy is combing the seas for them, with battleships, submarines, destroyers, cruisers, and that they're coming closer all the time, in massive numerical superiority. The scene is being set for a new war drama: the sinking of the German cruiser *Prinz Eugen*.

Seamen Bülow and Merx have been set to galley duties. And they have got themselves stuck in a hatchway. The huge mess tins they are carrying nicknamed 'barges' by the crew, pour onto the floor with a hideous clatter. Their contents, meat, potatoes, red cabbage and gravy spill out.

'Jesus, can't you be careful?' bellows Bosun Döhring.

'Get your own food if you don't like the way we do it!' Merx snaps.

'Are you crazy, man? I'll put you on a charge if you don't hold your tongue. You shit yourself all day, but your mouth's open and working, as if it had a life of its own. I thought you'd be the first to get the shits up . . . Go on, get that stuff cleared up and make yourselves useful!'

For a moment Merx stares at the bosun, his eyes livid with hate. Then he regains his nerve and decides to apologise. 'Sorry,' he says. 'Didn't mean it that way. You know, my brother was on the *Bismarck* . . . and I've never done this before.'

Döhring has pulled himself together too. He's no stickler for discipline in the usual run of things. Been wrecked with a minesweeper in his time. One of three survivors, and also one of the most popular officers on the *Prinz Eugen*. Always the soul of calm, particularly when things get rough.

He ought to report Merx. But he won't. He knows that Merx is one of the most reliable men on board if you treat him right.

'All right,' he says. 'I didn't mean it that way either. Everyone goes over the top once in a while . . . And I'm sorry about your brother. We'll have a beer together when all this is over . . .'

'Very good, Bosun.'

'Take it easy, and make sure you look after yourself. You've got plenty of time.'

'Yes,' Merx says, as if he meant it.

It is a piece of cake to take on fuel in this weather. The pipes are connected up, the oil tanks are already two-thirds full. The indicator needles slowly move right. In an hour or so it will be complete. What a miracle that there's still no sign of aircraft in the sky!

The message is received on the bridge: 'Convoy heading north sixty sea miles south-east of us.'

The captain acts immediately. The pipes are hauled in, the

refuelling halted. Orders to the engine room to engage maximum possible speed and set course for France.

The *Prinz Eugen* separates from the supply ship immediately. The men on the upper deck are grim. My God, the poor swine on the *Esso Hamburg*. What will become of them?

The 15,000-ton tanker has a maximum speed of only 20 knots. Goddammit, it'll be sitting there defenceless in the middle of the Atlantic, totally at the mercy of the enemy guns and torpedoes.

But can the captain of the *Prinz Eugen* do any different? Should he put his cruiser in danger in order to save a tanker that has already been condemned to death by the normal rules of sea warfare? Should he sacrifice 1600 men for the sake of 42?

The *Esso Hamburg*'s Aldis lamp flashes: 'Bon Voyage'. The *Prinz Eugen* returns the compliment. Most of the men on board don't have the nerve to even look back. They have a pretty good idea what will happen next. The *Esso Hamburg* is heading on the same course as the *Prinz Eugen*.

But she is going more slowly, much more slowly, and the enemy ships are gaining.

Esso Hamburg is escaping into her doom. To the most cruel fate that the war at sea can provide. Her time will come in a few hours. The enemy convoy has long since located her and started to draw closer. It is a convoy of 19 merchantmen, accompanied by three destroyers and an old cruiser. This formation has strict orders to avoid combat, even though it would be nothing for the destroyers to deal with the *Esso Hamburg*. Nevertheless, a message informing them of the situation and position of the defenceless supply ship has been sent to the RAF.

And somewhere, three aircraft take off.

Once out of range of the convoy, the *Prinz Eugen* slows down again, to spare the damaged starboard engine. My God, when will night come at last?

By about 16.00, it seems that the German cruiser's luck has finally run out. She now has reports that mean she is sitting in a trap between two convoys. Enemy ships both to starboard and astern! All they need to do is to fan out and they will have the *Bismarck*'s little sister encircled.

But they don't.

Perhaps they have precise orders and are not allowed to leave their pre-arranged routes? Perhaps – though it seems unlikely – their radar system is not as efficient as the *Prinz Eugen*'s. Perhaps they would rather leave the destruction of the cruiser to their own aircraft? Or maybe they are obsolete warships that daren't risk combat with such a modern cruiser?

Another hour gained. The distance to the enemy convoy to aft is closing. Captain Brinkmann steams away in a wide curve. Incredibly, the manoeuvre succeeds. If only they can remain undisturbed for another three or four hours, they will be saved. If only night would come!

The *Prinz Eugen* is back on her old course. The captain has decided to head for Brest. He informs Group West. If things go well, the cruiser will be within the range of German aircraft by the next morning. Perhaps the Navy will be able to send him some support.

Morale on board is slowly lifting itself off the floor. God, if they get to Brest, there will be leave for everyone. Good, long leave while the engines are overhauled. Everyone on board is his own navigator now, working out how far the ship is from the coast of Western France. Their route is obvious. The reconnaissance vessels *Kota Pinang* and *Gonzenheim* are informed that they no longer need to wait on the *Prinz Eugen*. The order reaches them on May 29th at 14.00.

The *Prinz Eugen* is steaming along the north coast of Spain. She will have to cross the Bay of Biscay by night. Group West has assured her of destroyer and air support as soon as she is running along the French coast.

Night saves the *Prinz Eugen*. The defective turbine holds up. By early the next morning, the cruiser is close enough to the French mainland for the Luftwaffe to supply protection. Tugs are already on their way to haul her into port. The little sister of the *Bismarck* has made it.

On June 1st 1941 at 17.59, the *Prinz Eugen* weighs anchor in the port of Brest, and goes into dock that same day. The heavy cruiser has stayed a happy ship – and a lucky one, too. Her captain and chief engineer immediately set to arranging for a complete overhaul of all three engines. The ratings, NCOs and officers leave the ship by division, to transfer to leave quarters around Brest. The *Prinz Eugen* will, it is reckoned, be combatworthy again by July 2nd. Or at least so the engineers calculate.

But they haven't reckoned on the Royal Air Force, which launches murderous raids on the port, forcing three German warships – the *Scharnhorst*, *Gneisenau* and *Prinz Eugen* – to flee into the open sea. Even there, they are heavily bombed.

Grand Admiral Raeder has every intention – despite the *Bismarck* débâcle – of sending them back to sea again to harry the British convoys. But Hitler refuses his permission, for – in contrast to his naval commander, who will shortly retire – he has realised that the time of the surface raider is past.

The hunters become the hunted, their only choice whether to be destroyed where they are or risk a dash up the Channel.

The question of what to do with the warships holed up on the French coast is an urgent one, but there are more pressing concerns as 1941 wears on. There is the Balkan Campaign, the Desert War, the landing on Crete, and, above all, the attack on the Soviet Union. For the moment, the Navy's dilemma on the Atlantic coast takes a poor second place.

Jump Into Hell

In those first shadows of evening, the three-engined aircraft look like flocks of dark vultures, waiting perched low over the rocks for their victims. Whistles shrill across the dusty airfield of Megara near Athens.

It is May 19th 1941, shortly after 21.00.

In no particular hurry, the men of III Company, Second Parachute Battalion, emerge from their tents. They are known by their neckscarves as the 'Green Devils'. They line up in three ranks, standing pretty easy.

'We shall be dropped over Crete tomorrow morning,' Oberleutnant Karsten issues their order of the day. 'We shall be landing right on top of an English camp near Malemes airfield. Gentlemen, I expect you to have got your beauty sleep before we take this on,' the company commander adds with a wry grimace. 'If we haven't taken the airfield by midday, we'll be in deep trouble.' His gaze flicks over the faces of his men. 'Who'd stand a chance of doing it – apart from us?'

The company roars its agreement. They stand shoulder to shoulder, 150 bronzed and fit boys, exuding courage and manhood. Very few of them know where Crete actually is, or even if it's a city, an island or a country in its own right, and ten minutes previously many would have thought it was a girl's name.

The company is dismissed.

'Well, here we go at last,' says Private Panetzky, fiddling with his nickle-rimmed glasses.

The others express noisy agreement. At last they can stop hanging around on this broiling airfield in the middle of nowhere. An end to that damned rotgut wine that Panetzky uses to wash his feet, and goodbye too to their sordid exploits in that little whorehouse in the dingy Athens suburb, with its ten 'artistically' draped girls.

And then there is schnaps. Three bottles per group. As he doles it out, the sergeant-major orders a ban on boozing that he doesn't even believe in as he says the words. Bernhard Ramcke, a man who made it from cabin boy to General of Parachutists, gave his men the motto: 'You can do anything you like – just don't get caught.'

The company disperses in the ruddy glow of the setting sun, past the aircraft where the groundcrews are working. Crates of weapons, ammunition and rations are being hauled over.

The heat is no longer so intense, but their uniforms are still stuck to their sweat-stained bodies. The powers-that-be forgot to issue the Green Devils with light tropical kit. Tomorrow morning they will drop on Crete wearing the same uniforms they had for the taking of Narvik in Norway.

Panetzky and Schöller reach their tent at the same moment. They slam down their mess tins full of schnaps on the orange box that serves as a table. Schmidtchen is busy removing his nude photos from the wall of the tent, with the most incredible care and skill.

'You want to take them with you?' asks Panetzky.

'You bet, mate,' replied the company's best soldier.

Wolfgang Stahl, known as 'the professor' because he has his school-leaving examination, is kneeling on the floor checking his parachute.

'What are you doing down there?' Panetzky asks with a laugh.

'Better safe than sorry,' says Stahl, blushing. Tomorrow is his first taste of combat.

'Ah, the Herr Professor has the shits up, eh?' Panetzky says with a deceptive softness.

Paschen gets slowly to his feet, draws himself up to his full, imposing height. 'Shut your mouth!' says the big Mecklenburger slowly. 'I get the shits up every time, worrying that the damned thing won't open. But if you're meaning that because of that I've got no balls . . .'

The troopers pile their ration pouches, pistols, magazines, water bottles and entrenching tools together in the centre of the tent. And then they go for the schnaps. It hits their throats like the proverbial water on the hot stone.

They even pour a drink for Mennler, the human beanpole, though he's one of the thirty men from each company being left behind because of lack of space in the planes and therefore not strictly entitled. The rangy private is sitting around looking like a kid who's had his sweets taken away from him.

The company commander had drawn lots to see who goes and who doesn't, but Mennler still feels it as a personal insult to be left out.

Paratroopers have their own special moral code, their own sense of humour. They fight far less for the reasons the propagandists always give, the 'Führer, *Volk* and Fatherland', than for the sake of the coloured scarf they wear round their necks in defiance of Wehrmacht regulations and for the privileges it confers.

Mennler, for example, launched himself at a bunch of mountain troops in an Athens bar, just because they were getting a little too familiar with the blonde Macedonian girl he was with at the time. There was a right royal punch-up, and the para came off worst, but Mennler was not about to give up, particularly when men from another outfit were involved. He tore the place apart literally. The next day, the alert was out for the 'culprit'. Everyone knew what he had done, but no one blew the whistle on him. The entire company was confined to barracks, but that did little to deter the Green Devils. When they want to go, they go. They just make sure they're back in time for reveille.

'Come on, cheer up, me old bar-wrecker,' Panetzky comforts him.

'Belt up,' growls Mennler.

'Leave him alone,' Paschen says. 'No use trying to get a happy fart out of a miserable arsehole.'

Mennler makes to go for the Mecklenburger's throat, but the others intervene and tell Mennler to go and see the old man, to try and persuade him he should be going to Crete after all.

No peace on the airfield. Drums of fuel are being rolled across the runway. A confusion of barked commands. Somewhere a portable radio is playing: '*J'attendrai – le jour et la nuit – j'attendrai toujours.*'

Oberleutnant Karsten and Leutnant Petri are sitting in front of their tent. One of them always seems to be glancing mechanically at his wristwatch. Mannler sneaks up to them from their blind side, stands quickly to attention and salutes. 'Permission to speak with the Oberleutnant.'

'What is it, Mennler?'

'I'm not due to go into combat tomorrow, sir,' says the boy, swallowing hard. 'I can't just sit and take that, Herr Oberleutnant. I want to go with you.'

'I'm sorry,' says the company commander, and shrugs his shoulders.

'Count your blessings, man,' Leutnant Petri tells him by way of consolation. 'You'd only twist your ankle anyway.'

Mennler turns away. Not like a soldier but like a girl in school. Tears are pouring down his cheeks. He tries to hide them, but that only makes it worse.

'It's terrible,' the Oberleutnant says to Petri. 'I just picked out thirty men at random. I can't do anything about it. I could hardly stay at home myself so that another one of them can come!'

A few more hours and the waiting is over.

'Ready to board!' comes the order.

'The sun shines red,' the young soldiers croak in the grey of dawn. 'Ready to fly! Who knows tomorrow if we'll live or die . . .'

The words of the paratroopers' song say 'tomorrow'. But tomorrow is now today. The paras swing up into the Jus and pack themselves tight into the holds, grabbing the handgrips as they squeeze in. One behind the other, like chickens on a perch. The professor can feel the weight of his parachute pack bearing down on his back. Schmidtchen, the perfect soldier, gives him a good-natured slap between the shoulder-blades. 'Come on, mate!' And Mennler is actually with them; at the last moment, he was picked as a replacement for a man who needed an appendix operation.

A monotonous roar fills the entire airfield. Aircraft after aircraft taxis in for take-off, kicking up cascades of black smoke over the runways. Motorised field kitchens dodge between the planes, issuing coffee with schnaps in a proportion of two to one. The paras crowd into the hatchways, hold out their mess tins. Their outstretched arms look as if they are grasping one last, desperate time for a hold on safety.

'Happy landings!' bays Panetzky.

And then comes the first disaster: the mass take-off has to be abandoned. The Luftwaffe had not reckoned with the sand. Each machine kicks up such a cloud of sand as well as smoke that the following planes have to wait five minutes for it to subside. The entire airfield is like one big sandstorm. It is the same on all the other airfields around Athens: sand, delays and abandoned schedules.

'Like a goat shitting into an electric fan,' growls Karsten.

His Ju rises slowly into the air with a low, long roar. The sun bursts through to bathe the interior of the plane with a buttery light. The men are packed together like sardines. Below them is the curve of the Greek coast and the gold-threaded Mediterranean.

The other aircraft bank and assemble in the pre-arranged airspace, though now later than planned. Whole squadrons of Jus are swarming together like great storks, so close that the men can wave and grin to each other through the open hatchways.

Suddenly the Ju banks sharply then pulls off into a wide, long curve.

'What the hell's going on?' roars Oberleutnant Karsten.

'We have to change our approach route,' the pilot shouts back from his cockpit. 'Too much anti-aircraft fire. The Tommies have got their entire fleet assembled off the northern coast.'

'That's a really great start,' says the company commander with a sour grin. 'How do you feel about that?'

'Great!' the men chorus back above the growl of the engines.

The schedule for the landings has gone completely haywire. The German attack will now come in two waves, because there were not enough transport aircraft available. The Jus are losing height rapidly.

The paras automatically keep hold of the grips. The sea below them is flecked with crowns of foam. Crete is in sight now. Yellow and sunbaked, sandy and bleak. The Green Devils stand up, stare at the island through the portholes, getting their first vision of the land that will soon be their battlefield and maybe their graveyard. Nothing but sand. Stones. Low, rolling hills.

Suddenly all hell breaks lose. The men hurl themselves to the floor of the aircraft. a crunch of breaking glass. The Ju is listing heavily, struck by light tracer fire. A lot of rattling, as if some stupid boys were hurling stones at the plane's fuselage.

'It's okay. This crate'll hold out until the end of the world,' says Mennler.

Karsen smiles that smile of his. 'And we don't need to wake up our friends down there, do we?'

The Ju to their left veers off and plunges into the depths, with smoke pouring from its engine. Only one man makes it out, a tiny black dot separating itself from the big aircraft. But his 'chute fails to open. The tiny black dot hits the sand, spreads slightly and just lies there like the thumb print of some mighty, careless god.

Their company commander is standing in the hatchway. Next to him stands Paschen, the man whose job it is to help all of them, including the reluctant ones, through the door into the drop. The klaxon sounds. The Oberleutnant jumps first, followed by Schmidtchen, then Panetzky and then the others. Stahl, the professor, fumbles twice as he goes to secure his 'snaphook'. Paschen helps him, gives him a shove. Stahl grabs at empty space. He hears Paschen shouting something after him, but he can make no sense of it. He is drifting earthwards from 300 feet; Mennler is following him.

Twenty to thirty seconds between the heavens and hell. The company commander is closest to the ground, and therefore to the enemy. He is staring skywards. Magnificent fellows: the white billows of the 'chutes are bunched like flowers above him. Below him: a forest of tents.

Soldiers are running about down there. Figures in khaki uniforms. Another 200 feet to go. There are thin, ragged salvoes coming from down there as the enemy begins to organise. During the time between his jump and his landing, a para is pretty well helpless. All that time he's like a dead man – and he can end up actually being one before he hits the ground...

The Oberleutnant releases the safety catch on his machine pistol. He fires a brief burst even before he hits the ground. He decides to ignore the usual landing procedures and crashes down right in the middle of the olive-green landscape, where the men in khaki are doing their strange little dance. He lands on his feet, rolls, stands up again in one easy movement, at the same time releasing himself from the harness of his 'chute. A happy landing, as they say.

Four or five figures are running towards him. Karsten stands four-square and levels his machine pistol from the hip.

A burst erupts from its barrel. Oberleutnant treats the weapon as if he was born with it in his hand. With one scything burst he hacks down the approaching Tommies.

Then he realises his disastrous mistake: these are not British soldiers but Italian prisoners who had been trying to draw his attention to their status.

'You bastards!' Karsten roars. 'Couldn't you wave your white snotrags, for God's sake?'

'Tank you, tank you, German comrade. *Graze tante,*' the Italian stutters.

There's ninety kinds of mayhem going on all around. The battle's really begun.

'Right! Get moving!' the company commander bellows to his men. 'You three here, get into that foxhole. The others off there to the right. Save ammo. Pick your targets!'

The company is gathering. A lot of casualties, but no time to count the cost. Paschen's group are on the right flank. Shells are dropping all around, exploding in the sand, throwing up showers of dust and stones.

Leutnant Petri, who was to have been the last to jump, got hit by a piece of shrapnel while he was still on board the Ju. The first death. Stahl, the professor, is hanging from a tree by his parachute, head down, desperately trying to escape. He is under fire from the English defenders, and bullets are hissing all around him.

'Mooooove!' bellows Paschen.

His group rushes across the level stretch of open ground towards the olive grove a way off. Schöller is clutching the big machine-gun as he runs; the reserve barrel is dangling between Panetzky's legs.

'Run, you arsehole!' Panetzky roars at the easygoing gunner.

Panetzky hurls himself into cover, gropes for his glasses, puts them on. In that instant he catches sight of the professor in the tree. He suddenly loses control, howls with anger, screams, starts to foam at the mouth. He forgets the tactical target, rushes up to the tree, making big strides. Behind him, Schöller and Mommer are putting up the tripod and the machine-gun. A bullet hits the steel leg of the tripod, takes a chunk out of Mommer's jumpsuit.

Panetzky can't wait. He leaps to his feet, rushes towards the grove, zigzags like a hare, then throws himself under the first tree.

'Idiot!' mouths Schöller. He grits his teeth, shoots as he has never shot before, a hair's breadth to the side of Panetzky, to give him some space.

'I'm coming!' Panetzky bellows. He reaches the tree, jumps up with his knife in his hand. He tries two or three times to do it safely. Then he leaves cover, lets the branches whip against him in full view of the enemy as he hacks at the harness straps. Bullets whistle to the right and the left. Finally the professor falls to the ground like a sack of potatoes.

Panetzky drags him behind the nearest tree. His crazy act of bravery has inspired the entire group. Karsten is on his feet, hurling grenade after grenade. The group set up a wall of grenades and bullets between their two comrades and the enemy.

Panetzky bends over Stahl.

'Willi . . .' the professor whispers.

Panetzky swallows hard in his emotion; the next second, a burst of machine-gun fire slices through his thigh.

It is May 20th, and the time is morning at almost nine o'clock. At this moment the German paras, divided into three combat groups, are fighting against overwhelmingly superior forces. On this side of the 30 kilometre-wide island, Group West – of which Oberleutnant Karsten and his men are a part – are due to take the airfield at Malemes and the Hill 107. Group Centre is detailed to take Chanea, the capital, Suda Bay, and the airfield at Rethymnon, and Group East is to concentrate on taking the airport at Heraklion.

The Mediterranean's fifth largest island has turned into an inferno. The flak positions shown on the invaders' maps are shown to be skilful fakes; the paras land in the middle of camouflaged strongpoints that have been constructed in just a few weeks on this island that has been turned into a fortress. All over the island, men jump from just a few hundred feet to be greeted by murderous opposing fire. Many die before they reach the ground. Entire companies are dropped in the wrong places. Friend and foe alike hammer each other without too much discrimination in vicious hand-to-hand fighting.

While on the ground there is bloody chaos, the Jus fly back to Athens – thanks to their air superiority, only seven aircraft were lost – to fetch the second wave. General Student is still in Athens. He has no radio contact with his men in their bloody trap on Crete. He still has no idea that his optimism about the taking of Crete has been so misplaced.

'The paras were dropped over their targets in dense groups,' writes W. Haupt. 'In many places, they land right in the middle of the enemy, who was well prepared and with his finger on the trigger. No one had expected that. Many paratroopers were hit by enemy fire while still in the air and arrived on the ground dead or seriously wounded. It was extremely difficult to identify the enemy defensive positions in the hilly and thickly vegetated country. And crates of weapons often fell right in the middle of enemy positions too, giving him an added advantage in firepower. In other places, the enemy managed to prevent the Germans from recovering the supply containers, at least by daylight.

'The Third Battalion of the Assault Regiment was hit by heavy enemy fire even during the descent and the landing. The battalion, whose companies were dropped over far too wide an area, suffered heavy losses and could not from that time be considered combatworthy...'

While Hitler had been concentrating his attention on England, the Balkans, long the powder-keg of Europe, had been threatening to explode. Stalin exploited Hitler's involvement in the West in order to pursue his own brand of brigandage. He absorbed the Baltic states. On June 26th 1940 he issued an ultimatum to Romania, demanding that Bessarabia and the Bukovina be ceded to the Soviet union. Hitler was in a difficult position. He needed Romania's oil and could not run his war machine without it – at the outbreak of war, Greater Germany had reserves of 2.5 million tons, and another 3.5 million tons of synthetic production, but in the first year of war Hitler's tanks, aircraft and other combat vehicles alone used 11.5 million tons. Fearing a war between Romania and the Soviet Union, he advised the Romanians to give in to the Russians' demands, so as to protect his oil supplies.

The ease with which the Russians acquired the disputed territory gave the Hungarians and the Bulgarians an appetite for Romanian land. The new disagreements also threatened to end in war; a welcome development from the point of view of the Russians, who might thus be able to absorb the entire oil-rich country and gain an economic stranglehold over Hitler.

The Axis powers held a conference in Vienna on August 30th 1940 – under the pressure of Russian divisions massing on the Romanian border – and enforced the so-called 'Second Vienna Accord'. The Russians protested, naturally. The accord added to the numbers of specialists of the Brandenburg Division and the 'military advisers' already in Romania, some camouflaged units that would soon help General Ion

Antonescu, boss of the pro-fascist 'Iron Guard', into power.

The unnatural alliance between Hitler's Germany and the Soviet Union began to show the first signs of cracking shortly after Hitler's secret decision to attack the Soviets. Nevertheless, on November 25th 1940, Stalin declared himself willing to join the Three-Power Pact between Germany, Italy and Japan, so long as the others recognised his territorial gains. Russia's brutal devotion did her no good, however: Hitler was already working on 'Operation Barbarossa'.

The situation in the Balkans was half-stabilised. It was not the Russians but Benito Mussolini, Hitler's friend and imitator, who put the match to the powder keg. He was jealous of his Axis partner's military successes and irritated at not being consulted when Hitler made major decisions.

Now, Mussolini decided, he would get himself a slice of the Balkans.

Although Hitler had agreed to halt all Intelligence-gathering activity on Italian soil, he got wind of the Duce's machinations and quickly arranged a meeting with his ally. When he got out of the train in Florence, he was greeted by a beaming Mussolini. 'Führer,' the Italian dictator said, 'we are on the march! This morning at dawn, our victorious Italian forces crossed the border between Albania and Greece!'

They didn't get far. Even by the time Hitler got back to Germany, it was clear that the Italians were suffering setbacks. Worse still, the British Army of the Middle East was sending help from its base in Egypt, which meant only one thing: general war in the Balkans. There was the danger that Anglo-Greek forces would attack the traditionally pro-German Bulgaria from the south and from there push on to threaten Romania's black gold.

By the middle of February 1941, Hitler had an army of 680,000 men assembled in Romania. On the 28th he crossed the Danube and established bases in Bulgaria, which became a member of the Three-Power Pact.

The Yugoslavs, put under severe pressure, hesitantly followed this example. Then, before Hitler could attack Greece, there was a popular uprising and a revolution. The German ambassador in Belgrade was attacked and spat on by angry crowds. Hitler went into one of his notorious rages and told Göring to destroy Belgrade.

In order to undertake this punitive expedition, and to enable him to throw the British out of Greece, Hitler postponed 'Barbarossa', his attack on Russia, initially for a month.

'The postponement of the attack on Russia,' William L. Shirer maintains, 'was probably the most serious miscalculation of Hitler's career. It is hardly exaggerating to say that with it he threw away his last chances of winning the war.'

That same year, Hitler will tell his generals that those four weeks would have brought them complete victory before the onset of winter.

Blitzkrieg in the Balkans. As swift and ruthless as ever. Or even swifter. On April 6th, German tanks roll over the Yugoslav border without a declaration of war, and at the same time his forces attack Greece. Belgrade is attacked by bombers and reduced to rubble; for a day and a night, the planes fly over the tormented city in great waves, secure in the knowledge that the Yugoslavs have no anti-aircraft defences. Hitler's outburst of temper costs the lives of 17,000 human beings.

By April 7th, the forces in Greece and Yugoslavia have linked up with the fall of Skopje. On the 12th, the panzers of the Wehrmacht are at the gates of Belgrade. The fall of the capital acts as a signal for the disintegration of the multinational state. The ancient differences between the Croats, Serbs and Slovenes flare up again like sores. Croat troops mutiny; entire units desert to the enemy. On April 15th, panzer spearheads reach Sarajevo; the following day, the Yugoslav forces surrender unconditionally.

The Greeks fight back with extraordinary courage; they were – as Hitler himself conceded – the only European army to stand firm in the face of Stuka attacks. They hold grimly onto their fortifications at the Metaxas Line, while their Australian and New Zealand allies are thrown off Mount Olympus and forced to undertake another Dunkirk, shipping their forces to Crete and Egypt with the loss of massive quantities of weapons and equipment.

German paratroopers are dropped near Corinth, open up the isthmus and the pass at Thermopylae to the advancing German troops; this time there is no Leonidas and no Spartans to stop them. 50,000 British troops escape during those last, frantic days, taking with them King George II of Greece. On April 27th, German panzers enter Athens. The swastika flag waves over the Acropolis.

'What Mussolini had not been able to achieve in a whole winter was dealt with by Hitler in a few days,' writes William L. Shirer.

'For all his pride in his victories, Hitler had failed to understand either the importance of the blow he had dealt to Britain, or the desperate position of the Empire. Instead of exploiting his success in the Mediterranean, he immediately turned his attention back to Russia. "Whether it will be possible to begin an offensive against the Suez Canal and finally drive the British out of their position there," he said, "cannot be decided until *Barbarossa* has been successfully concluded."

'The destruction of the Soviet Union was his first priority; everything else had to wait. That was, as we know now, his decisive weakness. At that moment, using only a proportion of the forces available to him, Hitler would have been able to deal the British Empire a grave, perhaps lethal blow; but he did not see his opportunity.'

The German Balkan campaign had cost only 1206 dead, 3901 wounded and 548 missing, but General Kurt Student, who had received a head wound in Holland, seemed to have an instinctive understanding of a foolproof way of bumping up the casualty figures: He suggested to Hitler that he could take Crete or Malta from the air alone, using his parachute troops.

The dictator hesitated at first with the decision, and then found it hard to decide between the two islands. Eventually he decided for Crete, since from the nearest part of the mainland, the Peleponnese, it was only 100 kilometres away. Greece had a coastline of 260 kilometres and mountains that reached 8000 feet. The main thrust of the assault would come in the more densely populated northern region. In the central region there was only a narrow, stony mountain road that the defenders of Crete would later dub the *Via Dolorosa* once they had experienced what it was like to use it for their retreating troops.

Hitler ordered the Wehrmacht to also land mountain troops from small ships and motor gliders, more or less in secret – the German dominated the air, the British the sea – and thus to sneak them onto the island that was defended by the New Zealand General Freyberg with 10,258 Greek and 32,382 British Commonwealth troops, plus the entire Mediterranean Fleet.

The German reconnaissance had been miserable. It was automatically assumed that Crete was defended by very poor quality troops; no one seemed to realise that the island's commander was a famous war hero and that many of his troops were from elite units. Even during the early stages of 'Operation Mercury' – as the landings were known – the British had cracked the German code and were busily translating everything into plain language and predicting all the German movements.

Freyberg knew all the points where the Germans were due to land, and he was able to fortify them. All he lacked was aircraft. For fear of invasion, the planes had been transferred to Egypt and the airfields largely destroyed so as not to afford support for the enemy invaders. The main emphasis of both the defending and the attacking forces lay around the western part of the island around Malemes and at Heraklion in the east, plus at Suda Bay, the British naval base.

On May 14th, planes of the German VIII and XI Air Corps had begun to launch air attacks to prepare for the landing. But serious difficulties occurred: the aircraft had to be refuelled by hand from barrels, totalling 3.6 million litres of petrol. There were delays in the air attacks. When it was realised that the island had not yet been sufficiently softened up by the bombers, 'Operation Mercury' was postponed, first to the 18th and then to the 20th May.

The Luftwaffe made ready an invasion fleet of 450 bombers, 502 transport aircraft, 60 transport gliders, four parachute regiments and units of the 5th Mountain Division – a total of 24,000 invasion troops. The parachute branch had been reinforced considerably since its baptism of fire in Holland, and its training had become much improved. It now possessed its own artillery, a special light gun with a calibre of 10.5 cm; a third of the gas-action recoil was lost behind when the gun was fired. One artillery piece needed five parachutes to take it down.

As soon as paratroopers reach the ground, they tend to acquire new strength, like the giants of ancient times, but here on Crete they seemed to have been condemned to a losing battle from the start, for they had no element of surprise on their side. At Heraklion Airport, the paras came up against English tanks and were shot to pieces, squashed, maimed and squelched before they had the chance to release themselves from their parachutes.

*

Even when the second wave came in, the artificial sandstorms on the airfields delayed the full arrival of the invading forces by up to three and a half hours. The units were not even able to start in the correct tactical order. They assembled over the targets in a less than ordered fashion. The backup provided by the bombers and fighter-bombers was frittered away. Most of the supplies landed in the midst of the enemy.

The commander of Group Central, Generalleutnant Süssmann, crashed in his transport glider on the approach to the island and was fatally injured. Generalmajor Mendl, commander of Group West, was seriously wounded shortly after landing. For some time after the landings, Airborne HQ in Athens had no news of their progress.

Group Central failed to take the airfield at Rethymnon. The thrust towards Suda Bay was pinned down under strong defensive fire. By the evening of the first day, none of the three airfields had been taken. All German efforts were so concentrated on the airfield at Malemes. The enemy dominated the terrain through his concentrated artillery fire from the top of Hill 107. 'The side that took Malemes would win the battle for Crete,' as one British military historian maintained.

Mountain troops were trying to reach the island in fishing boats and dinghies and any other vessels they could find. They had fought their way through 1500 kilometres of tough terrain in the Balkans only to be sunk by the British just before they reached the coast of their last destination.

Bad news followed bad news: the 12th Company of the Third Parachute Regiment had been dropped over a reservoir. Most of the men had been unable to release themselves from their safety harnesses and had drowned. Their colleagues from the 10th Company had jumped suicidally straight into the enemy positions at Daratsos. Despite the débâcle, one platoon succeeded in breaking into the enemy camp and taking four hundred prisoners. As they attempted to march them away, the Green Devils were subjected to heavy machine-gun and artillery fire. The few survivors now became prisoners of the men they had captured just a short while previously.

As the Germans landed on Crete, King George II of Greece was quartered at a manor house. He was able to watch through the window as, less than 100 metres way, the sky rained white parachutes. The monarch took to his heels and ran headlong to safety, crossing the mountains with his entourage and making his way to the coast. During the night of the 24th he boarded a British destroyer that took him to Egypt. From the safety of North Africa, the gallant monarch called upon the people of Crete to resist to the last bullet. His statement that the German commandos were all jailbirds and rapists had a shattering effect on the island's uneducated inhabitants: wounded men were massacred, corpses mutilated.

The first night after the German landings drew a veil over some unimaginable scenes of horror. Every metre that the Green Devils had conquered was drenched with blood. At this juncture, General Student, the commander-in-chief of 'Operation Mercury', was seriously considering calling off the whole assault. In the end, he decided that he could not desert the 7000 men already on the island, and so he ordered his last reserves in, on the principle that attack was the best means of defence.

The enemy general, Freyberg, intercepted the order, but he had also temporarily lost contact with his own troops. And so he was not informed in time that they were in the process of withdrawing from the disputed airfield at Malemes.

With the dawn, the German aircraft returned and beat back the British Navy. During the course of the eight-day battle, they sank the cruisers *Gloucester*, and *Fiji*, the anti-aircraft cruiser *Calcutta*, the destroyers *Kelly*, *Kashmir*, *Juno*, *Hereward*, *Imperial* and *Greyhound*. Damage was inflicted on the battleships *Barham*, *Warspite*, *Valiant*, and on the aircraft carrier *Formidable*, the cruisers *Orion*, *Ajax*, *Perth*, *Dido*, *Naiad*, and the anti-aircraft cruiser *Carlisle*, plus the destroyers *Napier*, *Nizam*, *Kelwin*, *Nubian* and *Decoy*.

By the afternoon of the second day, Karsten's company, supported by other units, had stormed Hill 107 – and had hardly the strength of a platoon.

They were forced to watch rations and equipment being flown into the enemy, had even used up their captured ammunition, had fought off a British tank attack with small arms, had captured a major anti-aircraft position and had also seen Schmidtchen, the perfect soldier, lynched by Cretan peasants who were under the influence of British propaganda.

Below them lay the sea. Hundreds of dead mountain troops were being washed up on the beaches down there.

'Follow me!' bellowed the Oberleutnant.

The remnants of his company dashed with their weapons and equipment down the same hill they had taken three hours to take – and they did it in three minutes. On the horizon they could see the clouds of dust kicked up by the retreating British.

They simply overran the last of the resistance, quite literally. Their commander was about to order a short pause when a despatch rider rode up.

'A Norton,' he said proudly, indicating his captured British motorcycle before he did anything else at all. 'The company is to clear the airfield so that our transporters can land.'

'Land?' the officer asked. 'Here? . . . Well, what do I care?'

While his men began to clear away the oil drums that had been laid all over the field by the British, the enemy artillery took a bead on the place. And immediately the first German aircraft came into land. It crashed. From then on, the Jus came in in packs, formation flying. Very tidy. They dropped swiftly, giving themselves a steep approach to the battered airstrip. A few were destroyed, others ended up belching flame before they could move out of the way of the artillery. The enemy shells were exploding between the taxiing Jus, which still carried on landing in comfortable, copybook fashion. Death was having a fine feast at Malemes airfield.

And in all the aircraft were packed mountain troops, brave lads from Upper Bavaria, from the Allgäu and the Tyrol. Most of them died before they could even realise what was going on in Crete.

The men of Karsten's company were forced to watch helplessly as the mountainmen were decimated by the enemy artillery fire. They stared at the aircraft that had managed to land and were ready to take off again just as soon as their human cargo had been tossed out through the hatchways. Two aircraft collided over the airfield and crashed to the ground like rotten planks.

The next ones prepared for a landing that was becoming near certain destruction. Smoke drifted across the field, providing a dirty blanket over the entire bloody drama. It took away men's sight, filled their eyes with tears, filled their lungs. It veiled for a moment the incredible scene as, by a miracle, aircraft continued to land and take off, and then return again a while later . . .

At the sight of the massacre of the mountainmen, big Paschen simply hurled himself into the sand and cried like a child.

Crete's premier airstrip was in German hands, and the reinforcements – even though they were only a fraction of their intended strength – had landed, opening up the way into the heart of the island.

A week after the beginning of the operation, the enemy's resistance at the capital, Chania, was broken, and a day later Suda Bay was captured. One of the last to die in the fighting was Private Mennler, who had been so insistent that he must go to Crete.

It was not until May 24th – after a delay of four days, during which hundreds of German mothers had lost their sons without even knowing they were in combat – the German High Command dared to issue a communiqué announcing the invasion of the island. 'The operation is proceeding according to plan,' the report concluded.

On May 27th, General Freyberg ordered the evacuation of the island. He was successful in getting away over 17,000 men – half the forces defending Crete – from exposed positions on the beaches, using all his naval forces to their utmost. The British lost 15,000 dead, wounded and taken prisoner, plus 2011 Marines and sailors.

The conquest of the island was scarcely complete before the High Command, obsessed with the planning of the attack on Russia, had forgotten it existed.

Hitler awarded Student the Knight's Cross. And he told the general who had proposed, carried through and commanded the entire operation, 'Crete has shown that the best days of airborne forces are past; they can only be used for surprise attacks, and these will not be possible in future.'

Soon events in the war in the Mediterranean and North Africa will show that Hitler conquered the wrong island. Malta, which Churchill once described as 'an unsinkable aircraft carrier' has, in fact, far greater strategic significance.

In order that the Führer can be wise after the event, 2071 German soldiers have died, 2594 been wounded, and 1780 posted missing.

And in contrast to the Germans, the Allies – having experienced the effectiveness of airborne landings in Crete – begin to build up their own parachute regiments as a decisive weapon of war. Another three years and the full wisdom of this will be shown beyond doubt.

The Frozen Victory - 1

The spring brings the storks to Russia - and other birds, too, though they cannot be seen or heard. Or located, for the Russians still have no radar. Specially-adapted aircraft of the German Luftwaffe take off in secret every day when weather permits, and they climb high over their bases before they set any course. Officially, even the ground crews have no idea where the aircraft are headed.

At the end of October 1940, Hitler had personally ordered these secret flights. By the end of the winter, the preparations were complete and four sections of Rowehl's squadron, which specialised in long-distance reconnaissance, were set fair to operate from bases in East Prussia, Western Poland, in Budapest and Bucharest. Hand-picked crews were soon at work inspecting Hitler's next theatre of war.

The good old He III, already ready to be pensioned off if the truth were told, could climb to 30,000 feet with special equipment. The modified Ju 88 could even reach 38,000 feet, a record altitude in the spring of 1941. It was the year during which Hitler reached the height of his power and the war escalated into a world war. In the face of all warnings, the dictator made the decision to follow the Nazis' original programme and seek *Lebensraum* - living space - in the Red East, 'Germany's India'.

The Soviets were not prepared for skyborne spies operating at such altitudes, and so they were able to cruise the stratosphere - or just below it - over the entire region between the Black Sea and the Sea of Aral, over White Russia and the Ukraine. The lonely crews flew deep into an immeasurably huge country, but they never reached Moscow. The cities beyond the Russian capital were seen as 'Bohemian villages', spread over thousands of square kilometres.

The Luftwaffe's systematic evaluation of the photographs at least clarified the situation in Western Russia. The aerial photographs were put together to form a huge mosaic of the territory covered. There was no military or industrial centre that the General Staff did not know intimately. All the Soviet airfields, even the camouflaged ones, were subjected to thorough inspection.

After every flight, the crew were once again enjoined to the utmost caution in their operations. Relations between Germany and Russia were to be maintained at a level of surface cordiality right up to the last moment before the invasion. The Russians were still making punctual daily deliveries of oil, foodstuffs, wood and cotton.

Hitler was preparing his 'last great campaign of the war', the attack on the Soviet Union, under the codename 'Barbarossa'. The Wehrmacht now had a strength of 180 divisions. More than three-quarters of all German troops were being secretly moved to the East. 'When "Barbarossa" becomes reality,' said Hitler as early as February 1941, 'then the whole world will hold its breath and be still.'

In the huge area between the Arctic Circle and the Black Sea, along a 3200-kilometre front and primarily under cover of night, a military force was being assembled that was unparallelled in history – and needed to be if, as the plans dictated, the largest country in the world was to be conquered in five months. Typical of the way the new front was camouflaged was, for example, the movements of the 35th Panzer Regiment, which for a few months had lived like a band of gods on the sunshine coast south of Bordeaux in France: the panzers went by rail to the Swiss border, from there to Strasbourg, across the Rhine and then right across Germany to Fulda. They then continued into the Protectorate of Bohemia and Moravia, and from there into the Burgenland district of Eastern Austria. After ten days, the entire transport sneaked back under cover of night and fog into Bohemia, to the exercise area at Warthelager, and then to readiness within the jurisdiction of Army Group Centre, just 100 metres this side of the river Bug, the border between Greater Germany and the Soviet Union.

'We dig slit trenches and camouflage our vehicles until they are unrecognisable,' Hans Schäufler remembers. 'Everything is quiet. No lights, no sound, no aircraft or vehicles, no soldiers visible. The world around us seems petrified. Every movement is slow and silent. An anxious silence around us, a depressing anxiety within us. We all sense that only a few hours separate us from an inferno. What will the immediate future bring? What price will it demand from us? We don't talk about it. A strange confined quality, a chilling narrowness, turns our chests to ice.'

3.2 million German soldiers are waiting for the order to move, divided into 19 Panzer Divisions, 16 Motorised Divisions and 118 Infantry Divisions, reinforced by Hungarian, Slovakian, Romanian, and later Finnish units, backed up by 600,000 motor vehicles all tanked up and ready to go and almost 3000 aircraft from the Luftwaffe, almost all that's left after the débâcle over England. The main thrust will come from the Army Group Centre commanded by Field Marshal von Bock, which will push for Minsk and then Smolensk. Field Marshal von Rundstedt commands Army Group South, which will launch an attack toward Kiev. Army Group North is ready in East Prussia, with the task of occupying the Baltic ports, storming Leningrad and Kronstadt, and then linking up with the Finnish army in Karelia.

As early as December 18th 1940, Hitler had issued the notorious Directive Number 21: 'The German Wehrmacht must be prepared, even before the end of the war with England, to conquer Soviet Russia in a swift campaign. The army will have to use all the means at its disposal, after allowing for the securing of the occupied territories. It will be the task of the Luftwaffe to release such strong forces for the support of the army that the ground operations will be concluded swiftly and any damage to Eastern Germany through enemy air attacks will be minimised. The establishing of our strength in the East is limited by the need for us to protect the entire combat and assembly area free of enemy air attacks, while at the same time not neglecting the war with England. The main emphasis of the Navy's activity will also continue to be directed against England, even during the Eastern Campaign. I shall order the massing of forces to begin eight weeks before the planned date of the attack on Soviet Russia. Any preparations that require longer are – inasmuch as they are not already in hand – to be taken in hand now and to be completed by May 15th 1941. Primary importance is, however, invested in the necessity that these preparations remain unknown to the enemy.'

The Balkan Campaign had set back Hitler's ambitious plans by some four weeks. He was now under pressure of time, for he would have to have shattered Russian resistance before the onset of the notoriously hard winter. From the classic military point of view, the dictator was a talentless dilettante. His personal interventions in Poland and France – against the advice of trained soldiers – had, however, led to clearcut successes. The Wehrmacht was now forced to pay a high price for Hitler's luck, since the Führer now considered himself to be a military genius, a delusion which led him to solitary, ever riskier strategic decisions. He allowed no gainsaying, and when disasters resulted from his own decisions he simply dismissed his commanders.

There were many objections to a war with Russia. A few generals remembered the words that the last Russian Tsar had said to the German Kaiser: 'One does not attack Russia: it is not a country but a continent.' The downfall of the great Napoleon, which had been caused by his invasion of Russia in 1812, was also in the minds of many military experts, though the chief and most vivid memory was of the disastrous two-front war that Germany had had to pursue in 1914–18. Generaloberst Kurt Freiherr von Hammerstein – who was in any case in the habit of referring to Hitler as 'that brown-shirted thug' – considered that victory in any war with Russia was out of the question.

'No one, no advisers, nor "tradition", nor any sense of revenge, had persuaded or forced Hitler to undertake this adventure,' states Herbert Michaelis. 'Even Göring, who had now lost many of his illusions and was inclined towards an attitude of resignation, tried to prevent the Russian war, as did Grand Admiral Raeder, who saw his naval plans threatened by Hitler's obsession with the land war in Russia. Even Ribbentrop and Keitel raised their feeble voices in cautious warning, as did the State Secretary at the Foreign Office, von Weizsäcker, and the boss of the Abwehr Intelligence organisation, Admiral Canaris. Weizsäcker wrote to Ribbentrop: "Russia is not a potential ally of England. To beat Russia and England – that's no programme for us!"'

But Hitler was totally fixated with the idea of a war against the Soviet Union, whose strength he underestimated to a fatal extent. His motivations were a mixture of racial nonsense, territorial greed, and ideological differences between the Nazi and Communist dictators, who on close inspection were very similar to each other in any case. Added to this was Stalin's own ruthlessly expansionist policy, which had exploited Hitler's involvement in the West to gain territory: the Baltic states of Latvia, Estonia and Lithuania had now been incorporated totally into the Soviet Union, while in the Balkans, Romania had been robbed of Bessarabia and North Bukovina. With these last acquisitions, the Soviet Union had brought two million human beings and 450,000 square kilometres of territory under the heel of the Red Army.

Hitler watched the Russians' westward expansion with increasing displeasure. Despite all the formal protestations of undying friendship, relations between Berlin and Moscow were becoming more tense: 'Things were not the same, whether Hitler and Stalin attacked a third party or whether they now began to move against each other.' (William L. Shirer)

The troop concentrations were complete. From the German side of the Demarcation line, Panzer General Guderian observed Russian cadets parading through the streets of the city of Brest-Litovsk. He had already conquered the city once, and in a few weeks' time he was due to send his tanks in again and make it yield to his guns.

Russian raw materials continued to pour into Greater Germany; the Russians were sending 52% of their entire exports to Germany, including so much oil that after the conquest of France, fantastic Allied plans were found which proposed the incendiary bombing of the oil fields of Baku and the Caucasus with specially-adapted long-range aircraft. Now Hitler intended to conquer them in the space of a few weeks. 'All we need to do is to push the door open,' he had told his generals. 'And the entire rotten edifice will collapse.'

East Prussia, June 1941, the hottest summer for years. The air is like brackish water. The sun is so hot that it seems as if it's out to burn the Brandenburgers' tongues in their heads – but they have a sure fire remedy.

The men are mostly from the 10th Company, Brandenburg Division. For days now they have been lounging around in a barn, waiting for the time to pass, listening to fat Melchoir telling them all about his adventures in Romania.

'At the end I had my own villa on the edge of the city of Bucharest,' he told them. 'Plenty to eat and drink. And women, women, I'm telling you: coal black eyes and hair and stacked like you wouldn't believe!' His plump hands traced fantastic female shapes in the air.

'Is that true, Jonas?' asked little Cerny.

'In outline, sure,' the Prophet confirmed, then grinned. 'But none of them let fatso near them.'

They all laughed wearily and dozed on. The Special Commando at Schönwalde near Allenstein consisted of young, untried rookies along with old hands. A good combination. And no one was enforcing the regulations too strictly at the moment; the Abwehr was allowing its boys a little living before they died. Jonas, Oberleutnant Schübler, and even fat Melchior, have this ability to sit and wait for the next crazy order, in the knowledge that being grilled by the sun is better than being roasted by Admiral Canaris.

Danger is their business, and the war now supplies opportunities in many different places: General Rommel has had to come to the aid of the defeated Italians in North Africa. While elsewhere, however, the Brandenburgers are leading the way in undercover operations, the Desert Fox forbade them to operate behind enemy lines. For his pains, he found himself the target for a British commando raid in his own headquarters, staged by men in German uniforms; it was pure luck that he escaped with his life.

They will, as usual, only find out what their superiors require of them at the last moment. Helping with the harvest, they were told at first. Then their commander muttered something about a sort of manoeuvres. A Special Operations Unit helping with the harvest? Manoeuvres in the middle of a war? Here in the East, a merciless war machine is coming into being.

For Operation 'Barbarossa', Hitler's attack on Russia, 153 German divisions totally more than three million men stand prepared, supported by three air fleets. The whole length of the Russo-German Demarcation Line is teeming with field-grey uniforms. Wherever you look, Panzers, artillery, supply columns, sapper units.

All 'helping with the harvest' - and the harvest will be a bloody one.

A unit of motorised infantry drives past the barn and kicks a mass of dust in the Brandenburgers' faces.

'Bastards!' says Melchior, sneezing and cursing at the same time.

'There's something going on there,' says little Cerny anxiously as he watches the unit passing. He is a mere eighteen years old, suffers from a Czech surname, which caused him to prove his patriotism by volunteering for the

Brandenburgers. Cerny is good raw material for a hero's death and no mistake.

'Well,' Melchior, 'where more than two Brandenburgers are together, there's something going on.' His voice betrays a mixture of pride and fear. He brushes the dust from his own face. 'And tonight we'll make a thing or two happen, boy.'

'I'm none too optimistic about that,' Private Pfänder cuts in. 'Especially if East Prussian women are like East Prussian horses.'

At last the evening comes, though it brings little relief from the heat.

'Come on, mates,' says Melchoir, always the first to break ranks. 'Let's piss off into Allenstein.'

No one is that keen on Allenstein any more, but most of them join in for a wander through the main town of the southern part of East Prussia, even though they have already seen all the sights: the Gothic church of St James, the old Bishop's Castle, the High Gate and the New Town Hall. And, of course, the cafés and restaurants, which are teeming with soldiers.

'A real male voice choir,' says Pfänder gloomily. 'Not a girl in sight.'

'True, our competitors have not been idle,' says Melchior. 'But they have to be back with their outfits by 22.00, got that?'

'Even the officers?' asks Jonas, and points at a few young Leutnants with girls on their arms.

But, in fact, the dance cafés (dancing forbidden to soldiers) start to empty as 22.00 approaches. Melchior starts to eye a plump peasant girl.

'She wouldn't win any beauty contests,' Pfänder says knowledgably.

'Just wait,' the fat man murmurs. 'She'll get prettier with each hour that passes, my friend.'

They take their seats at the counter, but instead of a flock of girls, it's the MPs who turn up. Field Gendarmes: a Leutnant, a Feldwebel, a corporal. A few soldiers and an officer make rapid exits. The patrol clears the place, then stomps up to the counter.

'We're clear through till reveille,' says Melchior smugly and presents his written pass.

'You must have friends at Führer Headquarters,' retorts one of the MPs.

'We're us,' the fat man smirks. 'And we write ourselves what we need.'

And then he sees the redhead. A real gift: a fine-boned, fair-skinned face, strawberry blonde hair, green pullover moulding itself over tempting curves.

'Now show what you can do, Casanova,' Pfänder challenges Melchoir.

And there isn't much time to lose. The officers in the corner are already measuring her up with their eyes when Melchoir leaves his stool and sets course for the redhead in green.

'Well,' he starts off with practised charm, 'another lock without a key –'

'Yeah. And another monkey without an organ-grinder,' she says dismissively.

His mates double up with laughter, particularly as the girl's companion has now turned up at the counter.

So afterwards they just sit and drink. One a.m. is closing time, but the place stays open. At two, they get their act together and stomp off through the woods back to their barn, singing dirty songs. They are checked three times by patrols, and none of the MPs can understand how privates and NCOs can have leave all through the night.

At last they arrive back at their barn.

'Well, we burnt a hole in our pockets, but not much else,' says little Cerny.

'There's always tomorrow,' Melchior growls defensively – and a few moments later realises his mistake.

'All leave cancelled with immediate effect,' says the Oberleutnant by way of welcome. 'Alert!'

'Why?' moans Pfänder.

'Canaris will explain that personally,' the Oberleutnant mocks. 'Provided he can find the time.'

No question of anyone getting any sleep. The air turns blue with curses. The rookies, who had not been expecting anything like this, are tense as over-wound watches.

'Just pull yourselves together a bit, will you?' Jonas says finally in irritation. 'You've been sitting here for days watching Panzers drive by. What did you think they were here for? The harvest?'

'I suppose you think you've got some kind of big wisdom,' Pfänder says.

'I've had a bit of experience,' murmurs the Prophet. 'If you want to enjoy what you've got left, get your head down and kip. Tomorrow the war starts. Seems like you want to start it a day earlier than anyone else.'

'What war?' asks Cerny nervously.

'Against Russia, you arsehole!' Jonas snaps.

Melchior and his entourage consider the entire thing a real shit-heap, while Pfänder proclaims that at least there's something to be had in the East.

Jonas smiles sourly. 'You're right there,' he says. 'A nicely chilled arse, that's what.' As the sole survivor of the commando unit that secured the Meuse bridges in Holland in May '40, he knows what he's talking about.

The first tint of dawning day rapidly develops into blistering heat. Thc Brandenburgers do their morning ablutions at a little farm pump. A big truck roars up behind the barn. Parcels start being unloaded.

'Just take 'em through into the front parlour,' says Melchior sardonically.

And then the smile fades on his lips: one of the parcels tears open by accident and he stares curiously at the contents, only to see the bottle-green uniform of the Red Army.

'So it's Russia,' he says in a voice tremulous with fear.

'Right! And off to the jolly old fancy-dress ball!' commands Oberleutnant Schübler with a far from jolly face.

The boredom and the timewasting are both over now. The men of Canaris's undercover outfit stand and stare at the uniforms.

'Well, isn't that something,' says fat Melchior as little Cerny, his eyes feverishly bright, gingerly strokes the material of the uniforms like a schoolboy with his first girl.

Sweat is pouring out of every pore; the boys' young faces are like shining masks of fear that dare not say its name. For the past few days they have been perspiring from the heat, but from now on it's pure terror, though none of them would admit it.

'Are they really good soldiers?' asks Cerny, anxiously running his fingers through his blond hair.

'Who?' growls Melchior.

'The Russians.'

'Aw shit,' the fat man says dismissively. 'Ever heard of the battle of Tannenberg?'*

Just as they are getting into the dress rehearsal, a

*The first great battle of the First World War in August 1914, in which the Russian Army invading East Prussia was routed by the Germans.

motorcycle despatch rider roars up and fetches Schübler to company HQ.

'Pack the stuff back in the paper and put straw over it,' he tells them. 'Wait until I get back. Don't speak to a soul about this stuff, all right?' He nods to them.

'Top secret!' he growls just once before he leaves. 'You'll be for the high jump if you don't keep your mouths shut!' and he's not wrong: any violation of the vow of silence at this level is punishable with death.

Schübler eases himself up onto the pillion of the bike. The rider steps on the accelerator pedal, turns as quickly as if the Russians were already after him. They bounce off along the pot-holed track, the young officer cursing like an ostler all the way until they reach the company's command post in the village school.

Schübler makes to give a formal report, but the Old Man just waves him to a seat and asks, in defiance of the ban on alcohol, 'Schnaps or Cognac?'

'Milk,' answers the Oberleutnant with a ghost of a grin.

'All right, my boy,' the Hauptmann chuckles. 'No need to be so pedantic.' He pours him a generous double. 'Cheers, Schübler,' he says, and claps him on the shoulder. 'Berlin have sent us a few really interesting propositions,' he adds then. 'I've saved up the most tasty for you,' he explains, baiting the trap. 'All right for you, eh?'

'Of course, Herr Hauptmann.'

'Good. How's your Russian?'

'Twenty words' says the platoon commander proudly, then does a quick mental check and revises his estimate, 'Maybe twenty-five.'

'Wouldn't do any harm if you learnt a few more,' the Hauptmann comments. 'Turn and face the wall.'

Even as he entered the room, Schübler had noticed the huge staff map on the wall. There was a big red line through the middle like a bloody cut.

'That's the Demarcation Line, the de facto border between Germany and Russia,' the chief explains carefully. 'Here's where we are. And there, roughly near Plaska, you'll sneak over to the other side. Don't worry. You don't need to make it to Leningrad. Can you see Lipsk?'

The Oberleutnant looks at the map for a few seconds. 'Found it.'

'Can you see the River Bobr? There's a bridge about a hundred metres long, wooden –'

'And I'm supposed to capture it?' says Schübler.

'You're a quick thinker. Get it in the back and hold it till the Panzers have covered the twenty kilometres from the border.'

'Nothing else?' the young officer asks sardonically. 'So it's the same shit we had in Holland.'

'In a way,' the Hauptmann says slowly. 'But we've learned a lot in the meantime.'

'I hope so,' drawls Schübler. 'I've got no more desire to die from a German bullet than I have from a Russkie.'

'Well, at the moment you're alive,' says the Old Man. 'Schübler - you'll pick your own men. All undercover and fancy dress. Various targets. So not a shot must be fired until the war is officially under way. That'll be around 3.30.'

'The Russians will declare war on us?'

'Kind of, yes. Just don't ask such awkward questions, Schübler; you know the Führer has ideas of his own.'

'I know. And what do I take with me?' the Oberleutnant asks.

'A road map. A Polish guide. And weapons. As many as you like,' the Hauptmann assures him quickly. 'Machine pistols, hand grenades. Even a light machine gun.'

'Great,' says Schübler. 'And how long do I have to teach my people to use Russian weapons?'

'What do you mean, Russian?' The company commander pours each of them another double. 'You'll take German ones. All cats are black at night.'

'That's crazy -'

'You're right, Schübler, his commander agrees roundly. 'But the craziness starts when you volunteer for a bunch of deadbeats like this one . . . All right?'

No answer to that. 'When do we start?' asks the Oberleutnant.

'Not today. Maybe tomorrow. Or the day after tomorrow. *Nichevo*.' He puts a hand on the young man's shoulder, escorts him to the door.

During the trip back, he gets another bone-shaking session, but that's not the reason he hisses at the rider to slow down.

It's just to gain time. The closer he gets to the barn the queasier his stomach. He will have to reach his decision, pick his men, and that will leave some long faces. The Devil knows why those boys are so keen to die.

The reasons are many. Firstly, no one knows what's in store for him when he volunteers. So-called 'racial' Germans find themselves shanghaied into the Brandenburgers before they can even apply for Reich citizenship, because of their language ability. Fat Melchior volunteered because the food was better. Little Cerny joined up to wipe out the 'shame' of his Czech name. Jonas was lured in by his friend Schübler, who in turn was recruited by a friend at Canaris's headquarters. A few real greenhorns thought they could win some medals and impress the girls. And Feldwebel Dörner, the bedrock of the platoon, volunteered because his wife had been playing around with another man.

'Have you counted how many of those goddamned uniforms there are there?' asks Schübler after his return.

'Ten,' announces Feldwebel Dörner.

'Tight, eh?' Achübler says with a grim smile. 'So we've got the question of who wants to stay at home.'

No one volunteers. As expected.

'Feldwebel Dörner and you, Prophet, will report to the Company Command Post immediately,' he says. 'Move!'

When he counts himself and the Polish specialist, that leaves six uniforms to be filled. 'Hands up those who speak Russian?'

Almost all of them reply in the affirmative.

'Don't give me that nonsense, you idiots!' He turns to Pfänder, who comes from the Baltic provinces, and orders him, 'Check their language skills, quick!'

Fat Melchior passes the language test. Schübler is glad to have him along, because the man is as reliable as a Panzer. The Oberleutnant is also happy to take Freudenreich, because he's reckoned lucky, and a platoon can always do with that. Sawitsky speaks fluent Polish. He had promised the gangling private a place in the next combat mission.

'Last uniform,' he calls, like an auctioneer. 'Two of you left, and we only need one.'

Grüber and little Cerny are the bitter competitors for the last place.

'All right,' says Schübler. 'We'll toss for it.' He takes a coin out of his pocket. 'You're heads,' he tells Grüber 'and you're tails, Cerny. Agreed, gentlemen?'

'Yes, Herr Leutnant.'

Schüber tosses the five mark piece through the air. It falls onto the straw, rolls away, finally settles.

'You've won, Cerny,' Schübler says. And the boy beams, even though the toss of that coin will probably cost him his life.

The Russians are asleep. On this the Western Intelligence

services and Canaris's Abwehr are, for once, agreed. Despite the huge German concentrations along the Demarcation Line, the Soviets have not placed their troops on alert, or reinforced them. Agents of the British Secret Service have already supplied Stalin with details of Hitler's plans, but the Red dictator's hatred of the Anglo-Americans has made him not only blind but deaf. And so long goods trains packed with grain continue to roll westwards instead of trainloads of Red Army soldiers.

Operation 'Barbarossa' is ready to move. An attack without declaration of war on June 22nd 1941. It will cost the lives of 20 million Russians, but it will also mean the eventual downfall of Hitler's Reich. More than three million men in field grey are at the starting blocks on the Führer's orders, and yet again the Brandenburgers will be sticking their noses out in front, staging yet another suicide mission a matter of hours before the rest of the Wehrmacht goes into action. In short, they are what the Japanese will later call 'Kamikazes'. The 10th Company is waiting all around Schönwalde near Allenstein, spread over barns and farmhouses, waiting for the order to go into action.

Shortly after midday, the volunteers leave the schoolhouse that serves as the Company's headquarters. The Hauptmann gave them no schnaps, but he offered them a good drop of wine, and now they are enjoying a double in the village inn. And then another. A drop to soothe the savage breast, the local brew they call *Bearcatcher*, East Prussia's honey-sweet favourite drink.

Dörner starts to press for them to return to their quarters, but the Prophet slows him down with the words, 'You're never too late for your own funeral.'

'God, this is a real bastard of a unit and this mission's a bitch too,' Jonas continues in commentary on their orders. 'I've done it all before. In Holland. They make gangsters out of soldiers – and mincemeat out of human beings.'

'There's something in that,' the Feldwebel admits gloomily.

'Well, I've just about had enough,' says Jonas.

'Yeah? Then why don't you get yourself a transfer out of this outfit?'

'Cowardice, really,' the Prophet says laconically. 'Tell me to be a hero and I'm too scared to disobey. Being a Brandenburg is like an illness; you get it and eventually you die of it.' He gestures to the barmaid. 'Let's try it the other way. Why did you end up in this weird crew?' he asks Dörner.

'Don't ask so bloody innocently,' says the quiet Feldwebel, suddenly talkative. 'Everyone round here's known for a long time that my old lady got herself another man.'

Jonas nods sagely. 'Then at least you know why you're meeting your maker tomorrow,' he says.

'And who says it'll be tomorrow?'

'If you like, you can make a bet,' Jonas concludes, realising they really have to go. 'Just ask yourself whether you'll actually be around to collect or whether you'll need to duck down in the heroes' cemetery to avoid paying your share.'

'Speak for yourself,' snaps Dörner sharply.

They are brought back in a Kübelwagen. Heavy traffic coming the other way. Units kitted out in full combat gear. Supply columns following really close behind in the *Blitzkrieg* way, which runs counter to all the classical rules they teach at the War Acedemy.

Both notice immediately that the atmosphere at the barn – now heavily guarded – is not exactly happy.

'What, worried we might get stolen?' Jonas asks his friend the Oberleutnant.

'Get yourself a uniform and hold your tongue!' rasps the officer.

And the fancy-dress party is under way. The Soviet uniforms are brand new. Probably from the Reich tailoring shops. They have been cut generously, to allow German uniforms to be worn underneath.

'And in this heat,' Dörner moans. 'Do we have to?'

'That's the question,' Jonas answers knowledgeably. 'Ask yourself whether you'd rather be caught by the Russians or blown to bits by our own people.' He pauses. 'I've also suggested, after my experiences on that Dutch bridge, that the Hauptmann have the other Brandenburgers divided up with the German vanguard so that they can identify us and save screw-ups like the one at Gennep.'

'Great idea,' Schübler says appreciatively, and taps his own forehead to show his regret at not having thought of the idea himself.

The uniforms are either too short or too broad. None of them fits anyone perfectly, and so they fit all of them. Laughter is hollow and brief. Little Cerny is as excited as a child peering through the keyhole the night before Christmas.

While the boy begins to drive them insane with his questions, a Fieseler Storch comes in to land in front of the barn; Oberleutnant Schübler is whisked away by the company commander.

'Have you been promoted to general?' Jonas shouts out after him.

They all watch the plane climbing and flying off southwards. Little Cerny grabs the Prophet. 'They all died, didn't they, except you . . . on that bridge in Holland?'

'Congratulations,' says Jonas. 'You've got the right answer. But next time you might be the one to survive, don't forget.'

'Cut that dismal crap,' growls fat Melchior, and starts to search among the straw until he finds a litre bottle of two-star brandy. 'Fire at will!' he says, and expertly uncorks the bottle.

•

The view from above is glorious, but the young Oberleutnant has more eyes for the positions of the various units than for the church spires and horses drawing ploughs down below. After twenty minutes, the Storch lands close to a heavily-guarded barracks building.

No one knows that it belongs to the Abwehr.

'You're the only ones I'm giving a guide,' says the Old Man. 'Because you've got the longest way to go. The others will find their way all right.'

'Is the man reliable?'

'We don't have much of a selection to choose from,' the Old Man admits. 'It's because I can't offer any guarantees that I'm letting you take a look at him first.'

They have their papers checked three times and then are shown into a sort of waiting room.

'Is the Pole being paid?'

'That too. But mainly he wants to go home. He comes from the area around Lipsk.'

'And what if the Russians have sent him over?' asks Schübler doubtfully.

'Then I'll pray for you,' the Hautpmann shoots back without hesitation.

The man in question is small, has a yellow face, slightly Asiatic eyes, spiky hair.

'Polski?' asks Schübler.

The man nods and grins.

'You nix friend Russki?'

The man brandishes his fist in the direction of the east.

'I'm sold on him,' the Oberleutnant says wryly. 'We'll take him with us.'

Their guide is first choice, basically because there's no second. And they're short of time.

That evening they are moved. In the twilight. They seem to each other as bizarre and shapeless as elephants: first the German uniforms, then the Russian, and finally a heavy despatch-rider's coat over the lot until they get through the German lines.

'It's like a triple-decker cake,' says fat Melchior.

'Christ, the bugger's thinking about food again,' Schübler growls.

Apart from the fat man, the little band consists of Freudenrich, their lucky mascot, Pfänder, the Baltic German, Sawitzky, who speaks fluent Polish, Jonas, and the guide.

As an escort, a party composed of Feldwebel Dörner, Zwecker, little Cerny and Rauchalles will follow a short distance behind. Should the two sections lose contact with each other, Dörner's group will find its own way to the bridge.

Even before they cut holes in the barbed wire on the Demarcation Line, they encounter their first problem. The Polish guide refuses to put on a Russian uniform.

'Tell him I'll change the shape of his face if he doesn't belt up and do as he's told,' Schübler orders Sawitzky.

From that point, the Pole is at least as afraid of the Germans as he is of the Russians – and their safe passage to Lipsk depends on that fragile balance.

Schübler is the first to make it through the barbed wire. He checks the terrain, waves. Melchior follows. Between him and Sawitzky comes the panting Pole, fully kitted out as a Russian and shaking with fear. Then there's Freudenreich, with Jonas bringing up at the rear.

It is 23.21. They still have a long way to go. Their route leads them through the Russian lines. The night is fairly bright. Darkness hangs over Oberleutnant Schübler's band of heroes like a widow's veil punctuated by tiny, twinkling stars. From their light years' distance, they looked down on these men selling their lives for a wooden bridge over a river. At the front, Oberleutnant Schübler, forced to hide his fear from his men; right behind him, Pfänder, the Baltic German, the only one of them to speak fluent Russian, on whom it will depend whether they survive if they make contact with the enemy. Behind him is fat Melchior, who thinks mainly of food even in the hottest spots. On his heels follows the Polish guide, who at least can show how shit-scared he really is. The rearguard is made up of Sawitzky and Jonas, who are also keeping an eye on the guide.

They are still in no man's land. At this point it is especially wide, with no barbed wire on the Russian side. But for the men who are wearing two uniforms, the utmost care is needed. They expect the Ivans to have pushed their advance sentry posts forward during the night hours.

Schübler hits cover. His men do the same automatically. Sawitzky claps the Pole to his breast. At first the Oberleutnant can only hear his own breath, and he feels fear because it is so loud. He probes the area with his infra-red field glasses and curses quietly because his uniform is soaking through in the wet, swampy grass. And he can see no sign of any Russians. Either someone in an office in Berlin has succeeded in discovering the one dead spot on the Russo-German Demarcation Line, or Schübler has gone blind. But if the young officer really takes the time out to be precise on that score, the stroll to the bridge is going to take until Christmas rather than at dawn tomorrow.

Schübler puts away his field glasses and points to the undergrowth. Maybe 80 metres away. If the Red Army has dug itself in there, it's keeping absolutely quiet.

Schübler leaps up. A few paces, then one shadow is silent again, indistinguishable from the darkness. The next. And another. No shots from the undergrowth. No flares. Not a single barked order in Russian. Really close by, a cricket is chirping, and somewhere frogs are croaking. A gentle wind plays with the rustling leaves.

Then they hear fat Melchior, who has made a full-length crashlanding in the undergrowth and is wiping sweat and dirt off his face. 'Just issue your orders, Führer, and we'll take the consequences!' he growls quietly.

'Shut your trap,' Schübler hisses. 'If you have to make that row, at least do it in Russian!'

'Can you speak Russian, Oberleutnant?'

'Arsehole.'

'Yeah, well,' says Melchior, concluding the conversation.

Onward. The raiders are now some 900 metres from the foremost German positions, which means that they have another 19 kilometres to go.

Schübler looks at his watch: twenty to midnight. They shouldn't be crawling but running to their target. Once dawn comes, they'll be in trouble.

The soaked Russian uniforms are now also covered in mud. Pfänder makes an attempt to shake it off. 'That's real shit!' he oaths before giving up and grovelling in the dirt behind the Oberleutnant.

They have done two kilometres now. To their left a village, to their right a wood. They avoid the village, even though it has probably long since been cleared of its civilian population. A huge cornfield that they cross at an easy pace provides them with some cover, but on the far side they really hit trouble.

Straight in front of them is a stream, ten metres across and not shown on any map. Also, not a single bridge in sight.

'And how the hell do we cross that?' asks Pfänder.

'With a spot of force,' his commander answers. 'And you might get your balls a bit chilled.' He wades cautiously into the new obstacle and tests the depth, holding his machine pistol high above his head to keep his powder dry.

He's lucky. The water only comes up to his navel. The current pulls him a few metres out of his way, but he lands on the far bank safely.

By midnight they have covered three kilometres, by a devious route, and still had seen no sign of a Russian. The border is obviously very thinly guarded, and if this situation is repeated elsewhere, the Germans' Blitzkrieg will really catch them asleep.

They move on. Their nerves are stretched to breaking point. Clouds of mist drift up from the surrounding swamps and give them more cover. They cross a meadow along a wide path. Their eyes probe the area ahead, but their thoughts are straying back across the Demarcation Line.

'Dear mother, dear father,' Oberleutnant Schübler had written to his parents. 'By the time you read these lines, I shall long since have this operation behind me. If anything should have happened to me, then I . . . to the last . . . In gratitude and love . . .'

'Cover!' he hisses, but his men have already seen the danger.

The sound of the truck's engines could be heard well before the vehicle's lights became visible. The big truck rolls slowly towards them, packed with infantrymen who are obviously dozing rather than checking the field for enemy soldiers in fake uniforms.

Schübler signals to Sawitzky to take his place next to Pfänder at the front, since from now on he intends to urge his men on from behind, 'And blue beans for breakfast!'

Time is passing. Schübler jabs a finger at his map, and the Pole nods eager assent without even looking at it.

The next village. A farm dog howls a love song to the night. And then they hear voices.

They hit the dirt.

'Damned peasants,' thinks Schübler in irritation. 'Sentries half asleep.' They keep lying flat and eating dirt. Pfänder keeps an ear out while Schübler checks out the Ivans with his binoculars. He fumbles with the focusing.

And then he sees them: three Red Army soldiers in a little hollow, much closer than he had thought. If the Ivans hadn't been talking so loudly, he and his men would have walked straight into their gun barrels. Well, Schübler told himself with a strange little burst of anger, for them it's peacetime, while we're already playing at war - before it's even begun.

He has the Ivans so thoroughly in his sights that he can see every detail of their solid, coarse-featured peasant faces. The village is obviously teeming with Soviets, and these three boys taking their night-time constitutional are supposed to be guarding them. But they're just chatting on - about women, as a deaf man would realise by the tone of their voices.

Schübler looks at his watch and considers what to do. He could take out this trio in no time. All he would have to do would be to press the trigger; by the time the Soviets in the village woke up, he and his men would be miles away.

But the little band under Schübler's command has orders not to get involved in any combat until X-hour, the official time of the invasion. It is now half past midnight. During the past few hours, other Brandenburg units have probably crossed into Russian territory on undercover missions. If he were to start making a noise around here, he would probably be putting the Ivans onto the other units as well. He thinks of Jonas, the Prophet, his friend; of little Cerny, who is trembling with a mixture of fear and eagerness to prove himself.

'They'll have to waste time by feeling their way to the right in a wide arc. They make it through, but they lose half an hour. They are already as tired as long-distance runners, but the real test has not yet come. The Oberleutnant is still in contact with Dörner's group; he reaches a little road, checks the time again. 'We'll never make it at this rate,' he says. 'From now on we stay on the road and play real Ivans.'

Pfänder looks concerned, but the others are glad to give up the hide-and-seek game.

'Right. To Moscow!' says Schübler, playing up the mood, though he knows better.

For a while nothing happens. Then a Russian artillery unit drives past them, heedless of their real identity. The guns are old German ones, sold to the Russians by Hitler as no longer of use. Then comes a motor-cycle despatch rider, who asks Pfänder the way to the Demarcation Line.

The Baltic German points behind. 'Just keep following your nose, *Tovaritch*,' he says with a grin. 'Then left, then right, and then put your brakes on . . . or the Germans'll have you off your saddle in no time.'

The man steps on the gas pedal and roars away. Schübler is astonished at how well it went. 'Christ,' he says in bemusement. 'You're a genius, man. I'll give you a special leave if we get through this shit in one piece.'

From now on he feels confident. Maybe a little too confident, but how else are they to reach their target before dawn? Things go well. Unexpectedly well. Most of the Russians are really asleep, and the Red Army troops who are on the move ask no questions.

From somewhere they hear a melodious, sad song. Many fine voices. Poor devils.

The Oberleutnant strides ahead powerfully. The others stick behind him. Suddenly he stops. Shapes are rising out of the ditch to the right of the road . . . Ivans!

'*Stoi!*' growls a Russian lieutenant.

Pfänder walks up to him, though his legs are paralysed.

'Password?' the officer demands.

'Smolensk,' says Pfänder.

'*Njet*,' says the lieutenant, and looks at the six with obvious distrust. The Pole is trembling with fear. He looks as if his eyes are about to pop out of his head. Schübler keeps his mouth shut. Pfänder is speaking like a native, and the words are rolling off his tongue like water from a waterfall, but he's just talking them all into trouble.

'Come with me,' says the lieutenant.

'Where?' asks Pfänder.

'To the Commissar,' the Soviet officer says, glancing at his three heavily-armed companions.

And once the Brandenburgers step into the light, the Russian will surely see their German weapons. And their suspiciously bulky uniforms.

Then they're really in it. One Oberleutnant and five men, making six candidates for the firing squad in all.

Dörner and his men watch unobserved as Schübler's group are taken prisoner by the Russians.

'Christ, you've got to do something!' says Cerny.

'No shooting,' the Feldwebel answers.

'Fuck that!' Rauchalles chips in.

'Schübler will get himself out of trouble,' Zwecker comforts his comrades.

'He's running out of time,' says Cerny.

They then shut up again, make themselves small and stare into the night.

The Russian lieutenant in charge of the patrol is obviously not easily fooled. He has a thick mane of hair, a face in which the skin is stretched taut over the cheeks. People with stomach growths look like that, as do fanatics.

'We're on a special mission,' says Pfänder in a last attempt to get them out of the mess. 'If you stop us from carrying it out, we shall make you responsible for the consequences, Comrade Lieutenant.'

'Don't give me that,' says the lieutenant. 'Move!'

They are flanked by four Red Army soldiers. The Soviets seem, in fact, still to believe that they are dealing with a bunch of deserters who have split from their units on the lookout for girls or vodka. The officer shone his torch on them very briefly so that he didn't even notice the German weapons. His aim is to get these miscreants to the nearest commissar, and then his job is over.

The escort and prisoners get slowly under way. Maybe 800 metres to the first houses on the edge of the village. Schübler's brain is working feverishly, but whichever way he calculates, he's still sitting right in the shit. If he lets himself and his men be taken to the commissar, then in a few minutes the Russians will know they are Germans, and that they have put on Russian uniforms to infiltrate Soviet territory. If, on the other hand, they open fire, then they will not only be disobeying an order but possibly also betraying all the other Brandenburgers who are roaming behind the Demarcation Line this perilous night.

Another 780 metres. What to do, for God's sake? he turns

to Melchior, and the fat man shows he has understood without letting the Soviets know. Then the Oberleutnant reaches for his machine pistol, as if adjusting the strap. His fingers are quicker than his brain. His lips become a thin gash of determination. He's a soldier, not a murderer, but if he wants to survive he has no choice but to pull that trigger.

Half a magazine of bullets slams into the body of the left-hand Ivan. The other Soviet whips round in astonishment, collapses headlong; even in death, his face carries an expression of almost childlike amazement.

Freudenreich has hit the ground. Melchior has the Russian lieutenant in his sights and has already pressed the trigger. Jonas is blasting away too. Murder, the child of necessity. Schübler fires on and on. The sound must be audible for miles around - but he gets the third Ivan, and that's what matters now.

The fourth is running for it, zigzagging from one side of the road to the other, then going headlong, squirming a few metres, back on his feet again, a real pro . . .

The Pole, meanwhile, has returned from the realm of terror and realised what's happening. The relief has gone to his head very quickly. He is pounding away with his fists and feet at the corpse of the Russian officer.

'Leave him be, you lily-livered bastard!' Schübler growls at him. 'Come on!' he bellows to the others. 'Just get out of here!'

There are shouts from the direction of the village. Flares are starting to hiss skywards. A score of searchlights scar the night, probing for the fleeing Germans. Their lungs are bursting, their knees trembling as they run. Their eyes imagine a thousand ghosts.

On! Faster! Get down! Up! Crawl! Roll! Into the night, into the forest, everything just like they practised in training, except this time it's a matter of life or death. If the Ivans realise who has killed their comrades . . .

They're being followed, but the hunt has no method or logic. They take cover, sense the night.

They can hear commands in Russian from quite close by. But it is obvious that the Ivans are looking in the wrong direction.

They move on. Their guide doesn't want to continue. Jonas and Sawitzky grab him under the arms and frogmarch him.

In the road, trucks are roaring by. Soldiers are all over the place, shining torches over the meadows and trees.

They take cover in a ditch close to a crossroads. Oberleutnant Schübler stares at the map.

'Where now?' he snaps at the Pole.

The man shakes his head. Schübler slaps his face with the flat of his hand, as hard as he can. 'Where to?' he hisses again.

'Straight ahead,' the Pole whimpers.

'Good,' says the officer.

They hurry on, headlong through the night. Soon it will be light. They have Russians behind them, Russians to the right and left. The enemy are so close that they can hear the sing-song accents of the Ukrainian dialect. They can see the glimmer of the *Papyrossi* cigarettes. Bastards, thinks Jonas – they can smoke.

Dörner and his men waited for a while at first, for safety's sake. They are still staying in cover. The Russians have come very close to them several times, but they still haven't been discovered. The problem is that they have now lost contact with their comrades up ahead.

'Shit,' oaths Dörner. Time is pressing on, but a Russian unit is barring his way through to Schübler.

He peers cautiously out ahead. The Russians are silent. They are under cover too. The enemy's woken up now, and he is on a war footing.

While the Feldwebel is still considering who he should send ahead as a scout, little Cerny has already decided to volunteer. The enemy's invisibility has really started to prey on his inexperienced mind. He sees a Russian behind every tree and a machine-gun post in every thicket. Given the chance, he would just like to spray bullets wildly through the night, and at that moment he hates the darkness, the mission, the whole Brandenburg outfit. He's scared of cracking up, and so he decides to fight his inner demons by volunteering for action. It can't be worse than this waiting . . .

He wriggles up until he is next to Dörner, whispers into his hand. 'I speak the best Russian,' he tells the Feldwebel. 'I'll go forward and see what's happening.'

'Be careful,' says Dörner. He suddenly feels queasy in his guts. This is Cerny's first undercover mission.

Dörner looks at his watch, takes another glance through the binoculars. Eleven, twelve minutes to go until X-hour.

Nothing to be seen or heard of the boy, and the Ivans are now so close you can see their cigarettes and hear their lowered voices. Dörner is relieved to see that the boy is trying to sneak past them in a wide half-circle. Training pays. Caution is the mother of survival. Cerny is moving a little fast for the Feldwebel's taste, but then this is his first combat mission.

Cerny creeps up from the flank towards the Russians. At least two platoons there, he estimates. No question but that they are pulling back. Great, Cerny tells himself and notes that the road to the right is free of enemy forces. He decides to make absolutely certain of that, and at the same time realises that his fear has gone. Completely gone: he is as astonished as a man who has been run over and can't understand why he feels no pain. Another 50 metres, he thinks, and then back to make his report, and a few days to wait until someone pins an Iron Cross on his chest and makes him a hero.

Cerny sneaks onward, at a crouch, very clear about his objective. He no longer has much time. If the Feldwebel doesn't know soon that he can move through to the right, the report will be no good to him. Another 20 metres. Suddenly he stumbles against a tree root, can't keep upright, lands noisily among the undergrowth, gets to his feet again hastily – but the Russians are already there.

Eight or ten silhouettes moving in on him, encircling him.

One of them calls out something, but Cerny has forgotten that he speaks Russian. He can't go forward or back. And he can't shoot, because after all those are orders. And the Ivans are nearly at him. The one in front is asking for the password.

Cerny shakes his head; he can't even lie.

'Where are you from?' the Soviet asks.

'The front,' says Cerny haltingly.

'Which unit?'

Question follows question, merciless and fast. Before the boy can even start to answer, he finds himself held fast by big, hard peasants' hands. He strikes out, tries to break free. His Russian tunic pulls up, revealing the Wehrmacht field grey underneath.

Cerny no longer has anything at all to say.

Whistles. Shouts. Dörner, Rauchalles and Zwecker cannot see exactly what's happening, but it takes very little imagination to realise that their comrade has fallen into a trap.

The Ivans are interrogating him. From time to time, a few scraps of talk waft across to them on the wind, and Dörner prays that the procedure will be drawn out, because soon the big noise is due to start: Hitler's invasion of Russia.

Are they hitting him? Is he screaming?

'No!' Cerny is moaning. 'You can't do that . . . !'

For Christ's sake, he should be speaking only Russian, Dörner tells himself dully.

'Are we just going to sit here while they kill him?' Zwecker snarls.

'Don't talk shit,' says Dörner without much conviction. 'They'll knock him about a bit, and then –'

Again they hear desperate screams echoing through the night. The sounds are inhuman. The shrill, horrified screams cut through the consciousness of the other Brandenburgers, as if it was they who were being tormented out there. They just burrow lower into the wiry, soggy grass and shut their eyes, feel the rope on their own necks.

'I'm a soldier!' little Cerny is screaming. 'You can't do that! It's . . . it's against international law!'

One of the Russians laughs. Dörner feels as if a knife is being slid across his bare nerve-endings. He puts his hand over his ears and shoves his nose down into the earth. Zwecker looks at his watch, puts his hand on the Feldwebel's shoulder, as if to steady him.

'If they harm a hair of that boy's head,' hisses Rauchalles, 'I'll make sure they won't be able to tell their arses from their eyes when I'm through.'

'Come on!' says Feldwebel Dörner. He doesn't give a damn about that deadshit bridge any more; this is for little Cerny.

The others follow him. They approach very close to the Ivans, then fire from the hip straight into the Russian position. To their surprise, they find that there are very few Ivans left there. They shot a few down, and the others bolt into the night.

'Christ, it's going to be an afternoon stroll to Moscow,' says Private Zwecker, and starts to look for Cerny along with his other comrades.

No sign of the boy.

They've probably taken him with them to the rear. He'll have to sweat it out a bit, poor kid, until the lightning German advance sets him free in an hour or two's time.

Dörner is the first to see him. And he can't get any sound out when he does. His gaze travels slowly upward, from the boots up over the Russian trousers, the German belt, to the chest, the neck, the face. Little Cerny is hanging so low and close to the ground that it looks as if he could dance on it with the tips of his toes. The branch he's hanging from is thin, almost fragile, but then so was Cerny. He wanted to prove himself, and they strung him up for it. Rough justice.

Dörner suddenly feels ill. He leans against a tree, throws up everything he's got. Then Zwecker moves up next to him, sees the dead man, still with his Russian uniform over his German tunic. Cerny's eyes are turned up; his bloated tongue lolls out of the side of his mouth. A hero's death, Brandenburg style.

'Sickening,' says the Feldwebel to Rauchalles, who is threatening to go berserk. 'Don't you think it gets to me too?'

'Yeah, it gets to you,' says Zwecker acidly. 'Then why did you send this... this beginner... out to do a man's job?'

'Maybe so that you didn't end up hanging from that tree,' the Feldwebel answers coldly.

At that moment, almost that instant, 7000 guns roar. The night sky turns sulphurous yellow. Low-flying planes swish across the terrain. Panzer engines roar into action. Far to the Russian rear, bombs start to fall from the sky.

The war in the East has begun - five minutes too late for little Cerny.

An hour before the official declaration of war, German bombers rain destruction on the major Soviet air bases. Before the Reds can overcome sleep and terror, their air force is in flames. Rata fighters try an emergency scramble at the military airfield at Brest-Litovsk. Even before they have left the runways, German bombs explode among them, and planes are destroyed in mid-air, blazing fireballs just a few feet off the ground.

The Soviet airfields are just as Rowehl's reconnaissance squadron photographed them: bombers, fighters, spotter planes, all crammed together, wingtip to wingtip, nose to tail. The German bombers wreak incredible havoc. Steep, dense clouds of smoke rise over the air bases, which will soon be in German hands, for they are very close to the border. The Soviets' carefully-built air power is eliminated in one swoop before it can even be brought to bear. 'The usual Soviet story: take it easy and pay the price,' as one Soviet colonel said to his German captors.

All combatworthy aircraft of air fleets 1, 2 and 4 had been

ready for combat since 2 a.m. The crews were under orders to fly over the Demarcation Line at extreme altitude and smash the Russian fighter bases just before X-hour. 'This tried and tested "first strike" ruse took many Soviet air bases totally by surprise,' Janusz Piekalkiewitcz writes in his book *The Air War*. 'It was followed immediately by the second wave, with a main force of 637 bombers and 231 fighters against 31 Soviet airfields. During the early hours of the morning, some 400 bombers carried out the next massive blow against another 35 airfields. A total of 66 air force bases were affected, which meant 70% of the entire Russian air force.

'As Soviet historians confirm, by midday on that first day, some 1200 Soviet aircraft have been destroyed, 800 of those on the ground. Lieutenant-General of the Air Force Kopets loses 600 of his aircraft on that first day without inflicting losses worthy of mention on the enemy. On the second day he commits suicide. Particularly hard hit are the air force units stationed on the Baltic coast (General A. P. Ionov). They are surprised by the Luftwaffe's attack just as many formations are returning from a big night exercise.

'Soviet sources say that because of a shortage of pilots, who were either on leave, sick, on courses or delivery flights, "on the first day of the war, almost half the aircraft in the five frontline districts were unable to take to the air." Thus the German Luftwaffe gained air superiority immediately and in all areas of the front, and this played a crucial part in the ground forces' successes . . .'

The confusion on the Soviet side was unimaginable. Their communications system was pathetic; many telephone lines had been cut by German agents just before the opening of hostilities. The German advance, when it comes, is vast and inexorable. The skies belong to the invaders. The German air cover is dense and totally lethal; as soon as an aircraft bearing a red star appears in the sky, it is shot down, be it fighter, bomber or reconnaissance aircraft. The troops advancing eastwards wave gratefully to the low-flying bombers and fighters.

Most of the Soviet combat aircraft are still totally obsolete. Stalin's air force has a total of more than 13,000 aircraft, so German experts estimate – and perhaps they are being ungenerous. But the confirmed 'kill' figures attributed to German fighters soon reach such astronomical heights that the underestimate doesn't matter. Yet. 'It was like a duck-shoot,' says Johannes Steinhoff, a fighter ace with 176 kills to credit, of those first weeks of the war in Russia.

The Blitzkrieg has been regenerated. The Ju 87s, which had been given such a bad time over England, are now monarchs of the air. Then, however, a few losses mar the brilliant record of those first weeks: a Ju 88 explodes, and then a Heinkel 111. Without any enemy action. No flak activity reported, or Ratas in the vicinity. No one can say why the pilots - mainly on return flights - seem to have found themselves sitting on dynamite.

It turns out that they had been carrying death in their bomb bays. The culprit is the new fragmentation bomb, the SD 10, which they are supposed to drop in bundles of four. Their lethal cargo often gets stuck in the bomb doors and explodes - if they get that far - on landing at the latest.

An even greater disaster are the 'devil's eggs', two kilo fragmentation bombs of the SD 2 type, packed into special 'shaker' containers. It turned out that a small amount of atmospheric turbulence was enough to set them off and cause horrendous damage. The bombs look like food cans with small fins. When they explode, they separate into 300 slivers of shrapnel that spread themselves over an area of about 12 metres. They are to be used by pilots against 'live targets', and they are also intended to have a demoralising effect, but they are feared by friend and foe alike because of their unpredictability: a large part of the responsibility for the 35 planes lost that day must be laid at the door of the 'devil's eggs'.

'The aircraft in the squadron were fitted with little hangers for each bomb, 96 altogether,' say Hans Ring and Werner Girbig in their book *Fighter Squadron 27*. 'These bombs became activated by being dropped, and were then timed to detonate a short time later. The SD 2 was planned to be a clever and effective weapon in air-to-ground support situations, but it involved a host of dangers in operation. Most frequently, the front rows of bombs hanging from the rack would stick under the effect of the air pressure, and only drop when the aircraft slowed down while coming in to land. Often they would explode in the process, but sometimes they wouldn't, because they were not yet primed. It was quite common for the pilot, in blissful ignorance, to come taxiing into his hangar or landing space with a load of primed SD 2s. Some of them would then drop and explode right behind the plane. If they remained unexploded, they could still endanger the following aircraft as they came in to land. The groundcrew became very reluctant to approach full-loaded aircraft after an SD 2 mission.'

A bloody reckoning. Suddenly, late on that first morning, Soviet bombers attack heavy, cumbersome-looking aircraft, making their way towards the German panzer spearheads, stubbornly in formations of 20, 30 or 40 each, without fighter support. They pay no attention to the German flak, just keep going on fixed courses. And they are picked off, formation by formation, by the German fighters as they make their approaches. All of them . . . And then the next wave goes the same way. It is no more than mass-suicide on the part of the Russian crews.

It's the same story all that day. Advances on all fronts. Just a few hours after the beginning of the war, all bridges over the Bug are in German hands and intact, and the panzers are flooding eastwards.

Swift advances, without any securing of the flanks. Supplies dropped from the air. Classic modern war of movement. Nevertheless, there are basic differences between this war in Russia and previous conflicts: firstly, it is clear that even the huge quantities of panzers and aircraft are already lost in the endless spaces of the country; and secondly, as early as March 30th 1941, Hitler had declared to his speechless commanders that the conduct of the war in the East would differ from that in the West, because it was a battle between two 'world views' and would be fought with pitiless harshness and without regard for conventional attitudes. 'We must,' he told the Wehrmacht high-ups, 'shift out of any notions of soldierly comradeship with regard to the Russians.'

At the same time, the Nazi dictator issued his notorious 'Commissar Order': the uniformed political advisers who were part of any Soviet unit were to be separated from ordinary soldiers and liquidated. At the same time, Hitler issued orders that civilians in the occupied areas were not subject to the normal military legal procedures, and that crimes by Germans on Russians were not to lead to prosecution.

It was a fateful step.

Neither Oberleutnant Schübler nor any of his men could

have said afterwards how they managed to reach the wooden bridge over the Bobr immediately before X-hour. It had been the shortest night of the year, but to them it had seemed like the longest. The Russians call the time after the summer solstice the 'white nights'; they will be the bloody nights, nothing is more certain.

The young officer achieved his goal simply by paying no heed to his pursuers and heading for the bridge by the shortest route.

Now he is sprawled in the undergrowth, probing for the river with his field glasses just as the first silver fingers of dawn show themselves in the east.

'Look at that, will you?' says the Oberleutnant. 'Not a goddamned soul on that bridge!' He gets to his feet, to show his men how unnecessary it is to take cover here. 'Christ, what a bunch - and they call themselves soldiers! They might as well still be fighting with bows and arrows!' He stretches himself comfortably, loosening the muscles of his shoulders and back. 'You can smoke,' he says generously. Then his voice is lost in the roar of distant guns. And shells land to their left and right - German shells. The Russians seem to be still asleep.

The Brandenburgers trot down to the bridge as calmly as a little flock of lambs. The Oberleutnant has enough experience to be especially suspicious of all things that run too smoothly, but he can see no guards on the bridge, no matter how hard he tries. Schübler stands and looks at the prepared positions there, laughs out loud and points to the empty dugouts. 'Really great guys, these Ivans,' he chuckles. 'They've even saved us some elbow grease!' He moves ahead of his men, jumps down into the dugout, examines it with a critical eye: excellent. Straight out of the textbooks. As if the Brandenburgers had done it in training at Quentzgut. And the Oberleutnant's thoughts are not so strange: after all, in the twenties the German Reichswehr trained the Red Army.

'They deserve a medal for this!' says Freudenreich, their lucky mascot.

'Need to wet the whistle?' asks Jonas, and hands Schübler his field canteen which is filled with schnaps.

'Just don't get caught, my boy,' the Oberleutnant mutters sourly, and gulps greedily at the raw spirit. He sees the Polish guide standing looking helpless and miserable. 'Go on!' he barks, and points to a dugout. 'You can move in there.

There's an apartment free on the block!'

Suddenly the fun is over. He sees Russians in uniform approaching. Sappers. The bridge's guards, he ponders, and then sees that they are carrying bales of straw and cans of petrol.

'What a thing,' he says to Pfänder, the Baltic German. 'They're out to set fire to the bridge like Indians in a Wild West story.' He laughs humourlessly. 'Just don't let 'em shoot me before I give the order.' And he grins like the cat who's got the cream. No worries.

The Russians still have no idea what's going on. Friend and foe alike are under cover, the Ivans on the right bank, the Germans on the left. Shells are landing on both sides. Heavy blighters from the big German guns.

'What a bunch of arseholes!' the Oberleutnant growls. 'We're risking our necks, and they're shooting us and that lovely bridge to shit!'

Dense formations of German fighters are whooshing overhead. Stukas, flying higher, are sweeping almost casually towards their targets. Sawitzky has to make a conscious effort not to wave to them. He is as proud as if he had invented the Ju 87 himself.

The first Russian units are approaching the bridge from the West. They are moving close to the bridge, still more or less orderly: an infantry detachment, trucks, scout cars. The wooden structure trembles. The damned thing won't hold up to that kind of traffic for long.

Then the situation starts to get serious. Obviously the sappers have been given orders to destroy the bridge. Even with the naked eye, the Germans can see a Soviet officer urging on the men with the petrol cans, spurring them on to work faster.

'Right. At last,' growls Schübler, and cautiously pokes the barrel of his machine pistol out of the dugout.

The others imitate him mechanically. The Russian officer must know that anyone who sets himself up as a target has only himself to blame.

Schübler takes aim on the Russian lieutenant and has no idea why he is hesitating. Perhaps because the man looks so decent. If you had stuck him in a civilian suit, he would have looked nothing like a Russian . . . But forget the philosophical speculations. When push comes to shove, there's only the old barrackroom saying: leave thinking to horses, because they've got bigger heads.

'Forward, in the name of lunacy!' Schübler calls to his men. 'Fire at will!'

They let rip. All at once. The Soviet officer sways for a moment, throws out his arms as he is trying to reach for the invisible enemy. Then he trips over and topples with his face to the wooden railing, and hangs there like a drunk.

The other Red Army troops go down like ninepins. This is not war, but slaughter. The Russians have one advantage, though: numbers. Those not caught in the first welter of fire realise quickly what is going on and take cover, pinpoint where the enemy is, begin to return fire.

The Polish guide raises his head out of his dugout rather incautiously, and is the first to die. A bullet through his head that means his home town of Lipsk will only see him again sealed in a coffin.

On the Russian side, a good NCO who knows what he is doing must have taken charge. He has realised that he has to get over the bridge and engage the Germans in hand-to-hand combat, to exploit his numerical superiority.

'Poor bastards,' murmurs Jonas, the prophet.

The first wave comes on, wavers, pulls back. Easy. The second also wilts under the power of the German fire. But the foremost Russians have managed to get dangerously close to the German position.

'Use hand grenades!' Oberleutnant Schübler orders, and ducks as he feels a Russian machine-gun burst above his head. They must be giving their people covering fire, he thinks; he would do the same in their situation.

'Let them come closer,' he calls out to Savitzky. 'Don't use the grenades too early.'

He watches the Russian attack with mixed feelings. One coming on, the other covering textbook stuff. But it's not good enough. In these well-built dugouts, the Brandenburg commando squad will be able to hold out for maybe another ten minutes, and by that time their comrades will surely have arrived.

'I'd like to know where that slackarse Dörner's got to,' the Oberleutnant grates.

'He and his mob'll have made themselves scarce,' Jonas answers. 'Not surprising after that firework display back there.'

'Yeah, and if we'd been heading for a whorehouse instead of a bridge, they'd have stuck like glue,' says Schübler cynically.

They can already hear the rumble of German Panzers. Small arms fire. Fighters banking and landing to refuel for their next ground support forays.

Suddenly the Brandenburgers hear the sound of fire behind them.

'Great!' roars Sawitzky. 'They're coming. Can you hear them? Our boys are on their way!'

He turns around, is careless for a second, and that's enough for the Russian machine-gunner. A burst slices through Sawitzky from left to right.

'You stupid bastard!' bellows Schübler. 'Stay under cover!'

But Sawitzky is in no condition to hear his advice - or anything any more. And the others are fighting for their lives, for they have realised that they are now faced with a miniature two-front war.

The Soviets are coming from behind as well as in front. For a moment it seems as if the Russians are going to go for each other. Between the two groups sits Schübler's halved commando group, busy deciding whether to deal with the threat from East or West.

The Ivans advancing over the bridge are now no more than 30 metres away. Pfänder, the Balt, and fat Melchior are covering the rear while Schübler is pulling the pin out of his last hand grenade and Jonas is switching his machine pistol to single shot. The damned wooden bridge over the Bobr is still standing, festooned with piles of Red corpses, behind which their living comrades are taking cover. Either the next German shell destroys the damned thing, or the Russians will capture it back, because four men can't hold it from both sides for much longer.

This time they have been well and truly catapulted into the shit, one of five Brandenburg squads sent on crazy undercover missions in the East immediately before the outbreak of war. And like the others, these men have about a snowball's chance in hell of coming back alive.

Schübler allows the next wave of Russians to come forward to within ten metres. He throws his last 'egg' like a man lost in the desert who is draining the last of his water. He pitches it precisely between two oncoming Russians. The grenade explodes and gives a short breathing-space. But now the game is up, because they can't fight with their bare hands, and in these - it now seems inevitable - last seconds of his life, the young Oberleutnant hears his commander saying, 'Cheers, Schübler, I have reserved the best for you. That's what you want?'

'You bloody bastard!' he oaths, and he's not sure whether he means himself or the Hauptmann. 'As the Herr Hauptmann wishes . . . orders carried out, Herr Hauptmann. Kiss my arse, Herr Hauptmann . . .'

The Russians are coming forward again. They have guts, there's no doubt about that. Or a commissar who doesn't allow any backsliding. 40 metres to go, maybe only 35.

'Hey, Melchior!' the Oberleutnant yells to the fat man. 'Can you lend me a hand grenade?'

But the man doesn't hear him, for in that moment an insanely loud roar drowns everything. The Russians start to bellow warnings to each other. Air attack. Messerschmitts.

Salvation comes in the wave of annihilation.

The Mes spit golden, tiny beads of death. Their wing-mounted machine guns and cannon clear a space behind the commando group, a space alike to a cemetery, and at the same time they force the Ivans advancing across the bridge to take cover.

Schübler uses the good fortune of the moment, leaps out of his dugout, draws the enemy's fire to him, avoids it by running in a zigzag, hurls him down close to the nearest Russian, takes the dead man's weapon out of his unresisting hand and prays that it's loaded.

He dashes back, and sees the greedy snouts of the Messerschmitts, which have turned and are coming from the other side. He burrows deep into mother earth, so deep that no one could burrow deeper. When the lethal hornets have passed over him, he sees that Pfänder has had it. A direct hit. A bloody bundle of flesh is all that remains of the German Balt.

'You goddamned morons!' he growls at the retreating Me pilots, despite the fact that they just saved his own life. He can't bear the sight of his dead comrade, tries to shut his eyes, but knows there's no point in dying blind. He lifts his head again, looks – and finds himself staring into the grinning face of a dead Russian, who has forgotten to shut his left eye. Wherever Schübler tries to look, he can only see this cyclops' eye.

'Shut it, you bastard!' the young officer moans.

'Jesus, Oberleutnant,' yells Freudenreich, their mascot,

loud as a fairground crier. 'We've made it right through the shit! Look at that!'

Schübler turns, sees with his first glance that the Russians flooding back from the Demarcation Line are turning to face the oncoming German Panzers and will be crushed by the German advance in moments.

'You just keep your big head down, then!' the Oberleutnant bellows to Freudenreich.

But the warning comes too late for the platoon's mascot to moderate his near-demented enthusiasm. His left arm has been shot to ribbons, but he can wave with his right, and he clambers up out of his dugout, stares down at the Ivans raising their hands in droves.

'Hey... You!... Fantastic!' he bawls at the Germans. 'You're late, but at least you came!'

'You idiot!' Jonas bellows.

'A walkover! A walkover! Don't be so timid, gents,' yells the mascot. 'We've got the goddamned bri –'

Jonas drags him back. Too late.

Freudenreich buckles onto his knees and drops slowly, as if in slow motion, with his face to the earth, caught from behind by a burst of Russian machine gun fire.

Jonas sees Rauchalles and Dörner jumping down from the leading Panzers and moving forward on foot, covering each other, to save the last of their comrades on the Bobr bridge.

Schübler is finished. He collapses, witnesses his own salvation as if from a dream state. Only now does he notice that he has been hit two, three times. Before he loses consciousness entirely, he sees the wooden bridge collapse under the weight of the panzers...

Greetings beween Jonas and his mates who saved him at the last moment, though they are brief and one-sided. Nevertheless, Jonas the Prophet had made it through alive a second time, and with him Schübler, which doubles the survival rate achieved on the bridge over the Meuse in Holland. He sits dully on a tree-stump, burnt-out, finished, vacant, with his Russian uniform tunic still on over his German uniform.

'Just the face I'm looking for,' says a Propaganda Ministry photographer, and sets up his camera.

He takes pictures of Jonas from every angle. The Prophet is staring into space, his jaw slack and his eyes empty. His hair is hanging down over his forehead. His face is filthy, devoid of hope – the face of a beaten man.

Two weeks later, he appears as the cover photo for a Wehrmacht magazine. The caption is: 'The Face of the Bolshevik Sub-Human'.

All the Brandenburgers who are still alive by that time laugh themselves halfway to death at that one. Everyone agrees it's the best involuntary joke of the war.

The Frozen Victory - 2

It took a whole day until everyone in the huge expanses of the Soviet Union was aware that Hitler had attacked their country. Even in the western parts, where the German advance was racing through the land like a fire fanned by the wind, there was still unimaginable confusion as late as midday. The German wireless interception units picked up messages: 'What are we supposed to do?' – 'We are cut off' – 'Urgently awaiting reinforcements' – 'Request support from long-range fighters'.

These cries for help got more and more desperate, the Russians' military position more and more chaotic. Stalin had been warned by the English and the Americans, and at the last moment also by the German-born Soviet spy Richard Sorge in Tokyo, but had chosen to ignore all these reports, including accounts from his own Intelligence services regarding the German concentrations on the Demarcation Line.

As late as a week before the outbreak of war, the Soviet government issued an official denial in every newspaper in the country that relations between Germany and Russia had in any way deteriorated. On the day of the invasion, *Pravda* led with an article about 'the people's concern about our schools'. Radio Moscow did not alter its usual Sunday schedules; it was not until almost midday that an important government announcement was slotted into the programme. The weather was fine and sunny. Most of the population were on vacation, innocently amusing themselves on the beaches and lakes.

Many Soviet officers had been taking part in midsummer's night parties when the Germans invaded, and were still drunk when they fell into German hands. General Dimitri Pavlov, the commander of the Western Military District, was watching a comedy in a theatre in Minsk when an Intelligence officer warned him of the German attack. 'That's impossible,' said the general, and proceeded to watch the third act with the same pleasure as before. By the time he got home from the theatre, he had nothing to laugh about.

Even Alfred Listkow, a soldier in the 22nd Infantry Regiment and an old German communist, who deserted to the Russian side only hours before X-hour to warn the Soviets, could not change their minds. It seemed that Hitler's victims were willing ones.

In London, Winston Churchill was woken up and informed of 'Barbarossa'. He had given instructions only to be woken in the case of a German invasion of England, and he berated his aide mercilessly before going back to sleep.

All over the world, leaders and people alike underestimated the importance of the Russo-German conflict. No one saw it as the turning point of the war, which would change the balance of power in the world for decades to come. The general attitude was one of grim satisfaction at a fraternal battle between two totalitarian systems, akin to Chicago gang warfare.

The former tie salesman and later US President Harry S. Truman said unequivocally, 'If we see Germany winning, we should help Russia, and if we see Russia winning, we should help Germany, so that they do each other as much damage as possible. I have to say that there are no circumstances in which I'd like to see Hitler win, but neither of them cares a fig for keeping his word.'

Those orders that reached the frontline commanders from Moscow were either incomprehensible or idiotic. One order, for instance, said: 'When counter-attacking, under no circumstances cross the German Demarcation Line'. Another: 'Comrade Stalin has forbidden the use of artillery against the Germans.'

General Boldin, deputy commander of the Western Military District, bellowed down the telephone line; 'Our troops are retreating. Entire cities are in flames. Everywhere there are masses of dead.' At this moment, the Panzer spearheads of three German Army Groups were driving deep into Soviet territory, cutting off the Russian armies from each other and threatening to encircle them.

Hitler had already addressed the nation with a speech on the Reich radio in which he told them; 'At this moment, we are witnessing the fulfilment of a military effort that in its magnitude and size is the greatest the world has ever seen.'

At 12.15, Commissar for Foreign Affairs Molotov spoke on Radio Moscow; 'The German fascist rulers have committed an unheard-of breach of faith. Not for the first time, our people has to face an insolent, ruthless assailant... The Red Army and our entire people is ready to fight another victorious patriotic war for our homeland, our honour and our freedom.' Molotov spoke emotionally, haltingly; he announced that 200 people had died in German air attacks on the cities of Shitomir, Kaunas, Kiev and Sebastopol. The declaration of war had been handed to the Commissar by the German ambassador half an hour after the actual invasion had started; despite this, they had separated with a handshake.

There was not a word from, Stalin, nor a sight of him. Nikita Kruschev, Stalin's successor, insisted that the Soviet Generalissimo shut himself in a room for two days and just simply drank himself stupid. The Soviet publicist Alexander B. Cakovski writes of his first encounter with Stalin and his closest advisers after the outbreak of war: 'He began to curse angrily. After that, he left the building, his shoulders bowed and his head sunk into his chest, got into his car and drove away. No one knows what he did for the next few days. No one saw him. No one heard him on the telephone. He summoned no one. And those who were waiting for hours on end for him to call, dared not call him without his prior permission...'

The Soviet defences had collapsed at the first blow. Of the 150 divisions in the West, 28 were eliminated from the conflict immediately, another 70 lost more than half of their soldiers and their equipment. It was not just the element of surprise that made the Russians so helpless; the eternally distrustful Stalin had unleashed an orgy of terror on his army between 1936 and 1938 that had made it literally headless. Marshal of the Soviet Union Nikolaevitch Tukhachevski, a hero of the Civil War and an exceptionally gifted commander, had been condemned to death and executed in secret on the basis of documents played into Stalin's hands by SS Obergruppenführer Reinhard Heydrich. The purge that followed had liquidated almost the entire army leadership. Three of the five marshals, fifteen army commanders, and a host of other high-ranking military men were jailed, executed, dismissed or demoted. Roy A. Medvedev, a Soviet historian, says; 'No army has lost as many high-ranking officers in war as the Red Army lost in peacetime.'

Romania and Italy joined the war against Russia immediately; Slovakia followed a day later. The Finns attacked Murmansk on June 26th. On the 27th, Hungary declared war on the Soviet Union.

The Panzers rolled on and on. On the 24th, Guderian's command vehicle struck a roadblock and was fired on by a Soviet tank from just a few metres' distance. At the same time, a truck stopped and a group of infantrymen stormed forward to counter-attack. When they realised that they were facing a German general, however, they were so terrified that they failed to use their weapons. 'The Russians must have recognised me, though, for their newspapers claimed that I had been killed in the incident,' wrote Guderian in his memoirs.

Two days later, his panzers had advanced 280 kilometres and were only 95 kilometres from Minsk.

Stalin was officially declared First Commissar for defence of the Soviet Union on July 3rd. His first act in office was to call on the Russian people to fight a guerrilla war against the invader. The English and the Americans, whom he had always dismissed as 'capitalist exploiters', were now 'faithful allies'. He also promulgated the 'scorched earth tactic', and called for every village to be razed before it fell into German hands, every can of petrol to be burned and every morsel of bread to be destroyed. In a move that was very skilled, he followed Molotov in dubbing this war of extinction 'the Great Patriotic War'.

In the Baltic regions, later in the Ukraine, and also in parts of White Russia, the German troops were often greeted with flowers, bread and salt. But the cruelty of the extermination squads who followed in the wake of the Wehrmacht's advance rapidly turned cautious allies into deadly enemies. The killers of the Reich Main Security Office were only following Hitler's orders. The Führer wanted no Russian allies; he intended to exterminate the 'Bolshevik subhumans'.

On July 8th, he announced his intention of razing to the ground the great Russian cities of Leningrad and Moscow. A day later, the first great 'cauldron battle' centring on Bialystok and Minsk ended with the capture of 330,000 Russian prisoners.

And the lightning advance continued. On July 9th, Minsk fell, followed by Smolensk on the 16th. 750,000 Russians were killed or taken prisoner, 6000 tanks and 5000 guns destroyed or captured. Franz Halder, Chief of the Army General Staff, a leading military expert and also an opponent of Hitler's regime, wrote in his diary: 'It would not be an exaggeration to say that the campaign against Russia was won in the first fourteen days.'

But as early as August 11th – the 51st day of the war in the East – Halder was saying: 'It is becoming increasingly clear from the general situation that the Russian colossus, which prepared itself deliberately for war, with all the ruthlessness of which a totalitarian state is capable, has been underestimated by us.'

Guderian's panzers were resting, well camouflaged and well cared for after their headlong advance. Their crews passed the time with cards. 'The skies over the endless plains are free of aircraft,' writes Wolfgang Paul in his book *The Battle for Moscow*. 'The roads are busy, and the break they had all been hoping for has begun. Now reinforcements and supplies are arriving. A few replacement engines have come. The panzer regiments are reclaiming their repaired tanks that had to be left by the roadside during the Blitzkrieg of the early summer.

'Everyone is clear about the next goal. It can only be Moscow, the enemy capital, for to take Moscow means victory. Generaloberst Halder calculated at the beginning of August that Army Group Centre outnumbered the enemy in this sector. With 750 kilometres behind them there are only 300 to go to their goal. Even the most sorely tested panzer engines can manage that.

'But the rest take turns into a waiting period in the vicinity of Smolensk. The roads that divide the whispering cornfields lose themselves in the limitless expanses to the east that seem to go on for ever . . .

'Guderian and his generals expect that they will soon advance along the highway towards Moscow with all their available panzer divisions, and they would like to lose no time. The rest need not last more than a week.

'The enemy is strengthening his forces around Moscow more with each passing day, as German spotter planes confirm. Why the delay?'

Moscow had been virtually undefended and Guderian's Panzers were standing around with nothing to do. The generals were almost unanimous in their suggestion that the army break through to Moscow, but Hitler, the 'creative genius' (his own description), stated on August 21st: 'The Army's suggestion of 18.8. for the continuation of operations in the East is not in accord with my views. The most important goal to be achieved before the onset of winter is not the taking of Moscow but the conquest of the Crimea, the Donets industrial and coal-mining area, and the cutting of the Russian oil pipeline from the Caucasus.'

Despite the generals' protests, the Panzer spearheads were redirected towards the Ukraine, and Kiev was surrounded. It was another perfect victory: 600,000 Russians were sitting trapped in a 240 kilometre long pincer.

But for all its superiority, the Wehrmacht was experiencing some unpleasant shocks: where it had estimated the strength of the Soviet Army at 200 divisions, it now discovered that there were 360. All the maps of the terrain were wrong, and even the routes shown as major roads were often found to be little more than narrow lanes. Instead of deserting to the Germans, the Russian civilian population showed an increasing tendency to support the partisans operating behind the German lines, who were very soon a major problem along the supply routes.

The fighting morale of the mistakenly despised Soviet forces also began to rise as the summer went on. It was true that more than a million Russian soldiers had been taken prisoner and that another 700,000 had been wounded or killed, and that the Germans had penetrated 800 kilometres into Soviet territory, but, as Oberst Dietrich von Cholitz stated: 'Countless cemeteries lined our advance, and they were filled with our own dead.'

Women's battalions, and even units composed of children, showed themselves to be bitter opponents. The pilots of stricken aircraft refused to bale out, preferring to aim the planes at German troop concentrations and thus take scores of the hated invaders with them to their deaths. One Soviet tank, peppered with shell-holes and blazing like a cauldron, continued to fire at the Germans until its entire crew had suffered roasting alive. And it was common for Soviet soldiers who had run out of ammunition to fight on with their rifle butts rather than surrender. Terror methods became more widespread on both sides: quarter was neither asked nor granted.

The Red Army conjured new armies out of the air, and autumn and winter approached without a decisive victory in Russia – a victory on the scale of the fall of Moscow, for instance.

In the South, the German conquerors were approaching the Donets Basin. In the Central Area, they were moving east of Smolensk. In the north, they were seeking the decisive battle for Leningrad. On August 13th, Field Marshal von Leeb's Army Group had captured the city of Novgorod, which lay on the main highway between Moscow and Leningrad. The Luga Line had been circumvented, and the commander-in-chief reported: 'One final push, and the Army Group North will have its victory.'

They are up to their necks in mud and have had a bellyful of this empty landscape, where only the lice and the flies seem to feel at ease. No roads, no human beings: now and again an old Russian woman, begging for a piece of bread from their ration packs.

'All in all, the biggest pigsty on the face of the earth,' says Private Kindler.

'Yeah. And if you raise that pudding head of yours so freely again, you're liable to end up in the other pigsty they call heaven,' Feldwebel Wendt corrected him.

A few of them laugh hoarsely. Rademann is too busy staring at his raw, bleeding feet. Drombach is rereading a letter from home, even though he knows it by heart. Ammunition, rations and post have arrived, and the men of the 42nd Infantry Regiment know what that means: they are about to advance.

Tomorrow, or better today, because anything seems better than sitting here scratching their arses, they'll be making for Leningrad. The main thing is to be going somewhere, and not sitting around in the mud, feeling their minds as stuck as their movements.

'When do we get underway?' Kindler asks his platoon leader.

'Don't worry,' Feldwebel answers with a laugh. 'You won't sleep through the great event.' He grins sourly. 'I'll wake you up personally.'

As evening comes, the mist descends, blanketing the hills and the dells, the forests and lakes in one huge shroud. The calm before the storm - on both sides.

The German assault on Leningrad has been set for 9.30 on September 9th 1941. And this day, of all days, there's no light. The boys in the infantry, who get rations of coffee and vodka, two to one proportion, look worriedly upwards, knowing that the promised air support won't be there for them if this weather continues.

And the Luftwaffe had assembled at the airfields of Dno, Saborova, Korovie Selo and Roskopolie and put together an airborne strikeforce just for Army Group North: 200 bombers, 60 Stukas, 166 fighters, 39 fighter-bombers and 13 reconnaissance aircraft.

'They're all sitting on the nest and waiting for us to do the dirty work on our own,' snarls Private Rademann with an edge of fear.

'Goddamned collar-and-tie soldiers,' says Kindler.

It is the first year of the war in the East. In the Baltic territories there had been flowers and welcomes; and then there was twenty different kinds of shit.

The 26 divisions of the Army Group, supported by Air Fleet 1, nevertheless made rapid progress. One after the other, Kovno, Dünaburg and Pleskov fell. While the 18th Army sealed the Soviet troops trapped in the Baltic states, the 16th Army reached the Sea of Alma on the 31st July, broke through here and on Lake Peipus, and this cleared the way to Leningrad - once Petrograd, and before that Saint Petersburg, Russia's second largest city, divided between many islands, a swampy Venice of the East.

The former capital of the Tsars is an enormously important communications centre, and a place that carries the name of the creator of the Russian revolution naturally has extra drawing power for a man like Hitler.

The swift capture of Leningrad had been assumed, until the Germans made the acquaintance of the local mud, in which Panzers became stuck up to their gun turrets. Instead of covering the infantry, the tanks were stranded, and the poor footsloggers were put to work building corduroy roads to put the colossi of the German war effort back into action.

The commander of the assault on Leningrad, Field Marshal Ritter von Leeb, knows that he must take the city in this September of 1941 or never.

More than three million inhabitants, the aged and the children, have been evacuated. Anyone who remains behind must fight: men or women. Worker Brigades are formed in the factories. When the first call for volunteers was made, 116,000 men and 32,000 women came forward. By the middle of July, three divisions of Home Guards have been created.

Stalin sends his Crown Prince, Zhdanov, as Defence Commissar, and Marshal Voroshilov as military commander to the city on the Neva. They publish the order: 'The direct threat of an enemy assault is now hanging over Leningrad, the cradle of the proletarian revolution. While the forces of the Northern Front are gallantly fighting the Nazi hordes and the Finnish Security Corps along the entire front from the Baring Sea to Reval and Hangö and are defending every inch of Soviet soil, the men on the North-Western Front are not always in a position to resist enemy attacks . . . As one man, we shall defend our city, our homes and our families, our honour and our freedom . . . Vigilant and merciless, we shall take up the struggle against cowards, panic-mongers and deserters. We shall enforce the strictest revolutionary order in our city . . .'

Until now, all Russia's cities have fallen easily to the German advance, but Leningrad will prove to be the place where the field-grey tide receives its first setback. The population has been fed a diet of atrocity stories, and work like madmen to save their city. In record time they build 4000 firebreaks, 4,600 dugouts, 700 kilometres of anti-tank trenches, 300 kilometres of roadblocks and 17,000 firing-slits.

Hitler has given orders for the capture of this city – Stalin for it to be held. Millions of human beings will be crushed between the commands of the two dictators, like peppercorns in a grinder.

'Make ready!' the order is bawled through the forward positions.

'Cheers!' says Drombach, and puts his mess tin to his lips. His mouth is so wide that his ears get visitors when he grins. 'You got troubles, you got some booze to help them.'

'I want to know how far it is to this dump they call Leningrad,' says Rademann.

'Oh, a good hour by car,' Kindler answers with a smirk.

'Find your car, you cretin,' says Rademann.

'I'll move fast, though,' Kindler promises him, hauling his machine gun up onto his shoulders. 'I just want to get into that lovely city. Just as far as a bathtub. That's all I need.'

'Quiet!' barks Feldwebel Wendt.

'Swamp-fever,' Drombach hisses with a grin.

And then, like a massive thunder-clap, the German

artillery starts up. Death spews out from a hundred fiery chasms, heading eastward. While the explosions slowly take shape miles away, the infantrymen's muscles are tensing, waiting for the 'Up! March, march!'

Engines are started up; aircraft crews stare at the clocks in their barracks and wait for a miracle to happen and the dismal, low cloud to be blown away by the wind and the skies freed for them.

The war machine is grinding into action. The German assault and – so its commanders hope – the final battle for Leningrad is underway. Just two hours after the beginning of the offensive, the heavens clear and the Luftwaffe is able to join the bitter battle. Late, but not too late.

During the first two days, the 6th Panzer Division is forced to fight for 32 underground bunkers and two armoured forts. On the 13th September, Krasnovadeisk falls. On the left flank, the attack progresses more quickly. From the bare heights overlooking the city, Oberleutnant Darius sends the famous radio message: 'I can see Leningrad and the sea.'

The First Infantry Division captures the troop exercise grounds at Krasnoie Seloe, the former summer residence of the Russian Tsars and the place where the famous Guards Regiment drilled. German forces break through the second ring of the inner defensive perimeter, and an advanced party reaches a tram stop at the end of the city's transport system, with the sign: '10 kilometres to Leningrad'.

By September 20th, the Russian front has been rolled back and the cauldron of Oranienbaum has been sealed. Three divisions are pushing along the railway line between Chudovo and Leningrad. An artillery platoon takes Sluzk as if by a miracle. A combat group takes the railway junction north of Mga, effectively closing off Leningrad from the land side.

Just one day after the beginning of the offensive, the advanced guard of the 424th Infantry Regiment spots Schlüsselburg. Feldwebel Wendt stares through his binoculars in astonishment. 'Either they're asleep,' he says. 'Or it's a trap.'

He rounds up a few men and makes for the deserted village, moving forward with expert caution. The regiment has long since fulfilled its duties and reached its objectives for the day, but no infantryman can refuse such a friendly invitation as this.

The patrol reports that Schlüsselburg is as good as

unoccupied. Oberstleutnant Hoppe decides to attack at 7.00.

The battalions move forward from three sides, as neatly and cleanly as if they were on the parade ground, men covering each other as they advance - but covering them against what? While the infantrymen prepare themselves for a desperate house-to-house struggle - their speciality - the Russians have already given them the place. They storm forward, but they find themselves pushing against an open door. The taking of the place is such an undramatic business that Feldwebel Wendt is able to hoist the flag at a leisurely pace on the undamaged church spire by 7.40.

And in 35 minutes the Stukas are due to arrive, to bomb Schlüsselburg into the ground.

'That's the trouble with your good deeds,' oaths Kindler, watching the desperate attempts of their radio operator to make contact with HQ, to avoid being blasted to kingdom come by their own Stukas.

No connection to Corps or Divisional HQs. No one knows that the Russians have been thrown out of Schlüsselburg without a fight. The radio operator's face is pouring with sweat. He keeps punching his keys obsessively, shaking his head like a frustrated child.

Eleven minutes to go.

The conquerors of Schlüsselburg keep imagining that they can already hear the sound of the aircraft engines.

And there's no cover. The wooden houses will crack under the bombs like eggshells. 'Just find yourself a nice little burial plot,' moans Rademann.

'Those arseholes,' Drombach roars. 'When you need them, they're never around, and then -'

'Christ, don't stand around with your thumbs up your bums,' the company commander growls. 'And stop that crap!'

'Yeah, we do our work and after hours those bastards turn us into mincemeat...'

'And I'll have your balls right now!' snaps Drombach, the company commander, and sneaks a look at his watch.

Six minutes to go until the catastrophe. In 360 seconds, not just one private but a whole unit will be blasted to hell.

'Made contact!' the radio operator shouts.

An artillery battery has picked up the message and passed it on to HQ, but the Stukas of the 8th Flying Corps have been in the air for a while now.

Seconds will decide life or death.

The bombers are already visible. The infantrymen wave wildly at the pilots, but their comrades in the air are in a hurry to get rid of their lethal cargoes.

They dip the noses of their planes, begin their dives.

The bombs explode on target, killing, wounding, destroying.

And while the survivors raise their heads out of the mud, the second wave comes, followed by the third.

With certain death staring them in the face, the victors of Schlüsselburg witness a miracle: the entire formation peels off at the last moment.

Slowly they clamber up from their foxholes and their piles of rubble.

'Jesus,' says Kindler to Rademann. 'That's the nearest I've come to a hero's death.'

But Rademann doesn't answer – corpses can't talk.

The main battle is raging south of the city.

Despite the Russians' embittered resistance, the metropolis on the Neva is obviously ready to fall to the German panzers. It is only a matter of time.

And then the inconceivable happens: the panzers are halted. By Hitler personally. He considers the fall of Leningrad a foregone conclusion and feels that he needs the panzer units for other parts of the front. They are withdrawn from Army Group North's theatre of operations. Leningrad, in the Führer's opinion now a secondary theatre, is to be 'spared'. Just when he is within an ace of conquering the city by force of arms, Hitler decides to abandon force and starve Leningrad into submission.

Thus begins a siege that will last for 900 days.

Three regular Soviet armies and 300,000 untrained, miserably armed men, dressed in rags, crouch in their ill-prepared foxholes in the suburbs. The world between Lake Ladoga and the Baltic is in flames. 700,000 old people had been evacuated from the city. The others are ready to starve, to freeze, or to die in a myriad other ways, for as winter begins there are many propaganda posters, little bread.

The flaming-red posters scream out defiance: 'Either the working class of Leningrad will be enslaved and its best elements liquidated, or we shall make Leningrad into a graveyard for the fascists!'

And close to the hoardings lie corpses that show no sign of

injury. These are men and women who have simply died of hunger. Even by the most generous calculations, there are only enough rations for a month. Children receive 300 grams of bread per day, 500 grams of fat per month. Soon there are no more horses, no more dogs, no more cats or rats left in the city. A girl extracts the gold teeth from her dead father, so as to have something to exchange for food. Teenagers hide their dead parents for weeks in the attic, so as to continue to draw their rations on their behalf.

The Russian defences are concentrated in six strongpoints. Weapons and ammunition are produced in factories that are actually under enemy fire. Inasmuch as they can, the Soviets move 92 big armaments factories from the firing line to the centre of the city. Near Kolpino, however, the German advanced units have to watch helplessly through their binoculars as hundreds of new T 34 tanks roll off the production lines and go - literally - straight into battle.

There is a shortage of aircraft on the German side. Most of the squadrons have been withdrawn, and the artillery alone lacks the power to flatten the Russian armaments factories.

The Soviet Baltic Fleet, brilliantly led, plays its part in the battle. The floating fortresses come in close to the shore and inflict serious losses on the attackers.

Immediately after the closure of the overland routes to the city, the Soviets start improving their sea port in the Bay of Osinovets. In the first month, though suffering severe losses, they manage to import 10,000 tons of food, at most a starvation ration for a week. After the fall of the supply centre at Tishvin on the Volschov, the situation in the city has become worse than desperate.

Military engineers, sappers, civilians and penal work parties are forced to carve a new road through the virgin forest, leading from Saborie in a wide arc via Lachta, Jeremina and Gora, to Novaya Ladoga.

When the lake freezes over, horses dragging sledges and carts will be able to cross it, and the city will once more be open to the land supply route.

Leningrad is the front that can't live and won't die. The besiegers now find themselves besieged in turn - by cold, shortages, sickness and also by numerical superiority. Elsewhere, German lightning victories are still the order of the day, but in front of fortress Leningrad the German advance has come to a decided halt. Now the soldiers of Army

Group North are threatened by the hell that will be the first Russian winter. For many of them, this melancholy landscape with its eternal damp mists will be their graveyard.

In October, it will be their infantry unit's turn to be relieved, and Kindler will be due for some leave.

Kindler has his pass in his pocket. He is dreaming of home, Königsberg, of his mother, his sister, his girl. At 22.00 he is due to be released from his duties. Drombach will escort him to the railhead. The times comes. They clamber up out of their makeshift home in the trenches, move along the communications trench, pass a small swamp, reach the clearing at the end.

There is not much going on. Some small-arms fire in the neighbouring section, and the usual distant rattle of light flak. The weather is no longer as cold as it has been, but this unhealthy damp is not much more pleasant. Kindler stares at the edge of the forest. Is that something moving there?

Nonsense. He can hear noises, but knows that it's only his own nerves. As if this damned war against the Red Army wasn't enough, he thinks bitterly, there's always the partisans to watch out for. No wonder a man starts imagining things.

'Hey, you're a lucky bastard,' Drombach says enviously. 'You'll maybe get out of here – and we ...'

'It'll soon be your turn,' Kindler says by way of consolation. Now he hears a sound to his left. But there's nothing to be seen, except for the dismal pea soup fog that drifts across this terrain and eats into the lungs like poison gas.

And suddenly the mist is alive.

Partisans ... Kindler thinks dimly. And then his throat is in the garrot. He fights back bitterly. As he fades into unconsciousness, he hears a shot and realises that Drombach has managed to fire his rifle and summon their comrades from the main trench.

They come quickly, but as they storm into the clearing they realise that it is already too late. Not a trace of partisans, except for two corpses: Kindler and Drombach – one strangled, the other stabbed; both dead.

'This war is shit,' says one of them. But it's something they've said so often that it has lost all meaning. And the siege goes on.

*

His victory at Kiev enabled Hitler to fix his gaze on Moscow once more. At his command, 'Operation Typhoon' began on October 2nd 1941. The Soviet capital was to be captured in one swift, decisive thrust. Moscow glowed for the exhausted, half-starved soldiers of the Wehrmacht like a will-o'-the-wisp in the distance. For them, Moscow meant warmth, winter quarters, rest, an end to this bastard of a campaign, and Christmas at home.

A day later, in his speech opening the appeal for the 'Winter Aid Fund', Hitler said of Stalin's Russia: 'Today I can say that this opponent has been broken and will never rise again.' These words were to count as his greatest miscalculation until Stalingrad, even though in the first phase of the battle for Moscow at Viasma and Bryansk on October 18th, another 663,000 prisoners had been taken and 1242 tanks and 5412 guns captured. The Blitzkrieg had followed its usual course, and Hitler, along with the commander of Army Group Centre, Marshal Fedor von Bock, took this to indicate that one more big effort would cause Moscow to fall into his lap once and for all.

Reacting to this grave defeat just in front of the gates of their capital, the Red propagandists took a different tack; where previously they had kept the population relatively calm by feeding them falsely optimistic or distorted reports, suddenly Moscow's newspapers were filled with dramatic warnings such as the headline: 'The barbarians are storming towards the heart of our country!'

'Such words would have unleashed anxiety in any country,' writes English author Nicholas Bethell in his book, *The Invasion of Russia*. 'But in the Soviet union, where the government habitually acted only under conditions of the strictest secrecy and subjected everything to rigorous censorship, the effect was terrible. Muscovites, used to hearing nothing but positive statements from the authorities, had learned since the beginning of the war to place the worst possible interpretation on any news. From wounded soldiers and from the rumours that spread constantly like wildfire through the city, they knew that at the fall of Kiev, which the government had portrayed merely as a tough defensive battle, the Red Army had suffered inconceivable losses, and likewise they knew the date of the German capture of Orel. In view of the disastrous news that was continually flooding in during the second week of October, they assumed that the fall of

Moscow was an immediate prospect.

'On October 16th, a mass panic broke out in Moscow, and the population began to flee the city. Within a few hours, all the roads leading eastward out of the city were hopelessly jammed with Muscovites escaping from the city – in chauffeured limousines for the bureaucrats, or in horses and carts, or on foot. There were jams on the railways too. The special train provided for the evacuation of the diplomatic corps took five days to complete the 500-mile journey to Kuibyshev.' Hundreds of thousands of refugees fought their way out of the metropolis on foot, or sat pathetically on suitcases and trunks at railway stations, waiting and waiting – even though the wait brought only despair.

The gold in the State bank had been shipped off to the Urals. Party cards and documents were consigned to the flames. Escaped prisoners roamed the city. Looters smashed the display windows of department stores. Women were conscripted to build defensive bunkers. Government circles discussed whether to remove Lenin from his mausoleum for safety's sake and take him elsewhere. *Pravda* was already being printed 'in exile'. Even the voice of the Red dictator sounded faraway as he addressed his people over the radio: 'We have lost cities and population, iron, coal and grain to the enemy . . . Six strongpoints have been given up against my orders. I have given instructions that all officers who took part in the withdrawals will be sent to the most dangerous parts of the front, to pay for their crimes in blood. Patrols have been initiated behind the front with orders to shoot any soldier who shows cowardice in the face of the enemy. So far as the Red Army is concerned, there is no longer such a word as retreat, only advance.'

Looters were shot on the spot, as a terror measure. Workers' Militias and women's battalions were drilled and trained in public squares. 5,000,000 people, including children, built barricades and made Molotov Cocktails. Close to 100 kilometres of tank trenches and more than 8000 kilometres of defensive trenches were dug at breakneck speed.

Russia was a highly centralised country, and thus all communications and economic priorities were concentrated in Moscow. He who held Moscow dominated all of European Russia, at the least. This was why Stalin regarded the holding of the huge city on the Moskva as a life-or-death issue. He ordered every third tank, 40% of his troops, 44% of his guns, and a third of his aircraft to be diverted to the defence of Moscow.

Many VIP's, including the members of the Bolshoi Ballet and prominent government officials, left the capital, but Stalin was not among them. 'We do not know,' wrote Raymond Cartier, 'whether it was his intention to die along with the city, or whether he was counting on being able to leave Moscow for the provisional capital at the last moment.'

During the night of October 29th, 32 German bombers attacked Moscow. Picked crews were ordered to attack specific targets. And, in fact, one bomb fell on a wing of the Soviet General Staff's headquarters in Kirov Street, killing a number of soldiers and wounding fifteen senior commanders, including the Chief of Operations, Colonel-General A.M. Vassilevski. Stalin gave orders that the General Staff would have to spend five days living on rations of bread and spread, which would be delivered three times a day by ordonnance officers.

The panic in Moscow had subsided to some extent, but the city was nevertheless showing signs of dissolution during these dark days. There were riots, shootouts with the police, mass escapes of deserters, who headed for the suburbs. Marshall Semion K. Timoshenko was dismissed and replaced by a officer from Leningrad, Georgi K. Zhukov. This excellent soldier, once a peasant's son and NCO in the Tsarist army, now a Marshal of the Soviet Union, would have been far more able to show his true abilities if Stalin – like Hitler – had not insisted on burdening him with nonsensical orders.

Zhukov took the situation in hand. First he had a number of deserters publicly executed. He declared a state of siege and called on Siberian reservists – elite troops, used to cold weather – even though it meant journeys of days and weeks to get them to Moscow. The military powers of the commissars attached to Red Army units were withdrawn, thus freeing operational commanders from political interference. Toughness became the order of the day, towards both the enemy and their own Red Army comrades. Anyone who fell into German hands was declared a traitor to the Soviet Union. His family could reckon on having their ration cards withdrawn. When Stalin's eldest son, a lieutenant in the Red Army, surrendered to the Germans, the dictator had his daughter-in-law arrested.

Stalin's propaganda underwent another radical change. Where before the ordinary German soldier had been portrayed as a victim of the Nazi elite, from now on all Germans were villains, without exception. 'From this moment, there is no curse more ugly than the word "German",' wrote the novelist Ilya Ehrenburg in his appeal to the nation. 'But we do not need to feel outrage about the Germans: What we really need to do is to kill them! If you don't kill a German, he will kill you! He will deport your family and torture them in his accursed Germany!'

So far as Soviet propaganda was concerned, Communism was now a dead letter; the emphasis now was on patriotism, which meant that it could now speak to many who had previously opposed the Soviet system. It was not that Stalin suddenly became acceptable, however; for them he was still the incarnation of terror, starvation, forced labour and massacre. But the atrocities committed by the murder squads that followed in the wake of the Wehrmacht seemed far worse than any of Stalin's crimes. 'The systematic transformation of the so-called "task forces" into murder squads had begun before the invasion of Poland, during the preparations for the war,' says the deputy director of the Bureau for the Clarification of National Socialist Crimes in Ludwigsburg, Heinz Arzt, in his book *Murderers in Uniform*. 'At the beginning of 1941, these squads began to be trained at the Border Police Training Academy in Pretzch on the Elbe and in the neighbouring communities of Düben and Bad Schmiedeberg. In all, some 3000 members of the Security Police and the SD were recruited...'

These men were Gestapo officials, SD men, drivers, interpreters, and large numbers of police reservists. 'These in particular were used as firing parties at executions,' Heinz Arzt discovered, using official sources to confirm figures of some 560,000 civilians murdered by these squads in the first eight months of the Russian campaign. 'While, when the squads began their lethal activity, they had their victims dig their own graves, which were then neatly covered over after the massacres, they later went on looking for large natural pits and depressions, or even anti-tank ditches, and using these as "graves". They found just such a ravine near Kiev. It was called Babi-Yar, and became a mass grave for some 33,000 Jews...'

The cavalry officer Oberst Rudolph Christoph Freiherr

von Gersdorff describes an eye witness account in his book *A Soldier in the Holocaust*: 'First the Jews had to dig big, deep ditches. Then in groups hundreds strong they were driven naked into the ditches and mown down by Latvian SS men with machine guns. Without anyone having checked for survivors, the next group of Jews were made to enter the ditch, trampling on the previous Jews, before being shot themselves. An SS man was seen hauling babies to their feet, shooting them through the head with his pistol, and then hurling them back into the ditch . . . Horrific scenes took place on the edge of the chasm of death. Desperate attempts at flight, and the attempts of young Jewish women to exchange their bodies for the lives of themselves and their children, ended the same way: in a merciless hail of bullets from the SS . . . Even a cursory check by us showed that the account was accurate in all crucial respects,' Freiherr von Gersdorff summed up.

Stalin's psychological ruse of portraying the struggle, not as a collision between two totalitarian systems but as a 'great patriotic war' – his next step was to abolish the system of political commissars – went into top gear. Everywhere the invaders – who in many places had been received with open arms, with bread and salt and flowers – experienced a complete turn around in the attitude of the population.

The invaders passed huge herds of dead, decaying cattle, burning houses. The only food they found was poisoned.

Red Army soldiers lay down with their arms full of explosive charges and exploded them – and themselves – beneath German Panzers.

Nevertheless, the next phase of the battle for Moscow was moving quickly. In the south, Guderian's panzers advanced towards Tula. In the centre, Hoepner's panzer group broke through the Soviet defensive cordon near Borodino, and Hoth's panzer group entered Kalinin.

Then, however, on October 15th, there came a dramatic deterioration in the weather. Russia's grey skies opened. Heavy falls of rain destroyed dams, swept away bridges, led to extensive flooding in the vicinity of rivers, and turned the ground into a quagmire. A Russian saying declares: 'In the autumn, a spoonful of water gives you a bucket of mud.' And so watercourses turned into rivers, ponds became lakes, meadows became swamps, and airfields were suddenly huge pools of mud. While trying to take off, aircraft found themselves stuck up to their wings in the slime.

General Mud became the Soviet Union's most successful ally. When the invaders tried to drag their heavy vehicles out of the mud and to clear the axles, they fell into the mud themselves and were forced to drag themselves and each other out time after time, to an accompaniment of curses. Motorised columns were forced to take to rafts. For hundreds of kilometres the infantry had lagged behind the panzers; now the tanks were slower than the horse-drawn vehicles. The heavens rained down without apparent end, pushing them all further into the mire. The mud got everywhere; filling the soldiers' boots, blocking the barrels of their weapons.

But the poor bloody infantry had even more to curse about when they saw a panzer division that had been sent to reinforce them from France arrive dressed in the tropical kit intended for the Afrika Korps - and this at the onset of the Russian winter! Instead of the 31 scheduled trains due to arrive every day, 15 at the most actually got to their destinations, which meant half rations, half ammunition, and half the quantities of mail due - if any.

The 69 German divisions that were due to take Moscow were stuck in a morass of mud and getting nowhere. Guderian had corduroy roads constructed, but even they made no difference. The advance remained paralysed, for the trucks, with their rubber tyres, found it far harder going than the tracked vehicles.

At the end of November, the rain was followed by freezing temperatures: first it snowed, and then the temperatures really dropped, to minus 30°, 40° and more. The invaders were still wearing their summer uniforms, and many were still in drill kit. The tracks of the panzers had to be hacked free with icepicks every morning, and the engines warmed up with open fires. The sudden cooling effect on the water led boilers to explode, this incapacitating freight trains bringing supplies to the front.

At Orsha airfield, five men put their weight on the propeller of each plane, but they couldn't budge them one centimetre. No air support.

When it reached minus 40°, even the fuel froze. A fill-up took an hour instead of a few minutes. And that didn't even guarantee that the aircraft would get into the air. Not even the Russians flew at such low temperatures, but even so the German groundcrews managed to get one plane in five airborne. They worked under unbelievable conditions, and had to relieve each other every few minutes. Despite this, many of them went straight from their work into hospital, suffering from frostbite. There was a shortage of cranes and lifting tackle, special tools and spare parts.

Motor mechanics injected acetylene gas from high-pressure cylinders into engines and – literally – blew the engines into life with this highly volatile mixture, a criminal way to treat machinery, but at least it worked. Or they would use the Russian method and thin the viscous oil with petrol. Any of these procedures would have brought the mechanics up before a court martial at any other time – but the court martials were a long way behind the front, and the battle for Moscow took priority over everything else.

'The Russian winter, unknown to West Europeans and therefore unimaginable for them, now took a hold with a vengeance,' wrote American author John Keegan in his book *Operation Barbarossa*. 'Guderian's Second Panzer Army made no more progress after reaching Kashira on November 25th, thus bringing to an end attempts to break through to the East and encircle Moscow . . . The simple Wehrmacht soldier at the front could scarcely move any more, let alone fight . . . Hitler had forbidden the distribution of winter clothing because he feared that any indications that he was preparing for a winter campaign would lower German morale . . . The army had, of course, begun to improvise, ordering the troops to wear their drill fatigues over their field grey uniforms, and advising them to stop any gaps with newspaper, but improvisation was not enough to protect the Army of the East from the Russian winter.

'Moreover, the Russian winter was also a decisive advantage for the Red Army. The winter months were traditionally Russia's most effective weapon against invaders, but cloud and snowstorms also provided an invaluable screen, behind which reinforcements could be summoned in safety and troop movements completed without the Germans' knowledge . . .'

The Soviet soldiers in their winter kit could withstand the cold far better than their opponents in their drill fatigues. In addition, they were now far more effectively prepared for the war from a psychological standpoint, and also better armed: The Soviet T34 tank, specially built to withstand winter conditions, became much feared by the Germans. It weighed in at 26 tons, had bevelled armour plating, which the German 3.7 cm anti-tank shells bounced harmlessly off, and which led it to be dubbed the 'knock-knock machine'; it also had very wide tracks, which made it extremely manoeuvrable. It was armed with 7.6 cm cannon. The new T34 was fit to take on the German Panzer IV at any time. In the battle of Mzensk, south-west of Tula, more German tanks were incapacitated than Soviet.

'The Russian tanks are astonishingly manoeuvrable and extremely fast in difficult terrain,' said an officer who had been one of the first to tangle with the T34s, to General Guderian. 'The explosion when they hit one of our tanks is so loud and of such duration that it is – thank God – impossible to hear the screams of the crew.'

While savage fighting was in progress on all fronts – Army Group South had taken the city of Charkov, the Crimea, and on November 21st the port of Rostov, just above the Don estuary – Moscow had been given a reprieve by the sudden arrival of winter.

And then suddenly the 'Stalin Organ' arrived also – a phenomenon that will never be forgotten by anyone who participated in the Russian campaign. This was a highly manoeuvrable rocket weapon. It was brought into position on basically-constructed trucks, built for Russian conditions rather than the sophisticated roads of Western Europe. It could fire 32 rockets from its tubes within 25 seconds; the nerves of the German troops were torn to shreds by the threat of the 'Stalin Organ' in much the same way as the French had been terrorised by the sirens fixed to the noses of the Stukas during the 1940 campaign.

In addition, the Anglo-Americans had promised the Russians 3000 aircraft, 4000 tanks, 30,000 trucks and at least 100,000 tons of fuel for the next few months – and if these had not yet arrived, the psychological effect was already tremendous. And the British Prime Minister, Winston Churchill, had also promised his new allies three million pairs of winter shoes.

As 'Operation Typhoon' ground to a halt, first in the mud and then in the ice, and as the storm-wind that gave it a name started to die down, a turning-point had already come for Army Group South: Rostov-on-Don captured only after savage house-to-house fighting in November, was retaken by the Red Army.

'A first sign,' said Guderian, commenting on the fact that to Leningrad, the city that the Blitzkrieg could not take, was now added Rostov, the city that the Russians had wrested back.

As the time approached for the oft-announced 'final blow', the temperature fell to minus 50°. The fuel froze in the tanks of the panzers, and the infantry had to take the bolts out of their rifles and keep them warm in their pockets before the weapons would fire. Packs of bandages were hard as steel; anyone who suffered even the slightest wound got instant frostbite. Each regiment had up to 400 losses to report from frostbite alone.

Even the new commander-in-chief, the slavedriver von Bock, described any continuation of the offensive as military nonsense; but at a conference in Orsha the General Staff Chief, Halder, declared that the Führer was unshakably determined to press home the attack.

An offensive without reserves: most panzer units could now rely on no more than 30-40 vehicles out of a nominal strength of 160. Aircraft were worse than useless. Even those that managed to get airborne soon lost themselves in the formless vastness of the country. Warm food was rare. One regiment was without bread for nine days; when it finally arrived, it had to be hacked free with axes. The 4th Army waited for two urgent ammunition trains. When they arrived, they contained not shells but red blocks of ice; by mistake, they had been delivered red wine in casks, a totally useless consignment - either to shoot or to drink.

The bolts of their weapons could not be opened any more. Optical instruments were useless. Automatic weapons could no longer be used, because the grease had frozen hard as stone. Many soldiers didn't even possess gloves; they had begun to make do with sacks, rags, woollen blankets, and so on. In these bizarre wrappings they stumbled on towards Moscow like drunks. Many fell into snowdrifts and froze to death. When they touched the bare steel of their rifles, their skin would come off in folds. To the west of Moscow, 73 dead Red Army soldiers had their legs sawn off so that Germans could get at their felt lined boots.

The 106th Division pushed its spearhead towards Krasnya Polyana and thus to within 27 kilometres of Moscow. Panzers reached 22 kilometres from the city centre in the suburb of Istra, and one advance party arrived at a tram stop right at the end of the line, from which the towers of the Kremlin were visible like some *fata morgana*.

The cold drove the infantry into the buildings, many of which had been mined and blew up, others of which were attacked by Soviet commando squads. The ambitious Guderian insisted to the commander-in-chief and the General Staff that they needed to call off the offensive and use the immobile panzers to build a defensive cordon.

But Hitler demanded that the attack continue, despite the fact that between June 22nd and December 1st 1941, 162,314 soldiers had died, 571,767 had been wounded, and 34,434 were missing. German field hospitals had so far registered 113,000 cases of frostbite. The soldiers who stole forward like thieves towards the capital had fought themselves out, were hungry, lousy, apathetic, defenceless, and – in many cases even their dreams had frozen to death in the snows of Russia.

Nothing's sane any more. In the section to their right, a young Leutnant is commanding a regiment and here, in the forefront of the 9th Army, Oberfähnrich Bäumler has just been blown to bits by an anti-personnel mine. Unteroffizier Dünnbier has taken his place as commander of the Third Platoon.

At the moment, he's lying flat on his belly and peering through a pair of field glasses.

The ground is shuddering. The heavens are on fire. Pillars of smoke mark the route of the invader, even though they have no accurate maps and in this witches' cauldron no one knows for sure where friends or enemies are. Moscow is up ahead, and behind the reinforcements are lurking.

'Come on, men,' yells Unteroffizier Dünnbier. 'Don't pretend you're tired.'

Somewhere, their armoured escort ought to be under way. Or maybe it's got stuck. Or maybe the Ivans have taken it out. The young soldiers curse and follow Dünnbier. They look terrible: ragged uniforms clinging to lousy, wasted bodies. The infantrymen are hungry as wolves, and they're furious at Dünnbier, the born leader – the man they wish would go to hell when there's nothing happening, and whom they run to like a father when the going gets rough.

'What's up?' he bellows, turning to the machine-gun crew.

'Take it easy, I wasn't born on a racetrack,' oaths private Lützelbuerger.

'Friggin' slavedriver,' says Vorndran.

'Yeah. Just look at that shit,' says Derber, pointing to his worn, ragged lumps of leather, once boots, which are his proof that since the opening of Hitler's latest theatre of war he has tramped his own good thousand kilometres, and walked the lot.

They hear the sound of engines above the din of the battle.

'Panzers,' says Corporal Vorndran. 'Wait a moment. They'll give us a lift.'

'You think so?' the Unteroffizier answers, and points to the narrow, rickety wooden bridge ahead. 'First, they could be Russian tanks,' he grins. 'And second, that thing won't take the weight.'

He gets to his feet, stands exposed against the bare terrain. 'Come on, boys! Just this bridge, then we'll be through for today!'

Suddenly Dünnbier hits the ground, and small-arms fire zings over the spot where he had been standing.

His platoon divides up into two sections: both attack at the same time. There are only a few Russians detailed to defend the bridge. They keep firing right to the end, defend their position grimly, and carry on fighting even when they run out of ammunition. No survivors.

Dünnbier takes the machine gun away from the gunners and hauls it onto his own shoulders. He is the first to manoeuvre his way across the shaky bridge. He gets to the middle and the second starts to come, then the third and fourth. All of them finally get to the far bank and get themselves organised for a breather.

And then it starts to snow again, as if it will never stop. A half a metre of snow overnight.

'So this is Russia,' growls Lützelbuerger, giving them the jewel of his experience. 'Slime, snow and shit.'

And then he stops talking, because he knows what lies ahead of them all. The Russians will come out of the snow: Siberian regiments, trained for winter fighting like hounds for the hunt. White landscape. White uniforms. White vehicles. White guns.

And white death.

The guard has to be changed every five minutes, to prevent their freezing to the spot. No warm food for days now. The soldiers stick their cans of rations in their pockets for hours before meals are due, so that at least they can thaw them out on one side.

In a nearby section of the front, an Oberst got frostbite in his arse, both cheeks, while using the latrine. 'But there are a thousand other ways of getting a cold arse in Russia,' Lützelberger tells his mates.

The desperate soldiers of Hitler's army can see only one solution to their hopeless plight: to move forward. To take Moscow.

'Help me, for God's sake!' oaths Lützelberger, who is busy trying to light a piece of frozen wood.

'Cut out that crap!' the platoon commander growls. 'You'll have the Ivans onto us!'

'Maybe,' says the private dourly, and pulls a dead Russian closer to the flame, to thaw out the corpse's icy limbs. Then he strips off the Red's padded jacket, swaps it for his own thin drill jacket. 'There you are,' he says, and admires himself with grim satisfaction. 'And now I'll find myself a decent pair of trousers.'

The ragged invading hordes keep moving forward. From the north, the west and the south, they begin to close their ring around Moscow. They capture Klin, Moshaisk, Tula. Many companies are reduced to twenty men, and combat groups once composed of 100 units now have a strength of no more than four or five. But they are in the suburbs of Moscow and can stare in fascination at the towers of the Kremlin rising between pillars of smoke in the distance.

As Unteroffizier Dünnbier, now acting battalion commander, takes the villages of Alabushevo and Kryukovo. The commander of Army Group Centre wires a report to Führer Headquarters on December 1st: 'In the requests and reports directed from the Army group to the Army High Command, which repeatedly indicated the threatening situation regarding combat strengths, it was assumed that the offensive will continue, and it was also emphasised that there is a danger that our troops will burn themselves out. The attack in progress at the moment is being conducted with full exploitation of all tactical possibilities and along the full extent of the front, but is nevertheless a frontal assault pure and simple. As we have indicated, the forces for a more flexible attack are not available, and nor by now can troops be moved in appreciable numbers. The attack will involve a bloody struggle for relatively limited ground gained, and may destroy a part of the enemy's forces, but it is hard to see any long-term operational advantage . . .'

But Führer Headquarters does not answer even this piece of indirect military desperation. All that the Field Marshal receives are a few ridiculous suggestions which shows clearly that in secluded, well-heated Rastenburg no one has any idea what units such as the 35th are having to suffer in the snows of Russia.

'Shoot, for Christ's sake,' Private Gerber hisses to his mate on the machine gun.

'What at, you prick?' says Lützelberger.

'Maybe that frigging sign,' Gerber mumbles, pointing to a legend that reads: Moscow 22 kilometres. 'I just want to warm my mits on the barrel.'

'You're a real clown,' cuts in Corporal Vorndran. 'When the Ivans come, you'll warm up fast enough. And you'll be glad for every bullet we've saved, too.'

Hunger is driving them crazy. The horses are eating the straw from the thatched roofs, and the troops are eating the horses. A thousand of the Wehrmacht's four-legged friends are going missing every day, making ten thousand so far. 'But tonight we'll be in Moscow,' says Unteroffizier Dünnbier. 'And there'll be warm food in our bellies.'

The men by his side can see the city suburbs with their naked eyes. 'They'll burn everything down before we get the chance,' says Langhoff miserably. 'The goddamnd place is blazing from end to end already.'

'What are, stupid?' Vorndran growls. 'At least where there's fire, you don't freeze.'

Most of them are too exhausted to speak, really finished and played out. They're sick and tired of Russia, but they're also determined to capture that city up ahead. How otherwise can they justify the insane suffering of the past weeks?

They cast one more glance at the conscript's idea of paradise before they finally trudge back through the hell that is Russia.

Officers who ordered a retreat in hopeless situations are risking their necks; and if they don't do it, they'll lose them anyway, for the Soviets are giving no quarter. The Wehrmacht takes its wounded with it, so long as this is possible. If they have to leave them, it's a sure sentence of death. The cold will save the Russians the work of killing.

Daylight comes only at 10 a.m., and disappears again at

4 p.m. But the burning buildings give the attackers plenty of light to see by.

The remains of the combat group have survived another night. Morning brings snow and then the sound of tanks. Unteroffizier Dünnbier hardly needs to issue orders. His handful of desperadoes split up and arrange themselves round their 3.7 cm anti-tank gun.

Diesel engines. T34s. They have got used to the noise in the past few days. Louder. Closer.

Where are the Ivans?

A sound of movement. Far too close for evasive action. The tank looks like an avalanche rolling across the flat snow towards them.

The commander of the gun crew throws his switch, turns, aims, fires.

Round after round.

Direct hits.

But for all the good it does, they might as well have been throwing soft-boiled eggs.

The foremost T34 grinds the anti-tank gun into the snow. Behind it are figures. The only part of them that's not white is their faces.

Hand-to-hand fighting. Anything that moves is cut down.

The Ivans move on. They are in a hurry As they disappear into the artificial snowstorm raised by their advance, Lützelberger sees that there are three or four survivors, not counting the seriously wounded.

'What's up?' he asks, and bends over Dünnbier.

'I've been hit.' The Unteroffizier is still clutching the rifle with which he finished off one Russian. But another came up behind him and did for him with a bayonet in the back.

The wounded man watches the swift exchange of glances between Lützelberger and Langhoff.

'We'll get you through this,' says the private.

'Crap!' the Unteroffizier growls. 'Just get out of here!'

The pair of them bend down to pick up Dünnbier, but before they can get hold of him, he has lifted his pistol to his head and pressed the trigger. The sound is almost non-existent; the roar of the fighting drowns the thin crack of the pistol shot in Dünnbier's case, as it has in hundreds of others.

The trio of survivors stumble onward, without tanks or Ivans in sight, starving and despairing. Tiny icicles hang from their eyelashes, the wind slashes at their faces. All navigation is by chance, and the living are as silent as the dead. Not a haystack or a stove in sight. All the villages and farmsteads have been destroyed, either by the German advance or by the Russians' 'scorched earth' policy.

Lützelberger is in the lead, behind him Langhoff and Vorndran, very close together to avoid losing contact. A man can't even see his hand in front of his face. When they see shapes in the snow, they could be trees just as easily as Ivans. The man at the front gives up trying to identify ambushes or enemy patrols; he just keeps pressing on through the terrain like a drunken man who seems certain to fall sooner or later.

He almost walks straight into the Ivan who is standing in the snow with a loaded rifle pointed at him.

'I surrender,' pants Lützelberger, and sticks up his hands. 'Don't shoot, don't shoot.'

Vorndran and Langhoff see the other three Red Army soldiers and also raise their hands high, in vain hope that the Ivans might be better than their reputation.

No movement.

No order given, not a sound.

No shots.

Then Lützelberger notices that he is standing opposite three dead Russians. They are all frozen solid and have been left leaning against a snowdrift as 'ghost sentries'. He snatches the foremost Russian's rifle, realises that it is a wooden fake. The other two Soviets are, in fact, empty handed.

Lützelberger collapses in a heap in the snow, laughing like a man who deserves to end up in a straight jacket.

And there's nothing worth looting from the three dead Ivans. Not even a Machorka cigarette butt.

At the beginning of that December, the entire Eastern Front was threatened with collapse. Soldiers who had once powered forward 80 to 200 kilometres in a day were now retreating metre by metre, mostly without their weapons. Many had torn strips of material from their coats and bound them around their hands to keep out the impossible cold. If they tried to touch their weapons with their bare hands, the skin was pulled off in ribbons; and that meant certain death from infection, as did the slightest wound. On December 3rd, the 12th Panzer Division of Army Group North reported that 63 soldiers had been killed in action and 325 frozen to death.

General Guderian flew to Headquarters in Orsha and suggested to his commander, Fedor von Bock, that they call off the futile attack on the Russian capital and create defensive positions, using his panzers as the cornerstones of the new line. This, he maintained, was the only way that the army would survive through to the next year's campaigning.

The Field Marshal and Guderian made a cautious approach to Führer Headquarters, where no one had any notion of the conditions the men were fighting under in Russia – whole armies trying to fight for their country in summer kit at temperatures of minus 40. Neither Hitler, nor Jodl, nor Keitel, nor von Brauchitsch had left the well-heated 'Wolf's Lair' this winter to inspect the situation on the Eastern Front for themselves.

The Field Marshal did not get far in his attempt to give the Führer some idea of the realities in the East.

'I want Moscow!' Hitler bawled him down. 'I will have Moscow! You will not stop me from having Moscow!'

On December 5th, Marshal Zhukov began a counter-offensive, using fresh, experienced winter troops.

The following day, Hitler was forced to break off the battle for Moscow.

German forces were now fighting in Northern Karelia and in North Africa; they stood on the shores of the Atlantic, and the battle for the Mediterranean intensified with each passing day. The man who was responsible for the suffering of millions of soldiers, both his own and the enemy's, issued the simple order that every position in front of Moscow was to be held 'to the last man'.

The extreme cold had turned the landscape into an ice field, in which soldiers, animals and vehicles slid helplessly. Guderian – known to his men as 'Fast Heinz' – made a decision on his own initiative to blow up any panzers that had been left because of battle damage, breakdowns or lack of fuel, and to withdraw the remains of his 4th Panzer Army. He communicated to his commander-in-chief that on the 168th day of the Russian Campaign, he was going to evacuate his forward positions at Tule, in temperatures of minus 50° C.

Fedor von Bock ordered him to visit the front line and to give himself a personal view of the situation.

'Where do you think I am?' the panzer general without panzers bellowed down the field telephone. 'I'm in Jasnaya

Polyana, and there's fighting going on outside my command post!'

And the fighting was desperate, a fight for bare survival. A military catastrophe of hitherto unknown proportions was in the making. While the Weekly Newsreel showed film of Russia that made it look like some idyllic ski resort in the Bavarian Alps, the entire Eastern Front was threatening to fall apart. For the first time in the war, Hitler's armies, so used to victory, were in headlong retreat.

Bad news from all parts of the front began to pour into the Wolf's Lair on December 7th. Hitler had already realised from an overview of the situation that the Soviet offensive was more than a localised counter-thrust. He had not yet understood, however, that a disaster of near-apocalyptic proportions was about to afflict his proud armies.

He stalked out of his map room, bent and exhausted. His head of chancellery, Martin Bormann, used his own authority to call Hitler's personal physician, Dr Morell.

The mood in the Führer's immediate circle at headquarters was uneasy, gloomy. It was as if everyone was wilting under the disastrous news from the front. No one envied the officers who had to keep taking communications to the Führer. Then, suddenly, a wild, excited figure appeared from the command bunker, without his usual hat and coat. It was Hitler, and he was waving a telegram in his hand.

'The Japanese!' the Führer screamed hysterically. 'Pearl Harbor!'

His commander stared at him in total astonishment. None of them understood what on earth he was saying.

'Now there's no chance of our losing this war,' Hitler yelled at them 'We have an ally who hasn't been conquered for three thousand years!'

355 Japanese warplanes had attacked the American Fleet at anchor in Hawaii without declaration of war, sinking or seriously damaging 19 American ships, destroying 177 American planes on the ground, and killing thousands of soldiers. The murderous surprise attack on Pearl Harbor, staged one sunny Sunday morning after a six-day covert approach by the Japanese fleet, surprised the commanding US Admiral on the golf course. The words of the officer responsible for watching the airspace became a classic. When informed that Japanese planes had been located on the radar, he said simply; 'Forget it'.

The outrage about the 'yellow bastards' ended America's dream of peace. US President Franklin Delano Roosevelt, at the highpoint of his power after being re-elected for his third term, spoke the famous words; 'A day which will live in infamy.' Except for an aging spinster from Montana – who had voted against American involvement in the First World War too – the entire senate voted for a declaration of war against Japan.

A committee of inquiry into the bloody weekend of Pearl Harbor later came to the conclusion that the success of the Japanese raid was due to American inefficiency and lack of vigilance. The US commander-in-chief in the area was stripped of his command and lost seniority.

The Japanese, who immediately began a whirlwind campaign of conquest in the Far East, were Germany's allies, but the treaty between the two nations did not commit Hitler to declaring war on the USA. His commanders and members of his entourage warned him against it; even Foreign Minister von Ribbentrop, usually a practised yes-man, was against war with America. But on December 11th Hitler announced the loneliest and most fateful of his decisions. While his armies on the Eastern Front were in full retreat that was threatening to become blind panic, the German dictator told the nation in his speech to the Reichstag declaring war on America; 'If fate has so willed it that the German people are not to be spared this struggle, then I am thankful that I have been entrusted with this leadership in a historic contest that will decide the next five hundred or thousand years, not just of Germany's history but of the history of the entire world. A historical change of unique importance has been entrusted to us by the creator.'

The demonic cheerleader of the masses had his usual frenetic response, storms of applause and approval. But the shouts would soon die in the people's throats as they experienced what havoc the American Flying Fortresses would rain down upon Germany's cities . . .

Hitler, the uneducated autodidact, who only listened to his advisers when they told him what he wanted to hear, was victim to his own wild underestimation of the military and economic potential of the most powerful nation on earth.

Roosevelt made a promise to build a ship every day, and as early as 1942 to produce 60,000 aircraft, rising a year later to 125,000. During the first year of the war, 45,000 US tanks would roll off the production lines; at the same time, the combat strength of the US Army was to be increased to 7.5 million men. Conscription was extended to all males above the age of eighteen, just as it was in Great Britain. From the first day of the war, the Yanks raised 130 million dollars per day for armaments; so far as the second year of the war was concerned, Roosevelt, who openly admitted that for the next few years the war would cost a half of the national income, spent 70 billion dollars. The USA had spent only 32 billion on the whole of the First World War.

Meanwhile, the war on the Eastern Front was still going disastrously for Germany. On the day of the Japanese attack on Hawaii, the war diary of the Wehrmacht High Command declared: 'As the catastrophic winter of 1941/42 broke, the Führer realised that no victory was possible from this point of the season onwards.' In the United States, the first units were being trained for transfer to Britain, and General Eisenhower had been named commander of American Forces in Europe with his headquarters in London.

On December 19th 1941, Hitler dismissed the commander-in-chief of the German Army. Field Marshal von Brauchitsch left the Wolf's Lair without a farewell or even a handshake. The ex-Corporal had already arranged for a successor: himself. His opinion: 'Anyone can do a bit of that operational stuff'. The Army Group commanders von Rundstedt, von Bock and von Leeb were sent home, and even Panzer General Guderian was relieved of his command, after a five-hour argument with Hitler.

The new commander-in-chief's first order was as follows: 'Halt! Not another step back! Not a foot of territory will be conceded from now on! Our forces are to be forced into fanatical resistance, with the personal intervention of commanders and officers at all levels; they are to hold all their positions without regard for enemy breakthroughs in the rear or on the flanks. This is the only way in which we shall gain the time that is needed for the reinforcements from the homeland and the West that I have ordered...'

But the invaders-turned-defenders mostly waited in vain for reinforcements, though at least trainloads of supplies from the Winter appeal launched by Propaganda Minister Goebbels were on their way east. The Minister's call for the German public to provide clothing and comforts had been so successful that shortly afterwards the fighter pilot Johannes

Steinhoff claims to have seen troops fighting in Persian lamb coats and fox furs. 'But the catastrophe was total,' the man who was later to command the Federal Air Force in West Germany states. 'In one single night, during which the temperatures went down to 50 below, the armies camped before Moscow became incapable of movement, and then it was this which beat them. So far as the troops the Soviets had brought in from Siberia were concerned, winter and cold were their natural fighting elements. On the German side, however, some real tragedies were being played out...'

The 4th Army was able to hold on, but on its right flank, the 2nd Panzer Army and the Second Army were forced to withdraw 150 kilometres in temperatures of up to minus 50° C.

And the Russians were attacking as they had never attacked before. One unit in three was from Siberia; cossack patrols ranged over ice fields that only saw daylight for eight hours in each day. All Soviet vehicles were fitted with chains; their engines were supplied with winterproof oil that the Germans had run out of. Even Russian horses were better trained for winter.

'The morale of the German armies had been broken,' wrote Raymond Cartier. 'Perhaps they would have surrendered – if the Russians had taken prisoners. An unholy terror of falling into Russian hands was what kept the German Armies moving during that dreadful winter. Those who were exhausted beyond endurance put a bullet in their heads or simply lay down in the snow and died there.'

Where Hitler had threatened to destroy Russia with one blow when the summer began, in winter Stalin now tried to do the reverse; he attempted to surround the 4th Army at the gates of Moscow and thus to force a decision in the East. Hitler's insane order for his troops to hold on at all costs played directly into the communist dictator's hands.

It was not until January 15th 1942 that the self-proclaimed commander-in-chief decided, after much hesitation, to give orders for Army Group Centre to withdraw from its positions at the gates of Moscow. It was to take up a 'winter position' to the west of the city. This limited permission to withdraw came too late. What motorised columns there were, or which could be set in motion, rolled slowly and hesitantly westwards, constantly under attack from Russian raiders.

The 'front' now consisted of isolated strongpoints going to

a depth of perhaps 150 kilometres. Headquarters became fortresses, defended by cook sergeants and soldiers who had never previously ventured out of an office chair. When the newly-appointed commander of the 9th Army, Walter Model, arrived at his headquarters in Sytchevka, his clerical staff was in the process of defending itself in bitter hand-to-hand fighting with the Russians; the Germans were pushed back to the railway station, where the Russians found several truckloads of cognac, which they promptly 'liberated'. The counterattack against the drunken Reds followed swiftly and wås successful.

But in this accursed winter, how often would they be lucky enough to have stores of cognac sitting around on railway stations?

Army Group Centre half-stabilised itself on the line Orel-Rshev, but at the junction point with Army Group North the Red Army pushed forwards from the Waldai Heights as far as the area north of Smolensk. 68 exhausted German divisions, whose strength existed mainly on paper, were fighting desperately against twelve Soviet Armies consisting of 88 infantry and twelve cavalry divisions as well as 24 motorised brigades. After a retreat of over 500 kilometres, they were making their stand on a very dubious line between the Duna and the Dnieper - and the winter was far from over.

The catastrophe could not be hidden from the German people. The myth of the German soldier's superiority had been shattered, along with the illusion that the Russian's couldn't fight. 'The Germans were no longer reckoned invincible,' writes Raymond Cartier. 'Adolf Hitler had lost his battle for Moscow, his war in Russia, and the war altogether. He would have had to beat his opponent in the first round, but his first blow had not been strong enough. Thanks to its enormous expanses, Russia had been able to gain the breathing-space that it needed. From now on, Russia could no longer be knocked out, and with the support of the western allies it was able to turn its full strength against the Germans. Whatever Hitler did from this moment on only served to delay the moment of his fall.'

In Army Group Centre's territory, single divisions, many at a third strength, have to defend unfortified stretches of front of up to 40 kilometres. The railway tracks come to an end 300 kilometres behind the supposed front. On their left flank, the Russians are pouring through a gap in the area of Vyasma-Smolensk-Vitebsk and attacking towards Velikiye Luki. East of Smolensk, Russian forces have been behind the German lines for months now, and are threatening to cut the vital supply line between Smolensk and Vyasma.

Alarming reports from all fronts: Rostov recaptured by the Soviets. The combat strength of the SS regiment 'Der Führer' has fallen to 35 men. Cholm is surrounded by Soviet forces. The most serious situation is in the area around Isyuin and Demyansk, a salient that sticks out like a balcony over the German route to Moscow. Six German divisions, some 100,000 men, have been surrounded here and could be overrun by the Soviets.

On February 8th 1942, the fighting in the cauldron reaches its climax. As General von Brockdorff-Ahlefeldt talks on the telephone with the 16th Army, demanding an assurance from Colonel-General Busch that everything possible is being done so that the Second Army Corps will not be left in the lurch, there is heavy static on the line.

'I'm hanging up,' the Intelligence officer says. 'The enemy is listening in.'

'Well, that seems to have been our last conversation until further notice,' the general remarks drily as he replaces the receiver.

Then he issues an order of the day to his troops, the only one during the entire Second World War that not only gave commands but also explained the true situation.

'During the coldest winter months, the enemy has managed to cut the Second Corps' communications with the rear by exploiting the ice covering the Sea of Alma, the usually swampy Delta of the Lov, and the river valleys of the Pola, the Redya and the Polist. These river valleys are part of a whole region of swampy, low-lying terrain that will become hard to cross, if not completely impassable, when the snows and the ice melt. Any traffic, and especially the enemy's supply traffic, will become immobilised.

'During the wet spring months, any supply route used by the Russians would have to be on hard roads, which means main highways. The main junctions on these roads, however – Cholm, Staraya Russa and Demyansk – remain firmly in German hands. Besides this, the corps, with its six experienced divisions, controls the only high ground in the area. It will therefore be impossible for the Russian, with his numerous forces, to hold out into the spring in these wet, low-lying districts.

'Our task, therefore, is to hold the road junctions and the high ground around Demyansk until the snow melts. Sooner or later, the Russian will give up and withdraw, particularly as we shall be reinforced by strong forces from the West.'

In the southern promontory of the cauldron, the men of the 12th Infantry Division, like their other comrades, got to know all the worse things that war and nature could heap on them. First it rained, until they feared they would drown in their trenches. Then came the mud, which stuck in great liquid cakes to their ragged trousers up to their thighs. Then the thermometer dropped to below minus 30. They experienced a cold that broke a man's spade in case he should try, on some insane impulse, to bury a dead comrade.

Hell was somewhere around Demyansk. At least for the 100,000 or so men who were waiting there, not knowing whether the Russians would slaughter them in that cauldron or whether their Wehrmacht comrades would really get them out of trouble.

'Jesus, how many days have we been stuck in these rat-holes?' asks Feldwebel Elsenbach.

'Take a look at your ready-reckoner,' Corporal Rössler says to his mate Schmelz.

The other corporal looks carefully around, gets hesitantly to his feet, and goes up to a fat tree trunk whose bark is covered with nicks. One for each day. He counts with his fingers. 'Ninety-seven,' he calls back to the others.

'And each day more wonderful than the one before,' says Elsenbach.

They hear the noise of the Jus, stare skywards, knowing that any dinner they get tonight will come from up there. Or letters from home. Or maybe nothing, because the fat, ageing 'aunty' Junkers often don't make it that far without falling victim to the Russian anti-aircraft guns.

March 21st 1942. The first day of spring. In the broad lowlands around the Waldai Heights, the snow is 60 centimetres deep. The temperatures are still around minus 30. It is 7.30 a.m. Heavy artillery have opened up on the Russian side. The Corps Group commanded by Seydlitz,

whose job is to break into the cauldron, is advancing.
40 kilometres to go.

Artillery rains shells on the Russian positions along a breadth of eight kilometres. Stukas attempt to blast the encircling ring open. Dense clouds of smoke mark the route into the cauldron. The relieving force, with its four divisions, is approaching from the area of Staraya Russa. In the centre, the 5th and 8th Rifle Divisions. On the flanks the 329th and 122nd Infantry Divisions. Direction of advance: Kalitkina and Vasilkovo.

The Stukas are preparing the way for them. The advancing forces are making good progress. Then the advance grinds to a halt in the snow-covered and icy forests in which the Russians have constructed five separate defensive lines. A pitiless battle, not just against the Red Army but against winter conditions at their most primitive and murderous.

Icy winds howl above the swamps. When the wind drops for a moment, you can hear the vicious crumps of the nearest 'Stalin Organ'. They are having to fight for every metre of ground. Wounded men are drowning in the mud. Horses sink into the narrow paths, neighing hysterically. Soviet soldiers with machine guns and rapid-fire rifles are behind every tree. Man against man. Trick against trick. Cunning against cunning.

No relief in sight. No reserves. Feldwebel Elsenbach hasn't seen his wife for twenty months. 'Home' has become too distant an idea for him even to imagine, or as Schmelz always says; 'When you start thinking about food more than about women, then you know you're really in the shit.'

'There,' bellows Corporal Rössler, pointing angrily at a stricken Ju whose left engine is in flames. 'Our mail!'

'Yeah. And those frigging Ivans can't even read,' Schmelz counters sourly.

'He's tryin' to make an emergency landing,' roars Feldwebel Elsenbach.

'Poor bastard,' Rössler says, and watches as the Ju plunges towards the thick forest, as the branches seem to reach up and drag it down like an octopus's tentacles. An explosion.

The shockwaves from the explosion reach as far as that forgotten German infantry position.

'We ought to get them out of there,' says the platoon commander.

'Suicide,' growls Schmelz.

'Then at least this shit'll be over,' Rössler shoots back with feeling.

And he is granted that small mercy.

The corporal is the first to die.

Killed by a Russian sniper.

They flew until they dropped from exhaustion or were shot down by the Russians. By the dozen. By anti-aircraft guns. By Ratas. They started off in the first light of dawn and did the trip several times a day.

Every hour, some fifteen Jus landed at the two tiny airstrips at Demyansk. It was the world's first airlift, created by Oberst Morzik, commander of air transport on the Eastern Front, and it was not just an organisational masterpiece but also the last hope for some 100,000 German troops.

'Can you do another?' the squadron leader asks the pilot who has just landed at his home air base.

The Oberfeldwebel has a raging headache. He hasn't slept for weeks. He has been doping himself up with pervitin; he looks like a skinny old hen, fit only for the soup pot. His stomach can hardly bear food any more. But he has seen the wounded men being unloaded from 'aunty's' plump belly just now, and he nods distractedly. One died because Curschmann had to make a detour to avoid a flak pocket.

'Any fighter escort?' the pilot asks.

'If you're lucky,' the squadron leader answers wearily. 'Otherwise you'll just have to bluff your way through, my boy.'

The encircled armies need at least 300 tons of provisions per day, and that means missing out on a third rations, half their ammunition, and three-quarters of the feed they need for their horses. Since the 500 aircraft that would be needed to do this in one trip are not available, the Ju crews simply have to take a double load of flying, through fog, snowstorms and flak.

Mail bags, cheese, cases of ammunition are loaded into the Ju. The old crate is overloaded, as always. In the bad light she looks like a fat, lazy bird, the skin drawn across her belly like a goose's.

Curschmann is back at his controls. He nods to his crew. Left engine, middle, right. He could do the routine in his sleep: full throttle, lift off, climb. Set course.

Beneath them, the longest battle of encirclement in the history of warfare is raging, and there is still no sign of a decision. For the first time in the Second World War, encircled German forces are having to be supplied exclusively from the air. The dwindling numbers of Jus fly through every sort of weather. Through thick snowstorms. Through the middle of the thick fogs that grip the region for days on end. Through lethal temperatures with their wings iced up. Tomorrow. The day after that. Again and again.

And their achievement is astonishing. They land 24,850 tons of provisions, fly 35,400 wounded out of the cauldron – more than a third of the forces originally trapped there – and land fresh troops right in the middle of the front line.

They fly on and on. 100 aircraft a day. Sometimes 150. Right into the jaws of hell. And out again. Back again. Commuting into hell.

No fighters in sight.

But there are puffballs from the ack-ack. The Ju shudders in the air pressure of the exploding shells: too far to the right, too low, too high . . .

'Let's hope they carry on missing,' bawls Oberfeldwebel Curschmann into his phones. 'Three shots for a mark, eh?'

The ack-ack is excellent for anti-aircraft use. It can shoot damned accurately – maybe because it was produced in German munitions factories. The grim irony is that these are not guns that the Russians captured, but weapons that were delivered to the Soviets – in exchange for foodstuffs – no more than six weeks before the Russian campaign began.

It is all right to attack a country without a declaration of war – but there must be order: morality and logic à la Hitler.

The right-hand engine is on fire. The plane is listing badly. Curschmann leans on the throttles to give the other engines more power.

Then the left engine goes out of action.

The crate lurches wildly, begins to lose height rapidly.

If only he can just reach the German lines! He hauls the throttle up and realises that blood is pouring from a wound in his right shoulder. He keeps up the pressure, even though his senses are swimming.

But the thick forest that he is heading for seems to be drawing the aircraft to it like a magnet.

He dimly hears the explosion.

Then all is night for him.

The pillar of smoke rises from the site of the Ju's crash as if from a sacrificial altar.

By the time Elsenbach's platoon reaches the scene, there are only six of them left. They are 200 metres away. Schmelz sees an Ivan going through one of the dead flier's pockets.

He aims.

The Russian falls on his face, his right hand still in the dead airman's pocket.

Two other Soviets make themselves scarce.

Feldwebel Elsenbach turns around.

He leaves three men behind to cover them, and moves cautiously forward with the others. Nothing remains of the plane, but the dead man whom the Russian had been robbing had been thrown clear of the aircraft on impact – and is in fact still alive.

Schmelz does an emergency bandaging job on the seriously wounded man's shoulder, while Elsenbach mechanically checks the man's name from his paybook: Oberfeldwebel Curschmann.

With some charred rations and a seriously wounded pilot, the platoon commander reports back to his lines.

No time to celebrate. Back to work.

At last the relieving forces are starting to get close. A sortie from the cauldron. The fixed fronts, at first seemingly frozen solid, start to become mobile again. On April 12th, Ramushevo appears out of the mud and the smoke, the crossing over the Lovat.

Soon there are German troops on both banks, waving at each other across the water barrier. Shouts of joy, drowned by the roar of the massive river. One important connection is made. Demyansk is linked with the main German forces by a thin umbilical cord. On May 15th, Cholm is also relieved.

The German corridor is narrow, damned narrow, and the Russians are hitting it with everything they have. If they succeed in a surprise attack on Ramushevo, then the entire connection could be broken once more.

August: fighting around Koslovo; in September, the forest east of Luka falls into German hands. Only now does the need for supply from the air end, and a military railway is built from Tulebya to Demyansk.

Quiet before the storm.

The Russians are preparing their next winter offensive.

Three armies will finally annihilate the Demyansk cauldron. By the middle of November, the Red divisions are ready. On November 28th 1942, the bloody battle south-east of the Sea of Alma starts again.

Massive artillery bombardments.

Huge formations of bombers rain death from the heavens. Against trenches and strongpoints. The avalanche of Russian tanks rolls forward against the barbed wire and the tank traps. Marshal Timoshenko's divisions grind inexorably westwards. Metre by metre. 200 metres in one day, 300 the next. Huge losses.

A Russian breakthrough is in sight when Field Marshal von Küchler decides on a desperate measure: he takes three divisions from the thinly-defended front around Lake Ladoga and throws them into the battle further south. They are brought down in a forced march and hurled into battle in a state of total exhaustion. The Grenadiers from Ladoga dig in grimly. They destroy 170 enemy tanks, but only 309 men survive from two entire regiments.

Steglich's battalion, part of the 12th Infantry Division, notes movements north of the village in the quietness of an early morning.

'Russian ski troops,' the foremost observation post reports when the Hauptmann reaches them. 'At least 400 of them.'

The Ivans are coming slowly closer to the German positions, drawn up in long lines in white uniforms that are scarcely distinguishable from the snow.

'Don't shoot until they're well within everyone's range,' the battalion commander orders.

They wait patiently. Minute after minute, lazily swinging the machine-gun barrels with them as they probe the landscape.

'Fire!'

A hail of bullets from machine guns and carbines.

The Russians throw themelves to the ground, masters of the silent disappearing act.

But then suddenly, and without apparent reason, they leap to their feet again as if they had St Vitus' Dance. Scream. Yell with pain. Collapse.

The Germans can find no explanation for the Ivans' suicidal behaviour. All they can see are strange, clutching movements, as if the Russians were trying to remove their coats.

The battle lasts five hours.

By the end of it, the Russian ski unit has been massacred to the last man. It is only when Hauptmann Steglich and a reconnaissance group come close to the site of the fiasco that he realises the reason for the Russians' strange behaviour: the Russians' felt boots, known as *valinkis*, had been nailed to the skis, because the Russians had run out of binding tape. When the soldiers tried to take cover, they were forced to take off their boots along with their skies. Tormented by the cold, they leapt to their feet - right into the enemy's line of fire.

The Demyansk Cauldron will be held for twelve months and eighteen days.

This bloody battle is one of the most glorious - and futile - victories ever achieved by the German Wehrmacht, for once both sides have bled themselves white there, the Demyansk 'balcony' will be voluntarily evacuated.

Demyansk, the world's first airlift, is a unique achievement that will have grim consequences. In the winter of 1942/43, Göring will guarantee that Stalingrad can be supplied from the air in the same way, ignoring the fact that he is dealing, not with six divisions, but with an entire army - a mistake that will be a sentence of death for more than 200,000 German soldiers.

But for the meantime, the defenders of Demyansk have survived, and can sport Hitler's Eastern medal - contemptuously known to his soldiers as the 'Order of the Frozen Meat' - recover from their frostbite and heal their wounds, and start to eat their way back to their normal weight. A short breather before the beginning of the summer offensive, 'Case Blue', on June 28th 1942.

Set Course For Death!

SOS calls from a point just off the American coast. Explosions right around Cape Hatteras. Threats to shipping in the St Lawrence River. Attacks in the Gulf of Mexico. Burning ships in the Windward Passage between Haiti and Cuba – the 'monsters of the deep', Germany's U-boats, seem to have increased in number since Hitler's declaration of war on the USA and to be omnipresent all over the Seven Seas.

In the first six months they sink more than 300 American ships. They operate in the Gulf of Mexico and in the coastal waters off Brazil. Special reports follow each other in rapid succession; Goebbels' propaganda machine mocks the mightiest military power on earth, because at this stage it seems powerless against the U-boat danger.

Roosevelt's forces are involved in a murderous struggle in the pacific. The Japanese 'lightning victories' seem to outdo anything the Germans have achieved. The American president nevertheless conceives of the war against Hitler as taking precedence. 'In contrast to a significant part of public opinion,' states Herbert Michaelis, 'which directed its anger chiefly against Japan, for Roosevelt the war against Germany took first place. Here too he enforced his will. Hitler's declaration of war helped him. He had always sought to be involved in the war of extinction against Hitler. He saw it as his historical mission. He intended, in his own words, not to rest or sleep, until Hitler had disappeared from the world. As early as spring of 1941, the general staffs of the British and American forces had agreed on a "Germany first" plot in the event of an American declaration of war. This agreement was now formalised by a conference called in Washington shortly after Pearl Harbor. It was confirmed that the two countries' joint strength would be concentrated against Germany, as was the case with Great Britain and the USSR.'

The Americans are much less prepared for submarine attacks than the English, but even their British cousins, who halted Hitler's attempt at direct invasion by their bravery in the battle of Britain, are showing the effects of his attempt to starve them out by a 'hunger blockade'. The conquest of France has given Dönitz bases on the Atlantic, and his U-boats, operating from Lorient, present a serious threat to the British Isles. His U-boats are 450 miles closer to their area of operations and quickly turn the time advantage into increased quantities of tonnage sunk. Even though – despite all the shipyards' efforts – the U-boats' numbers increase very little, their effectiveness seems to have grown out of all proportion. The Germans sink many more ships than their enemies can build. 32,000 of the 145,000 seamen of the British merchant navy die in the Second World War. They keep going into the danger zone, for a weekly wage of nine pounds and 'danger money' of twelfpence-halfpenny a day. Death lies waiting anywhere at sea, at any time of the day or night. Captain T.D. Finch, First Officer of the *San Emiliano*, gives a vivid picture of death on the British side. Surprised in his sleep by a direct hit from a torpedo, he leapt out of bed and dashed to the bridge, where he saw members of his crew with their clothing on fire jumping into the sea.

Finch followed them, reached a lifeboat and witnessed hellish scenes of destruction; he and other survivors heard cries for help, rowed against the wind and the current to aid one of their shipwrecked comrades. 'We realised that the first cabin boy had such serious burns on his body that we had to cut his hands free from the rudder with a pair of scissors,' the eyewitness reported. 'The third officer and I took care of the wounded and were horrified at the gravity of their wounds. Since we could not find any signs of life anywhere, we hoisted the sail and set course for Trinidad. It was at this time that the stoker died, having suffered terribly throughout the night, and a few minutes later we also lost the second steward, who had suffered appalling injuries to his stomach and serious burns. I went over to him, raised the woollen blanket with which we had covered him, and realised that his stomach had been very badly dressed and was quite exposed. He had been very patient throughout the night, and the only thing he had complained about had been the cold. We consigned both men to the sea. We had been sailing for one or two hours when the second mate called me over to him. He had suffered serious burns and was very badly wounded below the waist. He asked for water, which I let him have, even though I knew it was hopeless; a few minutes later, he also died, and as I spread the blanket over him, I also noticed that the first cabin boy was going too. He had been burned all over his body, and he died towards midday. He had been very brave, and throughout the entire time had tried to keep the others morale up by singing.'

After he had been saved, Finch noted that of the 48 men of the crew, only seven had survived, and of them three more died in action during the remainder of the war.

Despite the bravery and the contempt for death shown by British merchant seamen – the rate of fatal casualties was higher than in the fighting forces – the imports crucial to Britain's survival fell to half the pre-war level. As Mark Arnold-Forster states: 'Great Britain was faced with death by starvation'.

Under these circumstances, the German surface raiders had become a nightmare for the planners in the British Admiralty, and also for the British people; by using them in concert with the U-boat arm, or so London feared, Hitler would be able to enforce a total blockade of the British Isles.

The Sea Lords are quite well aware of what the situation looks like in the ports on the west coast of France. Hardly a day goes by without new reports from the Secret Service, which has built up a complete picture.

Scharnhorst and *Gneisenau*, fast, well-armoured battleships with 28-cm guns, are lying anchored under a fantastic cover of camouflage in the vicinity of La Rochelle. The *Prinz Eugen* is ready for active service again. The British have long had a tendency to overestimate the combat strength of the German Navy.

The Royal Air Force begins a near-suicidal operation. Time and again, its aircraft risk the lethal anti-aircraft fire and the ever-ready German fighters to launch bombing raids in and around the port of Brest.

Air raid warnings have become a part of daily life in Brest. The sirens howl so often during the night that no one really takes any notice of them any more. Night after night, the formations of big, four-engined bombers are decimated, devastated, turned into blazing torches. The British suffer between 10 and 20 losses every night. But they keep coming.

And the effect is minimal. All that happens is that the British bomber crews are crucified in the cruelly accurate German anti-aircraft fire.

On board the *Prinz Eugen*, the night of 1st/2nd July 1941

begins as normally as it is undramatic. At 20.00 hours, Leutnant Hane reports on board. He was not due back until the next morning, but the likeable flier has just returned from his honeymoon. After two false starts, he finally got to marry Ingrid.

'Jesus, are you ever on time!' was his welcome from First Gunnery Officer Paulus. 'Did it fall through again?'

'Oh, it was fine, Herr Captain.'

'Well . . . thank we all our God, eh? Was it nice?'

The Leutnant says nothing.

'You don't need to blush, man. In your place I'd have stayed a night more in Brest. You can bet that the commander of the watch will snap you up and give you something to do.'

'I don't mind, Herr Captain.'

'Right. Then good night, Hane.'

The Leutnant makes for the command centre under the armoured deck, where everyone goes who has no special duties during air raids. All they have to do is to wait, hold themselves ready for emergencies.

The ship is very peaceful. Changing of the guard. The officer of the watch and his NCO are making their rounds. The night is clear and bright. The heavy cruiser lies at anchor under huge camouflage nets. On the ordinary seamen's decks, skat is being played. Smuggled cognac from the town is being passed from mouth to mouth. The mood is relaxed, maybe a little cocksure.

Preliminary warning to the flak batteries and the coastal artillery.

Shortly after 22.00, the First Officer, Lieutenant-Commander Stooss, also arrives back aboard the *Prinz Eugen*. The stocky, red-haired officer had taken three days leave to be with his brother, who is also stationed near Brest. He had come back as quickly as possible, for he is so much a part of the ship and its crew that he suffers with every moment he has to be away from them.

'Repeat warning. Expected target Brest,' the air tracking service reports. But who's supposed to panic? Does any night here go by without an air raid warning?

'Air raid warning!' The alarm bells sound throughout the ship.

Ready for action! The artillery reports.

Report from the air tracking service: 'Enemy aircraft approaching from the north-west!'

They can hear the dull crump of the flak from a long way off, the angry response to the carpet-bombing from the British. A long way away. Even the men up on deck can see nothing of the vicious drama being played out up the coast, for the smokescreen canisters are pumping out great clouds of thick, evil-smelling gas that covers the entire dock and harbour area with a drifting, milky veil.

By 0.38, the noise of battle is coming closer. The artificial fog now blankets kilometres of coastline. If the British want to hit the ships at anchor, they will have to bomb through this fog at random.

The coastal batteries are giving the RAF all they have. Their rapid-fire screen colours the thick mist blood-red. A lethal duel between the flak and the bombers. The ship's artillery is silent, for fear of betraying the *Prinz Eugen*'s position.

The din of combat filters through to the *Prinz Eugen* vaguely, almost dreamily. It seems strangely distant, even though the batteries firing at the enemy planes are only 100 metres away. On board the ship, they are following the reports with the feeling that this fighting has nothing to do with their own ship; the crew has a sense of distance, like a crowd watching a football match without having to take part.

Suddenly the bombs are falling very close. To port towards the stern, to starboard forward of the ship. A direct hit in the dock showers the bridge of the *Prinz Eugen* with a fountain of water. The ship doesn't move - it is standing on blocks in the half-filled dock.

Gradually the nightly terror subsides. Raid beaten off! Everything's all right! Nothing else tonight!

Barked orders in all positions throughout her decks: 'Password!'

The answer comes in from every unit almost simultaneously, as they have practised a hundred times and as expected. The bridge hears it from the gunners, the radio rooms, the engine rooms, the command posts, from the Intelligence centres, the boiler rooms. Report after report is registered and ticked off. Everything okay.

One part of the ship is missing, however. The command centre, of all places, is silent.

The command centre?

Only now, minutes after the attack is over, does anyone aboard the *Prinz Eugen* realise that the ship has been hit.

The hit was on the port side of the upperdeck. A heavy armoured bomb able to penetrate walls up to 51 mm thick hit the ship on the water line, just under the stern section of the bridge. The opening was a mere 30 centimetres wide. This way, however, it slipped down inside the ship's wall, went through several longitudinal girders, was diverted by a latitudinal girder, penetrated the floor of the upper platform deck and only exploded here – in the very heart of the heavy gun emplacements, in the most forward part of the ship's communications and electrical system.

The rescue units finally fought their way through to the command centre. Past seriously wounded men whose faces had melted into black, hideous masks by the heat of the explosion, who were moaning for water and help, over corpses, past men from the torpedo control centre who had been saved at the last moment, who at this early stage were running around with terrified, vacant faces, pointing mutely in the direction of the command centre itself.

The chief engineer is the first to climb into the command centre. The shimmering light of his torch glides from the bulkheads, then down to reveal the dead man on the floor, who wears four gold stripes on his sleeve . The First Officer, Lieutenant-Commander Stooss, lies just a few feet from young Leutnant Hane, the flier, who is still wearing the wedding ring that had been ceremonially placed on his now lifeless finger by the parson just a week previously. The rescuers wrap them in blankets and carry them out. One after the other. The procession seems never ending. Men move out of the way to give them access, stare at the covered bodies, dare not ask who is under the blankets.

One after the other, they are brought to the dressing station and given over to Senior M.O. Dr Witte. Blankets are pulled off the lifeless faces for a just a few seconds.

'To stern!' he barks.

It is as if the doctor's job is to pronounce a final death sentence.

Men stand mutely around him, pull the blanket back over their dead comrades' faces, carry them out, lay them down next to each other in the stern section.

Another is brought in.

'To stern!' Dr Witte repeats gently.

'He's not dead, sir,' Bo'sun Keller protests forcefully.

Dr Witte turns back to him with a frown.

'This is Friedl Bergner, Herr doctor . . . My best friend.'

The officer is tempted to give him a tough answer, but then he sees Keller's eyes, sees the torment and the sadness in the petty officer's face. He pads over to him, puts a hand on his shoulder for a moment. 'Too bad, boy,' he says softly. 'He's really dead. I can't help him.' He gestures to the stretcher-bearers.

The coffins are arranged in two rows. The crew of the *Prinz Eugen* is standing to attention around them. 1600 men – minus 50 who will never stand to attention again.

The RAF's lucky strike puts the *Prinz Eugen* out of action for months. The repair work lasts until the end of 1941. The crew have mostly moved into shore accommodation. Many have been sent off to training schools. Painfully young recruits are sent to replace them.

The rapidly-escalating air war is turning the sky above the ports into a flaming hell. The bomber formations return again and again, to drop their loads on the *Prinz Eugen*, the *Scharnhorst* and the *Gneisenau*. By the end of the year, 12,000 high-explosive bombs have been dropped in 851 raids.

In the night of 18th/19th December 1941, 101 bombers appear over Brest. The next day, fighters escort 41 Liberators. The British are conducting massed raids, sacrificing men and materiel, drawing formations off from other targets just to get at three German warships, known these days by their crews – in grim jest – as 'bomber target service Brest'. In just six months, the *Prinz Eugen* uses up 3000 shells on aerial targets.

By the beginning of 1942, the heavy cruiser is fully operational once more. A hit on the *Gneisenau* has also been fixed up. The *Scharnhorst* has remained undamaged.

Both sides are expecting a decisive move. The enemy is afraid that the German flotilla will make a run for it any day.

But where to? And above all, when?

The Intelligence services of friend and foe alike are doing their utmost, feeling the pulse of the war, placing false reports, carrying out dummy manoeuvres and feints. False rumours are put into circulation, the ships' boilers stoked up for deception purposes, vast quantities of provisions taken on board and then unloaded again.

The tension is growing from day to day. Strange events are occurring. Now, of all times, just when the repairs should be coming to completion, the French shipyard workers are sent on vacation – except, of course, for the one man known to be a British agent.

The crew of the *Prinz Eugen* is issued with tropical kit.

Why?

Are they going to escape into the South Atlantic?

The marine commander in Brest is making preparations for a carnival celebration, is having halls booked, detailing sailors to put up elaborate decorations, inviting naval and Luftwaffe auxiliary girls to the party, hiring bands.

Now of all times? Just before the decisive passage of arms? Has the marine commander lost his mind? Can the German naval command put up with such behaviour?

The commander-in-chief of Group West is staging a grand hunting party at Fontainebleau, and he has sent fine printed invitations to the commanders of the *Prinz Eugen*, the *Scharnhorst* and the *Gneisenau*, requesting the honour of their company.

Captain Brinkmann has been taking an old hunting-piece out onto the beach and practising his shooting. A few days ago he had the gun overhauled by a specialist in the armoury. The entire crew has heard about it and has felt relief at the respite: if the Old Man is off on some big game hunt, that means the war at sea has been put on ice for a while.

The crews are given generous allowances of shore leave. The British Secret Service is there and listening intently at almost every café table where men from the surface raiders take their ease. All the reports sent in to London point one way. The big chiefs at the Admiralty shake their heads and wonder whether those damned Germans have gone mad.

Only the three ships' commanders know the game that is really being played. A huge bluff is being carried through, preparing for one of the most fantastic and adventurous undertakings in the history of naval warfare. An operation that only has a chance of success if the British are taken totally by surprise and unprepared; an operation that has to be started from an occupied country where almost every second working adult is a British agent.

This is Operation 'Cerberus', planned by the German Navy and co-ordinated with the Luftwaffe's Operation 'Thunderbolt'.

February 11th 1942.

When during the course of the afternoon, the sailors receive the order to board the ship immediately, none of them believe that it can be any kind of an emergency. The *Prinz Eugen*, the *Scharnhorst* and the *Gneisenau* are to take a trip out of the harbour that evening. Apart from the commanders, no one knows that the flotillas will never return to Brest.

The captain of the *Prinz Eugen* is under orders to attempt the impossible.

Since the Spanish Armada in 1588, no foreign fleet had dared to appear in the Channel. The straits are blocked with British sea mines, patrolled by bombers and covered by coastal artillery. In the area of the 'Channel Stop', the narrows between Dover and Calais form a neck, which makes the entire run through the Channel like a bottle with the cork firmly closed.

Any movement of shipping is observed from the air and by radar screens. It is only a matter of time before the British finally manage to sink the German surface raiders trapped in Brest. The British and German Navies are stalking each other like dogs in neighbouring yards: when one breaks his chain, the other will jump too.

At 21.02, fifteen flare bombs explode over the harbour. Nine minutes later, the first sticks of bombs whistle down. By 22.14, the duel between bombers and flak is over for the night.

Immediately afterwards, *Prinz Eugen, Scharnhorst* and *Gneisenau* make their run for it, with the Commander of warships, Admiral Otto Ciliax, aboard the *Scharnhorst*. They sail through the nets, the harbour's protection against enemy submarines, then assemble and set out in battle order, with the *Scharnhorst* at their head along with the crazy mission's commander. Hitler had opposed this operation because he considered it impossible...

By using all its fighters, the Luftwaffe's Operation 'Thunderbolt' will attempt to give the navy air cover on its great day. Commander of the air operation is the young General of Fighters, Adolf Galland.

It is 5 a.m. The first German aircraft appear in the sky. The British are still asleep. What are their radar stations up to? Their security people? Their air observers? The spotters attached to their coastal batteries?

The holes in the British radar screen had been part of the Germans' planning. A host of jamming transmitters had created a real 'airwave salad' on the British side in which it was impossible to tell friend from foe. In two hours time, if the plan is to go smoothly, the German flotilla must be level with Cherbourg. It is. Then it slows up, to allow the minesweepers ahead to mark a path through the newly-discovered minefields blocking off the Seine estuary.

Level with Le Havre, a flotilla of torpedo boats joins, to strengthen the security ring. Fast E-boats join further north. Fighters and fighter-bombers patrol constantly above the flotilla of warships.

At 10.48, the air observation service reports: 'Air raid warning in grid square 22 between Calais and Ostend.'

Minutes later, two-engined enemy aircraft are sighted. Now – finally – the information goes to the British coastal defences: 'Three heavy German ships and escort, twenty vessels altogether, full speed due east.'

The report is received at British naval headquarters and – not acted upon. They have the news confirmed by the aircraft, and then still shake their heads and tell themselves that the air observers haven't woken up properly yet and are imagining ghost ships that they are assuming to be German vessels in some sort of grand hallucination.

'The Germans were favoured by fortune,' says Mark Arnold-Forster. 'The big ships had left their anchorage late, because of the air raid and because a rope had become tangled up with a ship's propeller. That meant that the British submarine *Sea Lion* had left its watch at the entrance to Brest harbour by the time the ships finally emerged into the open sea. An RAF plane that had been fitted with radar and was supposed to keep an eye on the harbour entrance had developed a mechanical fault and had been forced to return to base for repairs. By the time the aircraft returned to its post, the German flotilla was already on the High Seas and speeding through Ushant towards Brehat Island near Roscoff. But this aircraft also had a fault in its radar. Some time around 6 a.m. on February 12th, the Germans reached the level of Cherbourg without an enemy force having noticed them at all. Worse still, no one in authority on the British side seemed to be aware that the planned observation flights had not been undertaken. The German ships had not been located, but on the other hand there was no reason why they should have been. The watchdog had not barked, for the simple reason that the watchdog had not been there.'

*

It is now 15.30, and apart from a few very occasional sightings of enemy aircraft, nothing major has occurred. Ships' speed: still 27 sea miles.

Then a fountain of water. An explosion!

The *Scharnhorst* has run up against a mine. The battlecruiser is forced to stop her engines and sit immobile in the water.

The rest of the flotilla - a further battleship, the heavy cruiser *Prinz Eugen*, six destroyers, a host of torpedo boats, minesweepers, patrol boats and E boats - continues, after the Admiral has gone aboard the destroyer Z 29. The *Scharnhorst* is left stuck, and - if she can't repair herself - will be the one to take the brunt of the dash up the Channel.

The seas are becoming heavier. Big breakers thunder over the decks. The cloud cover is a mere 300-400 metres above the German ships as they plough their way through the Channel. The *Scharnhorst*, still unable to move and therefore easy meat for the British, is now ten sea miles behind the others - but the British are still asleep.

The Admiralty had worked out a plan for just such an eventuality and named it 'Operation Fuller'. It started from the erroneous assumption that the Germans would conduct the entire operation - should they dare to undertake it - by night. The recommendations of the British Air Ministry said, word for word: 'It is considered improbable that the enemy will attempt to pass through the narrows in daylight. Should he, however, hazard such an attempt, then our submarine forces and the Royal Air Force will be presented with a unique opportunity to engage the enemy in concentrated operations, as long as he is still in the Dover Straits.'

A series of coincidences and disasters add up to a day of infamy for the Royal Navy: too late, someone realises that the chaos on the airwaves had been artificially induced by the enemy. Then there had been breakdowns in communication between the navy and the air units, which had reckoned on a day off because of the poor weather conditions. Their aircraft had been placed under tarpaulins, and many of them had not been prepared for takeoff. With such foggy conditions, you only took to the air, they argued if there was an absolute crisis on. But who would have thought that on this accursed February 12th there was a crisis on in the Channel such as England had not experienced for nearly 400 years.

The British coastal batteries had just been given a whole lot of recruits as replacements. While the rookies were still being knocked into shape on the parade ground, the German convoy was steaming past silent guns, because the experienced personnel among the gunners had been sent on home leave almost to a man.

Aboard the *Prinz Eugen*, the mood of guarded optimism is shattered by an announcement over the ship's loudspeaker system: 'To commanders on all decks!' barks an officer. 'Warning! Air attacks expected!'

A squadron of Swordfishes are approaching, near-suicidal volunteers, led by Lieutenant-Commander Esmonde, who had inflicted such lethal damage on the *Bismarck* with a low-level torpedo attack a year previously.

With German fighters breathing down their necks, the two-man biplanes fire straight into the ship's flak. The leading aircraft is blown up in mid-air; the second explodes in the water; the third is also destroyed by a direct hit; the fourth is shot down by a German fighter as it banks away from its target.

Then two Blenheim bombers literally drop out of the clouds, hurl their bomb loads right close to the stern of the *Prinz Eugen*, climb back into the cloud immediately, and make good their escape. The main action follows the prelude almost straight away. A substantial force of bombers assembles, heedless of the wild flak fire, getting ready for a concentrated attack.

Combat orders fly thick and fast.

'Cäsar low-level fighters 160 degrees!'

'Aircraft flying astern!'

'Dora ready for action... Two two-engined aircraft, 235 degrees high!'

Using codewords such as 'cyclist!', 'lemon above the ship', and 'hedge', from his position aboard the *Prinz Eugen* the Luftwaffe's fighter guidance officer urges his formations to hound the enemy. The Mes respond swiftly. Around 16.30, an incredible report goes the rounds in the heavy cruiser. The usually dry and matter-of-fact voice of the announcing officer has an edge of real emotion for once.

'Attention! *Scharnhorst* has started up engines again!'

Fortune could not have chosen a better moment. Now, during these critical minutes that will decide victory or defeat, a safe return home or destruction, the crew needs confidence, needs to suck in courage, needs to believe that luck is on their side.

Because for the first time in the now 20 hours-old Operation 'Cerberus', the enemy is throwing warships into the fight against the German flotilla.

At 16.43, the witches' sabbath begins. British shells explode behind the ship's stern! The British are scarcely visible, but their fire is returned. *Gneisenau* and *Prinz Eugen* take up their slack and move into top speed, to avoid the enemy's torpedoes. The ship's observers report a cruiser and several destroyers. The duel lasts for a few minutes, and the strict formation of the German vessels is blown apart by the need to avoid torpedoes; but the enemy's fire is inaccurate. Suddenly there is a pillar of flame on the horizon. A hit!

An enemy vessel is ablaze fore and aft. She looks as if her ears are on fire. The destroyer *Worcester* is on fire. Hopeless! The enemy ship limps away, still in flames and so badly damaged that the Wehrmacht report announces that she was sunk. In fact, *Worcester* reaches her home port, still ablaze.

And the adventure continues, with a constant rhythm of air attack and all clear. The British lose 41 aircraft this day, but they keep coming, falling on the German flotilla with unbelievable panache and bravery, constantly exposing themselves to the lethally accurate German flak, paying the price as they fall like burning stones out of the sky and explode on impact with the swirling surface of the sea. Others follow them into attack, as if begrudging their comrades the privilege of a hero's death.

When there are no loudspeaker announcements, when the electric lights flicker, when they can dimly hear the noise of battle down below, then the men at their action stations in the lower decks find themselves hesitating. There are hundreds of them, with their hands on thousands of buttons and levers. Then the questions they have been asking themselves for hours become overwhelmingly urgent, and they probe the man next to them, even though they know he knows just as little about what's really going on around them as they do.

'Jesus, where are we at the moment?' asks Able Seaman Herbst anxiously.

'When I get the time, I'll go up top and ask,' Leading Seaman Hinz retorts with heavy irony.

'They could tell us more.'

'Thank your stars they're not saying anything, mate,' says Hinz. 'When they do, it's usually bad news.'

Just at that moment, there is a loud boom. Both of them look at each other in silence for a long moment.

'What was that?' asks Herbst.
'Our own guns,' Hinz says.
'How do you know?'
Hinz laughs. 'In me bones, mate.'
'Cut that crap.'
'Keep quiet, you two!' bellows Chief Engineer Petty Officer Weber.
'Where are we?' asks Hinz.
'In the Channel,' Weber answers coolly. 'Surely you know, that, eh?'
'Well, I've travelled with more speed and comfort, I'm telling you,' grates Hinz.
Weber goes into the next door cabin.
The combat alert slowly tails off. Everyone asks what time it is. Everyone is waiting for nightfall. Everyone wants to go home. Everyone is shit-scared. Everyone is trying to hide the fact.
On the bridge, Chief Leading Seaman and steersman Lorenzen asks the captain, 'What are we smoking today, captain? Roll your own or live ones?'
Without a word, the commander hands Lorenzen his tobacco pouch. The Chief Leading Seaman and his slogan: 'The captain and I steer the ship', are known throughout the *Prinz Eugen*.
The leading British ships have pulled away. The heavy cruiser has passed the eastern exit to the Channel. Her escorting destroyers can no longer keep pace with her.
The night they have all longed for has arrived. The *Prinz Eugen* is now far ahead of the rest of the German ships. The petty officer in charge of the ship's speed can't take his eyes from the rev counter. Then the needle nudges the red dash on the dial, which means: 'Maximum speed reached!'
All eyes are on the instruments. The openings in the ventilators, the steam temperature, the temperatures of the engines, the pressure turbines, the cooling system, the oil pressure are all watched with grim concentration. No problems, no failures, no disasters, no suspicious noises, no signs of deterioration in any of the ship's mechanical functions. The officers responsible each raise their hands, telling each other, 'Everything okay.'
Beaming seamen crawl out of the bilges, nod to each other enthusiastically. Verbal communications are impossible because of the noise of the engines. The men in the engine

rooms know that it is up to them to ensure that the ship steams as quickly as possible, for every minute brings them closer to home. They have no idea what is happening on the bridge, in the gun emplacements, on the signals deck, in the radio and radar rooms. All they are aware of is the steady ringing which proves to them that the ship is steaming at full speed, that all three turbines are operating with the same peak efficiency. They wipe the sweat from their foreheads and work on, even though they are almost collapsing from the heat. Except that they cannot collapse, for the spaces are too narrow.

Their radar finds the buoy that marks the safe area through the minefield. British aircraft fly over the German heavy cruiser a few times, as if they can't believe that she has escaped.

The two battleships cannot match the *Prinz Eugen*'s luck. Shortly before 21.00, the *Gneisenau* reports a direct hit from a mine, and an hour and a half later the *Scharnhorst* has her second stroke of bad luck – another mine! Admiral Ciliax has to suffer a second humiliation: he is forced to change ships again – from the destroyer Z 29, which is losing speed because of engine problems, to the destroyer *Herbert Schoemann*.

The next day, February 13th 1942, the *Prinz Eugen* is the first of the ships to reach the mouth of the Elbe, to pass through the Brunsbüttel lock gate of the frozen Kiel Canal, and to tie up by the gate after a brief docking manoeuvre. After her, the others follow, every one finally arriving safely.

'The "Channel Dash" ended in a big tactical victory,' Cajus Becker states. 'No one could, however, ignore the fact that with the evacuation of the French bases the fleet had already begun a strategic withdrawal of crucial importance.'

Desert Fox Versus Desert Rats!

They were the first soldiers from the 5th to step onto North Africa's hot earth, and by way of welcome they hit the dirt, for safety's sake, and eat sand. The British low-level fighters are swooping down, screaming so low over the first units of the Afrika Korps that the soldiers main fear is of having their heads sliced off by a wingtip. And bursts of tracer fire from the Spitfires are etching deadly patterns in the sand.

By the time they fly off to beat up the Italian positions, Oberleutnant Honig's company has lost three dead and four wounded.

'Nice place,' oaths little Muggelbauer, and fumbles for his glasses in the dust. He is not the only one to have contacted permanent diarrhoea and to be constantly off with his entrenching tool under his arm to build a desert shithouse for himself. Anyone who thinks that's funny finds it's their turn next, because the desert respects no man's guts for long.

The 5th is a light division, and after their hasty landing in North Africa it could even be classified as feather-light, because a good part of their weapons and equipment has been sunk by the enemy and is currently resting on the bottom of the Mediterranean. And so the Feldwebel has taken them to Tripoli to organise more or less honestly what they need, or whatever he can get: captured British vehicles, German Kübelwagen jeeps, Italian trucks, decrepit motor cycles.

And a few drums of petrol.

This venturesome procession first took the main coast road, heading in the direction of the front line, towards Syrte. The Royal Air Force chased them off the highway, and since then the column has been grinding its way across the desert sands. Most of the vehicles have no anti-dust filters, and almost all have normal tyres, and so the wearisome old crates often only make 100 to 150 metres before getting stuck in the sand.

The men leap down from the vehicles, dig the wheels free of the enveloping sand, shove, curse, lay down tarpaulins and uniform jackets, gas masks and steel helmets – anything to get the bloody things on the move again. Engines scream, the wheels throw up huge cascades of sand that get into all the men's faces. The wheels turn uselessly, as if they were on sheer ice.

'This is like winter in the mountains,' says Private Zorbetzki perceptively.

Corporal Prinz is overcome by anger. He picks up a handful of sand and shoves it in Korbetzki's mouth. The man spits, coughs and wheezes at the same time.

'There you are: a snowball, mate,' Prinz grins. 'Should do something for your thirst.'

'The 'beer baron' – his nickname comes from the fact that his family have a brewery in Westphalia – ought to know about quenching thirsts. Prinz enjoys the utmost respect throughout the battalion since the time last Christmas that he conjured up several barrels of beer – not the watery wartime apology for beer, but strong, dark country beer like you can get in peacetime.

Towards midday, the hot desert wind, the simoom, becomes too much for them. Giving up the unequal struggle against the swirls of dust, the panzer grenadiers of the 5th Light crawl under the trucks and tarpaulins. They look like miners coming off shift into the light, looking forward to having a beer in the next pub.

But there is no pub. No air. Nothing to see. Just sand everywhere, nothing but sand. Sand in your lungs. Sand in your nose. Sand in your eye sockets. Sand in your trousers.

'And even between the cheeks of your arse,' moans Private Giraff, who is only 1 metre 65 tall, because he has almost no neck.

As evening approaches, most of the column is installed east of El Agheila, in positions prepared for them by the Italians. And even while the tailenders are still struggling through the desert, the company commander has been summoned to battalion, from there to regimental HQ, from there to a conference with the all-highest Desert Fox himself.

It is March 1941, and the Second World War is in the process of dreaming up another theatre to keep German soldiers busy: the desert. The Germans sent to Africa were prepared neither climatically, nor psychologically, nor militarily, for what they found there. Suddenly they were issued with old-fashioned tropical uniforms not unlike those worn by General von Lettow-Vorbeck's* troops in the First World war, and after that they gradually started to get into the swing of it and see their Italian allies as their 'askaris'.

Shortly before the end of the Western Campaign, on June 10th 1940, Mussolini had thrown his troops against the French, hoping by this cheap trick to gain the whole of North Africa – he already possessed colonies in Libya and Tripolitania. Hitler's peace treaty with France did not allow this, and the Duce got no more than he deserved for his very slight pains.

He was, however, determined to wage his own war in the style of the Führer. The strategic situation in North Africa was favourable from the Italian point of view. Using their colonies of Eritrea and Ethiopia, they could thrust north across the horn of Africa in the direction of the Suez Canal, at the same time moving west from Libya into Egypt and thus cutting one of the main lifelines of the British Empire.

But if the Duce wanted to emulate the German example of the Blitzkrieg, his Italian troops were nowhere near so well armed, and their military leadership was pathetic. As for the mass of Italian soldiers, they showed themselves to be masters of survival – they certainly lacked the death-defying courage of their northern allies. Food, wine and love were more to their taste than a hero's death.

Their fighting vehicles proved to be too thinly armoured, their generals to be too old. Relations between officers and men were tense. Even in the desert, Mussolini's officer corps would not give up their feudal habits and attitudes. The ordinary soldiers had to content themselves with a choice of two kinds of goulash stew, while the officers received their own food – and enjoyed the services of female auxiliaries who were rarely seen by the men and whose skills clearly had little to do with the efficient conduct of war.

Lord Wavell's Army of the Middle East pre-empted an Italian attack from the South by moving into Ethiopia, which Mussolini had annexed in 1936. Two Indian divisions attacked the north, while a force mainly composed of South African troops invaded the southern part of the country. 'The Italians did not put up any particularly strong resistance,'

* The governor of German East Africa (Tanganyika), who organised spiritied resistance against the British in the colony between 1914 and 1916.

says the British author Mark Arnold-Forster in his book *The World at War*. 'The most potent enemy of the Allies was malaria. The capital, Addis Ababa, fell on April 6th. The Duke of Aosta surrendered on May 16th, and by the end of May General Wavell was able to devote his thoughts and his forces to the main battle in the Western Desert.'

Moving westwards from Libya, General Rodolfo Graziani came only as far as Sidi Barrani, where he constructed a defensive line 80 kilometres long. Here the Italians planned to wait until a water pipe had been constructed; they intended to resume their mini-offensive in December 1940 at the earliest.

Even this fate was subject to postponement, and immediately before dawn on January 3rd, the British attacked Bardia, in the middle section of the front, and began the first desert battle of 1941. They attacked with two infantry brigades, supported by 23 tanks. Australian troops were facing an enemy who outnumbered them five to one. But after only three hours of fighting, the Italian line broke and Mussolini's divisions were in full, disorganised retreat. 40,000 Italian soldiers marched into captivity, laughing all the while.

'The desert was the only thing that put up a real resistance to the British,' Raymond Cartier writes.

Wavell's forces swarmed forward with a wild, victorious energy and drove their beaten enemy back 1000 kilometres from El Agheila to Tripoli, coming within 200 kilometres of the Tunisian border. The English armoured division started up on muddy tracks by moonlight, and within 24 hours it had covered 150 kilometres and had overhauled a huge column of Italian vehicles on the Via Balbia.

By the time the first British counter-offensive was open, ten Italian divisions had been routed and 130,000 troops had marched off into captivity, for the additional loss of 180 medium and 220 light tanks. The British had captured 845 guns and had acquired a quite arrogant sense of superiority over their main opponent in North Africa. The one-man armoured vehicle that had been displayed with such pride at parades had proved to be a tin coffin.

If the British Middle Eastern Army continued to move forward at this rate – and who was going to stop it – then it would conquer all North Africa.

Hitler, heavily committed to the coming invasion of Russia, had viewed the desert as a minor theatre at first, but during the course of the Italian retreat he had offered Mussolini German reinforcements. The Duce had refused. 'If we once let the Germans in,' he told his aides, 'then we shall never be rid of them again.'

He was, however, currently in the process of 'getting rid of' the whole of North Africa, and he made an urgent request for German help. At first it consisted of a single man – but his name was Erwin Rommel and he was the commander of the 'Ghost Division' in the French Campaign, a dynamic officer more popular with his own troops than with the Wehrmacht High Command. In those rarefied quarters he was seen as a good leader of men, but several leading military figures, including chief-of-staff Halder dismissed him as a 'crazy fool'.

The newly-appointed commander of the 'German Afrika Korps' – which as yet existed only on paper – paid little attention to such political struggles. He had arrived in Tripoli on February 12th 1942; three days later, he was sitting in a Fieseler Stork and flying over the British lines, despite enemy dominance of the air, to acquaint himself with the true situation.

The situation was miserable, even if in the meantime the 10th Air Corps had been transferred from Norway to Sicily, where it had set up a headquarters in the Hotel Dominico in Taormina. They were the first units to get to grips with the enemy within the framework of 'Operation Sunflower', the code name for under which the Afrika Korps was being assembled and shipped to Italian North Africa.

The British, who controlled the Mediterranean through their bases at Gibraltar and Malta – even though the Duce, with his usual vanity called it *Il Mare nostro*, 'our sea' – had already sunk the first transports to come by sea before they knew that they were shortly to face a new opponent in the desert. It was only when a British spotter plane reported an eight-wheeled vehicle of non-Italian manufacture – it was Rommel's command vehicle – that the British realised that the Italians were to be granted German reinforcements.

The first unit to be landed was the 5th Division, with its decimated equipment. Gradually other convoys got through, some carrying heavy weapons, some only soldiers who brought with them only their lace-up boots and their identity tags. Finally – and too slowly for the impatient commander – the 15th Panzer Division arrived, in dribs and drabs, as if reluctant.

Rommel was supposed to wait for further reinforcements and for orders, but patience was never one of his virtues.

It was for this reason that he was now calling together the officers of his slimly-based Afrika Korps, somewhere at his mobile headquarters. His words to them leave no room for doubt: He intends to make contact with the enemy without further delay and, if he can find a weak spot, to attack.

Rommel is formally subject to Italian supervision, but he has his own reasons for not discussing his strategy with them too intimately. In any case, his real superiors are in the Wehrmacht High Command. And even in their case, the general is only too well aware that he is not sharing with Berlin what he is now telling his own officers.

He lacks everything he needs for his planned attack – except for optimism and imagination. And his officers are given orders that seem more like heat mirages.

Or April fool's pranks, thinks Oberleutnant Honig as he drives back to his company's positions near Syrte. The fun is to start on March 31st, a day before All Fools' Day. Just the right date for such a good joke. Nevertheless, the young officer is irritated by the fact that his unit has been detailed to the deception operation; their job will be to raise great clouds of dust that look like a huge force of armour that doesn't, in fact, exist.

Oberleutnant Honig attempts to hide his disappointment from the Feldwebel, who heads straight for him with businesslike intent the moment he arrives back at the line. 'Reinforcements?' he asks him.

The Feldwebel laughs. 'Yes. Four armoured gun-carriers and seventy-four men.' He grimaces. 'And they all went to the bottom of the sea,' he adds, and hands the officer a piece of paper. 'But the documents have arrived.'

'Then at least we've got something to wipe our arses with,' the Oberleutnant says. 'And I need skilled men, ones who can write, paint, work with wood and generally make themselves useful,' he continues without a pause. 'Do we have them?'

'If not, we'll make some, Oberleutnant,' the Feldwebel says gravely.

The general mood of the men is fair to low, but, compared with the day's hardships, it is almost festive. The men are having a shooting competition using tubes of instant cheese. The bucket is already half full. You can do almost anything with the damned stuff – except eat it. Corporal Prinz is trying to bandage off his bow legs by wrapping elastic bands around his ankles, but the fleas and sand flies are refusing to recognise this demarcation line and forcing him to take increasingly desperate measures.

'Why do these frigging beasts pick on me?' oaths the beer baron.

'You smell the best of all,' Muggelbauer says with a sly grin. 'Raised on beer nuts.'

'And how are we smokers doing?' asks Müller.

'Dead quiet,' Muggelbauer growls.

'Oh really?' Prinz interrupts his almost balletic leaps and with a broad grin on his face pulls a green pack bearing an Italian brand name out of his pocket.

'Did you pinch them?' asks the Unteroffizier delightedly.

'No, swapped 'em,' Prinz answers with a harsh laugh. 'For some nudie photos I got in Paris.'

'Haven't the maccaronis lost their taste for that?' asks Müller II.

'They're not as dumb as we are,' Prinz retorts. 'So far as they're concerned this war can kiss their arse.'

'Yeah. And I'd rather have naked women than a cold arse,' chips in Giraff, returning to their favourite theme.

'Attention!' bellows the Unteroffizier, seeing the Feldwebel approach.

The Feldwebel dismisses their lame salutes with a lazy wave of the hand. 'Who's a craftsman here?' he asks. 'Any cabinetmakers or metalworkers?' He looks along the line of men. 'Or at least, who hasn't got two left hands?'

A long, lazy fart from the back row is his only response.

'Who was that swine?' the Feldwebel asks uselessly. 'Right, then it has to be all of you,' he adds, and orders them all off to join in the soul-destroying work.

Supply columns continually bring along wood, cardboard, material, pieces of tin, buckets of varnish. Finally they deliver burned-out vehicles - a complete graveyard of military vehicles. The men of the company begin to put together a little panzer army out of wood and rags. Carbonised cars are brought alive and made into tanks by the addition of long wooden 'guns'. Wrecks are turned into the latest thing in armoured combat vehicles. No limits are put on the boys' imaginations; only when Muggelbauer, feeling artistically inspired, paints a naked Venus on a papier-mâché gun turret, complete with jutting breasts, the Feldwebel bawls at him; 'You're supposed to be making tanks, not thinking of big-titted women!'

Overnight, the jokes die on everyone's lips and the prank becomes as serious as it could be. Hours before the offensive, Honig's panzer group - made of tin and paper, with a few genuine armoured vehicles mixed in, moves into 'action.'

The desert is freezing. The nights are cold. When the engines stop, you can hear the hyenas. The sand has been solidified into clumps that crackle under the tracks of the vehicles.

The company advances cautiously, only slightly concealed by the darkness, for it is a moonlit night. The genuine tanks are at the head, with the fakes behind.

The column has been under way for an hour now. No contact with the enemy. The searchlights probe the sky. Purely routine. Time check: 0.02.

Suddenly the left flank of the company collides with an English forward position. A brief exchange of fire, and then an armoured gun carrier moves forward and reduces it to rubble. The men wait for a concerted counter-thrust. But the night remains quiet. The English have obviously decided to view the fighting as a routine night skirmish.

Then, suddenly, flares light up the sky, illuminating the progress of the phantom column. The English, spoiled by the Italians, can't believe their eyes, but then the guns open up and they have bullets whistling around their ears, kicking up fountains of sand, putting the fear of God into them.

They report hastily to headquarters that a German panzer unit, possibly the advance guard of an entire division, is heading straight for them. They are ordered to withdraw - and then, all at once, the heavens come afire and seem to plummet down onto the tormented earth.

Hundreds of guns belch death from their barrels. Engines roar into life. Chains rattle. Wounded men are screaming. The wide, endless desert between the 34th latitude and the 10th longitude is transformed into a fiery hell.

Oberleutnant Honig has fulfilled his mission. But when he realises how feeble the opposition really is, he pushes on beyond his operational objective and brings his dummy vehicles with him.

When daylight comes, British reconnaissance aircraft appear in the sky. He has a broad grin on his grimy face as he orders his men to take cover as far as possible from their home-made tanks.

Twenty minutes later, fighter-bombers circle above the paper panzers, then dive and attack, slaughter the cardboard comrades in the turrets and probably radio to British HQ that they had destroyed a panzer spearhead that seems to be able to call on limitless reinforcements, for in the times between the reconnaissance flights and the bombing raids, the company leaps out of its foxholes and glues the entire bunch of dummies together again in slightly different order.

The company is making the English work hard, but the real work is going on elsewhere. Rommel had at first made an attempt on a frontal attack. He encountered stiff resistance and immediately veered off into a narrow track between two unnegotiable stretches of smooth, deep sand. The Tommies suspect that he is outflanking them; in order to avoid being cut off, they withdraw in more or less good order and without offering resistance. They have been thoroughly out-thought. They had become used to hardly any resistance, let alone offensive activity, so far as the Italians were concerned. They had committed the fateful mistake of withdrawing two of their divisions and sending them over to Greece.

Rommel reaches Agedabia, his objective, almost without loss. Here the Afrika Korps is supposed to halt, but the Desert Fox has no such intention. Dividing his forces into three mobile columns, he continues to advance further and further, crosses the Djebel el Akhdar and turns what had been an orderly withdrawal by the enemy - a mixture of English, Australian, Indian, French and South African units - into a disorganised, panick-stricken route.

Tripolitania, the western part of Libya, and the eastern part, the Marmarica, are huge, lifeless deserts, Cyrenaica, with its capital at Benghazi, has been colonised and transformed into a fertile, productive and civilised region. Bardia has been turned into a major port by Mussolini's governor. A road 2000 kilometres long stretches from Tunis to Egypt; 800 kilometres of it leads through a waterless sea of sand. The coast road is to become the route of advance and withdrawal for both sides over a period of years, a frontline of its own whose boundaries are never clearly drawn.

During the second night, Oberleutnant Honig abandons his game with the dummies, snaps up a few captured vehicles and joins in on the left flank of the forces pursuing the enemy.

The column rolls onward. The rhythm of the wheel axles

hammers at the brain. Headaches, thirst, sleepiness and exhaustion.

Onward.

Eastwards. Now and again a vehicle is left behind. No one bothers about it. Corporal Giraff is riding in the last vehicle but one. He is sleeping with his eyes open. Now and again he stares at the sand and actually believes it is water. Beer is just a distant, forgotten dream these days, even though the beer baron is sitting next to him.

He wakes with a start. 'Jesus, I'm ready for the garbage dump,' he says to Prinz.

The engine coughs unhealthily. Giraff stops for the fourth time to clean the carburettor. The last vehicle in the column rolls on past him.

The repairs only take a few minutes, and then the corporal steps on the gas pedal and they are off.

But where are the others?

Finally he sees the clouds of dust, quickly catches up, finds a place in the column that is moving across the desert swathed in its cloud of dust, the vehicles one behind the other and dumb as a herd of cows.

Half an hour, forty minutes. It will soon be light again, and then the fighter-bombers will come - which will mean all hell will break loose, but at least there will be a chance for a breather in a foxhole.

The roar of the engines. Sand creeping into every crevice of skin. The warm contents of their field canteens taste of a mixture of tar and sand.

The vehicle in front of Giraff's stops suddenly.

'Watch out, you camel-fuckers!' he oaths. Then he shuts up very quickly indeed; he has recognised the men who are jumping out of the vehicles ahead and forming themselves into a talkative little social group among the dunes. How could anyone mistake those wide, flat helmets?

'Tommies!' he grates to his mate Prinz.

'You're friggin' observant,' the boy from Westphalia hisses, and jumps out to warn the men sitting on top of the truck.

The others are off their perches in seconds, quick as monkeys.

One burst of fire into the group of British soldiers whose column Giraff had tagged onto all unawares. The astonished Tommies throw down their weapons, raise their hands high.

44 prisoners, five vehicles packed with supplies captured.

'And seven packs of the finest English cigarettes,' Muggelbauer reports with a leer. He looks at the pack in his hand and quotes, 'English blend.'

Soon incorporated in the attacking forces, Honig's company storms onward. German ground fighters blast their way open. The Italians, inspired by the panache of the offensive, find their self-confidence again and become serviceable combat troops. Rommel is in the process of taking back the whole of Cyrenaica when he is suddenly faced with a far more serious problem than the entire British 8th Army: he receives orders from Führer Headquarters to halt the offensive.

The Desert Fox has a kind of civil courage as well as military valour, however – a rare quality in German generals. He rejects the order and allows the Afrika Korps to advance as far as Benghazi. His victory is a direct result of disobedience of orders.

The exotically moustachioed Italian General, Italo Gariboldi, who is Rommels nominal superior, chases after the Desert Fox with orders to slow him down. But Rommel changes his command post so often that the Italian can't keep up. The Afrika Korps' commander flits around the desert like a will o' the wisp, always turning up where he is least expected; he leaps from a truck in the front line, lands right in the middle of his advance troops from a Fieseler Stork, appears in a panzer turret, or takes to a Kübelwagen to urge on his vital supply columns.

By the time Gariboldi reaches him, the Afrika Korps has already advanced so far that the Wehrmacht High Command rescinds the order to stop and gives him a free hand.

The swift panzer thrusts throw the British into complete confusion. The 3rd Indian Brigade, recently introduced to reinforce the British forces, has neither artillery nor anti-tank weaponry. There is no systematic resistance any more.

Rommel is aware of the enemy's disorganisation. His panzers have no fuel and no ammunition any more, but from his Fieseler Stork Rommel can see the British supply dumps at Derna and Mechili. He is determined to get petrol and weapons from the enemy.

During the night of April 6th, a week after the start of the offensive, a German advanced party stumbles on a British staff car and takes three British generals captive, including Richard O'Connor, who is still wearing an Italian medal on his tunic from the First World War. The old war horse will not remain a reluctant guest of the Germans for long. His third escape attempt succeeds, and he is soon back in the saddle as a leader of men in the hottest part of the fighting.

The German panzers fill up on enemy fuel and race onwards. Tobruk is besieged, holds on, beats off several German attacks. The town, supplied from the sea, is surrounded by its Australian defenders with a 48 kilometre long defensive perimeter which the Germans fail to penetrate. They hold Tobruk from April 1941 until they are relieved in December, presenting a permanent threat to the Afrika Korps' advance. 'If Tobruk had fallen - particularly during the early attacks,' writes the American author James W. Stock in his book *The Battle for Tobruk*, 'Egypt would undoubtedly have been seriously endangered. We can, of course, only surmise how much farther Rommel would have been able to drive his troops forward, exhausted as they were from their headlong rush through Cyrenaica. If he had managed to push far enough beyond the border to endanger Alexandria, the Wehrmacht High Command might have finally consented to build on Rommel's success by increasing the rate of reinforcement and supply.'

Benghazi falls on April 6th, Bardia five days later; a second massed assault on the fortress of Tobruk is beaten off, but in ten days Rommel has retaken the territory lost by the Italians and become the legendary 'Desert Fox' to friend and foe alike. He is now threatening to push forward to Cairo and the Suez Canal. And Honig's happy band of men are not the only German troops who dream of the delights of leave in the fleshpots of Egypt.

Rommel is waiting impatiently for his supplies, which must first reach the coast in one piece and then have to be transported along the apparently endless road route to the Egyptian border. Before the Desert Fox can begin his push for the Suez Canal, General Wavell starts a counter-offensive in June, but after some initial successes it is beaten back.

On May 27th, the Desert Fox takes the Halfaya Pass on the Libyan-Egyptian border. Prime Minister Churchill unfairly decides that his commander in the Middle East is a loser and on June 27th he replaces him with General Claude Auchinleck. The new British commander faces a man who in this short time has become the most popular general of World War Two.

'Rommelitis' is also endemic on the British side, and so the new commander-in-chief feels moved to state in an order of the day to his commanders and staff officers:

'There is a real danger that our friend Rommel is becoming a kind of magician or bogeyman for our troops, since they talk about him far too much. He is in no way superhuman, although he is actually a very energetic and capable commander. Even if he were superhuman, however, it would be highly undesirable for our men to ascribe supernatural powers to him.

'I ask you to use all the means at your disposal to dispel the impression that Rommel is anything more than an ordinary German general. The main thing at the moment is to ensure that they do not refer only to Rommel when they mean the enemy. We have to always refer to "the Germans" or the "Axis forces", or the "enemy", but certainly not always talk about Rommel in particular. Please ensure that this order is put into immediate effect, and let all commanders know that this matter is especially important from the psychological point of view.

(signed) C.J. Auchinleck, General, Commander-in-Chief Armed Forces Middle East.

P.S. I am not jealous of Rommel.'

Someone else on the British side is also aware of the need to counteract Rommel's magic, though in this case there is talk of more than fine words. This man's name is Admiral Sir Roger Keyes, the British commando chief, whose forces represent the equivalent of the Brandenburgers on the German side. Keyes has decided that on the eve of the British offensive he will mount a wild raid that will lead to the death or capture of Erwin Rommel.

It is November 18th 1941. The wind is whipping the sand up into clouds. The darkness covers the two MPs on guard duty like a hangman's mask. The only signs of life are the masked lights of the trucks moving along the highway towards Tripoli.

'The weather's changing,' says Private Gelhoff.

'Sun or rain,' mutters his mate Radinsky. 'It's all shit!'

'Plenty of Africa,' Gelhoff says darkly. 'Not too much beer-hall fun.'

Directly before the beginning of the British 'Crusader'

offensive, the atmosphere at German headquarters is like a calm before the storm.

Corporal Radinsky stares towards the tall cypresses surrounding Beda Littoria, attracted by a sudden noise. But all he can see are sand dunes, which are covered with rustling bulrushes. 'Didn't you hear anything?' he asks his sidekick.

'Sure,' growls Gelhoff. 'A sentry's fart.'

Beda Littoria is an important place, for the entire supply system of the Afrika Korps is directed from here. Some very important staff officers have established themselves in the substantial stone building behind them, and it is not unusual for the Desert Fox to turn up - always unannounced - to stamp through the building, make sure his officers are on their toes, and then disappear again as suddenly as he came. This man, a legend, has become for the Tommies a miraculous figure, more of a danger to their morale than all the panzers in the world.

Since the last battle, the British have dubbed Halfaya Pass 'Hellfire Pass'. In the requisitioned prefect's building of Beda Littoria, all is still and dark; the officers and men are catching up on sleep, for during the next few days they will scarcely have a chance to get out of their clothes.

There are still lights burning in a few rooms, and despite the blackout curtains they are still visible at the edges of the windows. On the first storey, Leutnant Denglert is crouched on an upturned crate writing a letter to his girlfriend in Überlingen. Writing is not his particular skill, but if he had her here, he would know what to say.

The entrance and exit, at the front and behind the building, are guarded. A few men are sleeping in the ammunition and weapon stores, to be on hand if needed.

But when will they ever be needed?

Corporal Radinsky is seeing ghosts, and his mate Gelhoff is looking at his watch: two minutes to midnight.

In a half-hour they will be relieved, and then let someone else stare into the night and see ghosts.

Footsteps?

Phantoms - but Radinsky is turning around, and before the burst from a machine-gun hits him he glimpses a tall, wiry man with his face blacked, dressed in a kind of tracksuit.

'Heeelp!' bawls Gelhoff the next moment. 'Eeemergency!'

Before a burst smacks him against the wall, he realises that all the lights have gone out in the building.

The private collapses, sprawls on the ground, seriously wounded.

He has lost consciousness. And men run by him in their silent rubber-soled boots.

'On June 17th, everything went to pieces,' wrote Winston Churchill in his memoirs with regard to the last British counter-offensive, and the British General Staff's report stated: 'Rommel's victory was a victory of leadership, of the superior fighting qualities of his troops, and of his superior weapons.'

This flattering account of the Afrika Korps was true of the previous British offensive, but tomorrow the next one was due.

Soldiers in their characteristic flat helmets, supported by tanks, were waiting for the artillery bombardment that would blast them a way through the German lines, it was hoped.

They are aware that the plans have been worked out in minute detail – but not, however, that a top secret mission is to be their chief weapon: an attack on the Desert Fox himself.

The headquarters of the 'Rangers', a crack commando unit, is in Cairo. By the banks of the Nile, a lot of time and effort has been spent in deciding whether it might be possible to hit Rommel in the apparent safety of his own headquarters.

While the new commander, Auchinleck, made his preparations for the next offensive, wild suggestions were being made in commando circles: surprising the Desert Fox in his sleep, kidnapping him or – if he resisted – just shooting him down.

If they succeeded in cutting off the head of the Afrika Korps, it was felt that the body would flounder and fail.

Lieutenant-Colonel Haselden has been organising espionage against the Germans behind the lines, living among the Arabs as an Arab.

His agents have told him that Rommel is in residence at Beda Littoria.

This town, a mere dot on the map, had been a model Italian settlement. It bordered on the ancient settlement of Kyrene, founded by the Greeks and in 88 BC conquered by the Roman gourmet and general Lucullus, who claimed it as a Roman province. The place became famous for the Venus of Kyrene, a unique work of art.

Once it had been decided to attack Rommel's headquarters, a hundred volunteers were sought from among the men of the Long Range Desert Group for this virtual suicide mission.

They were brought to London and there subjected to a brutally hard training programme: fractured limbs, accidents with explosives, weak hearts and circulatory problems reduced this select group to 53 men.

The men received plenty of booze and high pay, and – if they could still move – as much leave as they could manage, like Roman gladiators who were celebrating life just as they were about to die.

Immediately before they went into action, Churchill himself visited them. 'If we eliminate Rommel,' he told them in a short address, 'victory will be ours. We shall have got rid of the Desert Fox shortly before our new offensive, and the panzer troops in Africa will be without a leader.'

The time had come.

In November 1942, 53 hand-to-hand combat experts under the command of Major Keyes, the son of the Admiral, were flown to Alexandria and divided between the submarines *Torbay* and *Talisman*.

They went on board with their faces blacked up, kitted out with boots that had extra-thick rubber soles. Weaponry: a dagger, a revolver and an automatic pistol. Each of the volunteers was trained in karate; all of them knew that their chances of getting out of this thing alive were very slim.

'Stop both engines!' shouted the commander of the *Torbay* from his conning tower.

He looked through his telescope, followed the rush of the surf beating against sandbanks.

He summoned Major Keyes.

Both officers had to hang tight onto the steel rail to prevent themselves from being tipped overboard by the breakers.

'Shit,' said Keyes laconically.

'Indeed,' the commander answered drily. 'Launch the rubber dinghies.'

It was crazy, but it was necessary – necessity of war.

The boat was lowered into the water on the lee side.

The raiding party paddled themselves away from the shadow of the steel shark, only to find themselves seized on by huge waves and overwhelmed.

The dinghy overturned.

The Rangers trod water, grabbed handholds on the rubber boat, righted it - and were promptly tipped right back in the water.

'Hold fast to the ropes and swim to land!' the major ordered, with no regard how shit-terrible the operation had been in its short life so far.

Meanwhile, the *Talisman* had hammered its way into the bay too.

There were some losses here too: death by drowning.

Of 53 Rangers, 31 reached the beach - and that was when this genuine suicide mission was supposed to start.

They padded their way over to the assembly point, unobserved by the German coastal watch.

Lieutenant-Colonel Haselden had arrived an hour previously.

He introduced them to three Arabs. 'Your guides,' he said. 'It's all right; they are reliable.'

He would gladly have joined in the mission, but he had to disappear again to his Arab village to nurture his network of spies and pursue his role as the Lawrence of Arabia of the Second World War.

23.00 hours. The first silent figures reach the cypress grove.

They gaze at the shape of the prefecture building.

'Rommel's asleep in there, boys,' Major Keyes encourages his men. 'If we can settle his hash, then our boys will be on easy street tomorrow.'

He divides his men into two groups.

He takes personal command of the section that will infiltrate the front entrance. Captain Campbell will try to get through the rear door.

23.55. 300 seconds before X-time.

Major Keyes claps his explosives man, O'Hara, on the shoulder.

The NCO will put the building's lights out of action immediately before the attack; the fuse boxes are in an unguarded building next to the prefecture.

A few seconds to go.

The major stares at the two sentries at the front entrance. They are MPs from the Parachute Regiment. The left-hand sentry, Corporal Radinsky, is right in the sights of Keyes' automatic, but if possible the major would like to deal with him silently, so as to avoid waking up Rommel and his escort.

But the Englishman realises that the two Germans have spotted him, and so he leaps to his feet, presses the trigger, waves his men on.

They know that everything will be decided within the next few seconds.

The machine-gun burst outside brings Feldwebel Lenters and his men to their feet at their posts in the store rooms.

They stumble into action, reach for the light switches, realise that there is no electricity, shake off their sleep, realise that they are being attacked.

Unteroffizier Kniola leaps out of the top bunk and lands smack between Lenters' shoulders, bringing them both down in a heap, but within a moment they are on their feet again. They dash outside, and within a few metres of the door they collide with a ghost: a black mass out of which a pair of eyes and some white teeth are the only visible things; it is Major Keyes.

Ghosts have no eyes.

The Feldwebel raises his pistol and presses the trigger as Keyes pulls the pins out of a pair of hand grenades.

The Feldwebel hurls himself to the ground.

Kniola, standing behind him, reacts too slowly and catches the shrapnel from the explosion.

He drops down dead.

Shouts, whistles and footsteps in the house.

An incredible chaos.

Lenters has used up his entire magazine. He crawls back to his bed in the darkness, reaches for the spare magazine from his holster.

Leutnant Denglert, the letter-writer, fell out of bed at the first alarm signal. Within moments, he collides with a fast-moving Tommy.

They fire simultaneously, but the German is a fraction of a second quicker.

Bullets tear at walls and doorframes.

The screams of wounded men echo through the corridors in two languages.

The Rangers who made the original break through the front entrance can't hold out for ever, but they still have a chance – when the men who came in the back way storm up on the Germans from behind.

But where are they?

The second group had met with a disastrous setback.

The rear door was sealed shut.

The English, who had been trained in picking locks, had expected that – but they had not expected the door to have no lock at all.

It leads into a room where two privates are asleep. Since they had not wanted anyone to disturb their rest, they had pushed water containers up against the door and reinforced them with filing cabinets.

As the intruders realise that their skeleton keys will get them nowhere, the two Germans are brought to their senses by the alarm bells sounding on the other side of the building.

They grab their weapons, join in the defence of the prefecture.

The hopes of total surprise have been dashed, and with them the chances of taking the building in one swift, deadly rush. Within a few minutes, the beams of torches bring some light into the chaotic hand-to-hand struggle.

The defenders are still hitting each other as often as they do the Tommies, but now it is only a matter of time before they deal with the enemy commandos.

'Let's go, boys!' roars an English officer at the last possible moment. 'Up, up and away!'

The survivors run outside, dash headlong into the open air and into the cypress grove again, heading for the dunes.

That same night, light is cast on the bizarre attack that had cost the lives of four Germans.

They find the corpse of Major Keyes. A burst of gun-fire tore out his heart and lungs.

Captain Campbell is lying near the entrance. He is still trying to escape, despite his shattered leg, and is found next to Gelhoff, who is still unconscious.

The two are lying next to each other as if placed there by some careful hand, and they are both taken off to the same military hospital.

At first the authorities in Beda Littoria are not aware that the attack had been aimed at the Desert Fox, for Erwin Rommel, only an occasional visitor to the place, had been somewhere between Gazala and Grambut in anticipation of the British offensive.

Night still provides protection for the surviving Rangers.

They dare not go back to the beach for fear of drawing

attention to the submarines that are still waiting there.

They make contact with the Arabs and have been provided with safe hiding places by the time German and Italian patrols start to comb the countryside come the dawn.

Pino Bellerini, a sharp-witted Italian *carabiniere*, finds the solution: he has a regular Arab girlfriend, and so he knows the language and the customs of the country.

'For every Englishman you deliver,' he tells his girlfriend and her relatives, 'you get eighty pounds of flour and twenty pounds of sugar.'

That was worth far more to the average Arab than any good words the Senussi chief might have for the English, and by the morning of November 18th almost the entire Ranger team had been captured.

The offensive that follows the big thirst of summer starts with torrential rain in which soldiers actually drown. It is the Tommies' 'Big Push', and it is soon clear that it will not be the decisive battle of the desert war.

At the moment when the Rangers are being rounded up, the man who they were supposed to be kidnapping is in the vanguard of his troops organising a defence against the onrush of a thousand tanks; and within hours he knows that Tripoli is safe.

But it is not only the Desert Fox's military prowess that is becoming the talk of the world; he is also becoming known for his humanitarian acts.

After the attack on Beda Littoria, Hitler issues orders that all the commandos involved in the raid are to be shot. Rommel instructs his aide, Oberleutnant Westphal, to burn the Führer's order without allowing it to become known at headquarters.

Captain Campbell is nursed back to health in a German hospital and Major Keyes is buried in a military cemetery next to his four victims.

It is more than a chivalrous gesture. The fact is that the Desert War was a cruel one, because of the landscape and the nature of the fighting; thousands of human lives were lost in terrible ways, but the men involved did not completely lose sight of humanitarian values. It was not uncommon for men who had just been fighting bitterly to the death to suddenly become jointly involved in a rescue operation. Germans would find themselves being dragged out of the burning wrecks of their vehicles by Englishmen – and vice versa – to be rolled in the sand to extinguish the flames on their clothes.

The report of a British eyewitness is typical of this attitude: 'There is one particularly unpleasant way of ending your days, and that is to be trapped in a tank that explodes and then begins to burn,' writes Hugh Daniel, a dispatch rider attached to a British armoured unit. 'No one who has witnessed it will ever forget that feeling of fear and horror at the screams of men who are trying vainly to escape from their tanks. When a tank caught fire, it didn't matter which side of the line it was on – the crew just had to get out. I don't know of a single case where men, after they had escaped from their tank, were shot down by machine-gun fire. It was enough that they had to face the elements, the sand and the thirst and the hunger, and the fact that they had no vehicle and had to make their way back to base somehow.'

This time the Afrika Korps had to retreat and thus evacuate Cyrenaica again. At Christmas 1941 the Allies recaptured Benghazi, beat off a combined German-Italian counter-offensive and secured a gain in territory of 555 kilometres.

The front line was back at El Agheila, where Rommel had set out for his first offensive. But the Desert Fox had no intention of giving up. He intended to hit back again in January.

His supply lines were now shorter than when he was on the Egyptian border, but the entire issue was still a problem. The supplies had to be brought by sea across the Mediterranean from Sicily and Southern Italy, and the sea was swarming with British bombers and submarines. The rocky island of Malta, a total of 246 square kilometers, dominated the entire 500 kilometre expanse of sea between Sicily and Africa. The side that had Malta could observe everything that happened in the Western Mediterranean, and could send submarines and aircraft to anywhere they were needed. Malta threatened Rommel's desert victories like a running sore which, if it was not surgically removed, would sooner or later lead to infection and death.

Rommel, with his gaze set towards the Suez Canal, at first underestimated the importance of the island fortress and hoped that he could achieve his goal anyway. The Luftwaffe offered to capture the island – as it had Crete – from the air, with a plan codenamed 'Hercules', but for Hitler the cost in blood was too high; added to which, the glory-hungry Italians insisted on overall command of the operation. The problem was that their proud fleet had scarcely ventured into *mare nostro* since the Battle of Matapan at the end of March 1941, in which it had lost three heavy cruisers and two destroyers.

But their German allies demanded Italian convoy escorts, which resulted in frequent and costly clashes with the superior British fleet.

Even the English needed supplies and reinforcements, and their convoys were also bombed and shot up with remorseless determination by German aircraft. Operation 'Felix', which had proposed seizing the English naval base at Gibraltar by a bold surprise attack, had long since been consigned to the archives. Rommel had demanded German U-boats in plenty. By the beginning of 1942, 21 were active in the Mediterranean though five had been lost during the past months.

The German submarines were under orders to torpedo outward bound British supply convoys between the Syrian and African coasts, particularly in the area between the Suez Canal and Tobruk. 'This meant that the U-boats were operating mostly in the Eastern Mediterranean,' writes Karl Alman in his book *Grey Wolves in the Blue Sea*. 'Individual vessels were, however, also sent into the western part, for Malta was also being supplied from the west. Torpedo missions and minelaying expeditions – the latter only in the Eastern Mediterranean – alternated with each other. Both kinds of missions were, however, equally dangerous and often meant heavy loss of life.'

The frequency of fine weather and calm seas, which makes the Mediterranean such a magnet for tourists, is very problematic for U-boats, since it makes it easier for the enemy to locate them and pursue them. So far as the U-boats were concerned, however, any form of attack was made considerably more difficult.

The sending of supplies by sea was slow and dangerous; an initial loss quotient of 15% increased as time passed to 50%, which meant that when the worst happened, every second ship ended up in the realm of the fishes rather than in an African port. The air hop from Italy to the dark continent was quicker but also not without danger. Of 14 aircraft belonging to Combat Squadron 26 that took off from Cosimo in Sicily, three – incompetently guided by Italian ground personnel – collided at the air base in Benghazi and were destroyed.

At first, most of the air traffic to the front was routed via Tripoli. Even fuel had to be brought in by squadrons of Ju 52s and then be transported to the front by truck along with water. The groundcrew, who had to service the desert air bases and protect them from dust and sand, worked under intolerable conditions; temperatures in the cockpits could reach 70° C. In the intense heat, the Jus could only start when they had cooled down somewhat, which meant either in the early morning or the cool of the evening. Once the groundcrew had actually got the aircraft into the air, the pilot and his crew began their suffering. In one combined Ju-87 and fighter-bomber attack on Tobruk, Sergeant Ellis of the RAF shot down three Stukas, one after the other. At this stage, there were still no German fighters in North Africa, but four days later the first Me 109s of Fighter Squadron 27 landed at Ain el Gazala airfield and went into action the very next day.

The battle for North Africa was a war of tanks and aircraft; but panzers, like planes, were huge consumers of petrol and ammunition. For the four divisions of the Afrika Korps, which was soon renamed 'Panzer Army Africa', the sea route remained a lifeline. This once again meant that Rommel, despite all his bravura and verve, must lose North Africa sooner or later if the island fortress of Malta could not be neutralised.

'The supplying of the Afrika Korps with its constant need for provisions, fuel, weapons and munitions was shown to be extremely difficult right from the start,' writes Franz Kurowski in his book *The Afrika Korps*. 'A sea controlled by the enemy lay between the transport convoys' home ports and the African ports. In this sea, the enemy had three flotillas of submarines on active service, all of them very sound and efficient . . .

'A total of 320 tons was reckoned to be the basic need of the 5th Armoured Division alone. Then there was the vital water, some of which had to be shipped in in tankers. To get the 9000 tons necessary every month from the port of Tripoli to the front 630 kilometres away, they would have needed a far greater tonnage than they actually had at their disposal. Each column that drove to Tripoli, loaded up, and then drove back to Arco dei Fileni to dispose of its cargo, needed a total of six days for the journey both ways. This meant that the one column, which the 5th had at its disposal, could only supply 1600 tons instead of the 9000 needed.

'For this reason, a coastal shipping service, using small and even tiny motor barges and launches was quickly organised and expanded. This made things easier. Once the front was taken on to the area of Tobruk and then Bardia, however, the distances grew to 1500 kilometres and more...'

'Rommel was running away from his supplies,' Johannes Steinhoff says. 'In fact, the supply situation was the real Achilles Heel of the Axis' war in North Africa. The chance of taking the island of Malta, however, and thus solving the problem, was never taken.'

Between the toe of the Italian boot and North Africa lay the hell that Rommel's soldiers had to pass through before they were delivered up to the inferno of the desert war.

'Forget it, kid,' says Unteroffizier Grasser to young Moratzky, and stares at the sexy Neapolitan girl as she passes, unable to hide his own hunger. 'Looking is all that you'll get to do.'

'Yeah? Well, it's better than nothing,' mutters the eighteen-year-old private.

Both of them are part of an army flak battery and are waiting to embark for North Africa, passing their time with sun, Marsala wine and hours dreaming of women, always women.

It is August 1941. The hot sun means day-long sweat. The war is in its third year. The radio fanfares are still sounding for the victories. Supplies and reinforcements for the Desert Fox are being readied in Naples. Convoys packed with troops, munitions and vehicles are steaming out of the port almost every day.

'I'll be glad when we get over there and can do some fighting,' says Moratzky with all the wisdom of youth.

'The main thing you'll be fighting with is your digestive system,' says Unteroffizier Grasser, who has done some medical courses and reckons he knows the score.

Quite suddenly, both of them are called on board.

The time has come.

Their ship is a fat old freighter called the *Maddalena Odero*, an Italian vessel displacing 8000 tons. Not exactly a youngster, but the cruise to North Africa is not a long one, and the six-ship convoy had been assigned an equal number of destroyers as its escort.

And so they tramp on board, are squeezed in like sardines in the tin, carrying their lifesavers around their necks. 'Oh, you're from the anti-aircraft crew, are you?' says a Feldwebel from the 21st Division to Unteroffizier Grasser. 'Then you must know the difference between the flak and an old man?'

Neither Moratzky nor Grasser have heard the punchline, which the Feldwebel announces with a loud, booming laugh, 'Well, the flak can't get 'em down and the old boy can't get it up!'

The *Maddalena Odero* is steaming at the head of the convoy. Not because she is the best armed, but because she has the slowest sailing speed. 'And the first shall be last,' quotes Grasser, using – or abusing – the biblical saying.

The sky is blue, the sea is calm.

No problems.

The convoy has just passed the island of Lampedusa – about the size of Helgoland.

'I've no idea why they make such a fuss about this crossing,' says little Moratzky. 'We're as safe as in the bosom of Abraham.'

The air-raid warning comes almost immediately.

English torpedo planes.

They come straight out of the sun and attack from low latitude.

The flak blasts away with all it's got.

But the gentlemen from the enemy side calmly take up their attacking positions, shoot their deadly loads, and curve away out of the ship's anti-aircraft fire.

Seconds later, direct hits blast into the big cargo steamer. The aft section is blown open, the poop hit. The big freighter rocks violently in the waves, without engine power or direction.

'Abandon ship!' The Italian captain bellows an order which is swiftly obeyed.

Hundreds of soldiers are treading water, congratulating themselves on obeying the very order that they had been cursing a few minutes before: the compulsory wearing of lifesavers.

While the other ships of the convoy stubbornly continue on their way, English aircraft return and give the freighter another pasting.

They realise that the *Maddalena Odero* has been abandoned, and with some fairness bank away to avoid endangering the rescue operations. Once the British have gone, the destroyers collect up most of the swimmers and steam on towards Tripoli.

Grasser and his mate Moratzky missed their connection. They are still floundering around in the water along with 50 men from their unit, knowing that they will have to get back on board the freighter for better or for worse.

The *Maddalena Odero* can neither sink nor sail, but her cargo might still be saved. And so during the night of August 18th two destroyers come back and attempt to tow the paralysed cargo ship back to Lampedusa.

The 50 unwilling – and now dry – shipwrecked soldiers stand on the upper deck and pray that the night will last an hour longer.

It is also miraculous when they reach the island still under cover of darkness, just as dawn is about to break. British reconnaissance planes watch them from a great height.

Dry land sits a hundred metres from Unteroffizier Grasser like the promised land, but an idiotic order forbids the 'guests' to go ashore.

So they are forced to await their formal incineration between 200 barrels and two million litres of petrol, plus several waggonloads of munitions of various calibres.

They sprawl on crates of chocolate, stare in disgust at Bavarian beer in cans, salami, jam and biscuits.

'Where the hell are they?' moans little Moratzky anxiously, and keeps glancing at his watch.

Hour after hour goes by.

The enemy reconnaissance aircraft are still circling the motionless ship like vultures keeping watch over a dying animal.

Either the English bombers have found more worthy targets, or they are aware that the 8000-ton monster cannot escape them.

13.00 hours.

The sound of engines and warning sirens seem to merge in one terrifying monotone.

Incredible: just a single bomber.

A four-engined aircraft.

Coming in low.

And not a single piece of flak, or a German fighter.

The Tommies take an airborne stroll to deal death.

Bombs hiss from the bay.

Each one a direct hit.

First the trucks on the upper deck burn. Crew and passengers jump overboard, swim for their lives.

The *Maddalena Odero* is in flames from stem to stern, is burning like a torch.

But still no explosion.

The men of the Army Anti-Aircraft Regiment swim towards the island of Lampedusa with powerful strokes, without knowing that they have just avoided certain death for the second time.

Unteroffizier Grasser is one of the first to reach dry land and shrug of his confusion. He helps other shipwrecked men onto shore, confirms that all 50 men of his unit are safely off the ship.

'Quick!' he bellows to little Moratzky, who is a slow swimmer.

The next moment, an ear-splitting explosion.

The 8000-ton freighter goes up in one huge pillar of flame.

Burning barrels of petrol scatter through the air, smash into the shore, turn it into a sea of flame.

Slivers of panzer armour whizz through the air.

The *Maddalena Odero* no longer exists.

But all her passengers had jumped overboard in time.

Private Moratzky is still a few metres from the shore. His mate Grasser jumps back into the water to haul him ashore.

The boy is unconscious but alive: serious burns.

Hours later, the survivors of the catastrophe are shipped back to Naples.

To help them, recover from the shock – and perhaps also to make up for the stupid and lethal order to stay on board the ship – they are granted fourteen days' special leave.

But little Moratzky gets no leave. For him it is a question of 'see Naples and die'.

He succumbs to his injuries in hospital.

On May 27th 1942, Rommel, after an uncharacteristic wait of four months, continues with his desert offensive. His old trick: two Italian infantry corps – as an 'iron corset', infantry units of the German 90th Light are spread among them – fake a frontal attack.

At 20.30 Rommel – at this time still a Colonel-General – issues the codeword 'Venezia'.

In the northern section, trucks with aircraft engines and propellers mounted on them kick up wind and dust, while in the south of the desert the sand is being kicked up by real panzers.

10,000 vehicles of the German Afrika Korps begin their advance. Five divisions roll through the night, heading south-east. By the next morning, when the glowing fireball that is the sun is forcing sweat, thirst and inhuman temperatures, the spearhead is already moving around the southern tip of Bir Hacheim and turning back north-east.

The 8th Panzer Regiment is the first to hit the enemy. The English resistance is shattered. Now the German spearheads are rolling along the coast towards the fortress of Tobruk.

The 21st Panzer Division is the first to reach Acroma, while panzers from the 90th Light are taking El Adem.

If the 90th succeeds in capturing the desert fort of Bir Hacheim, defended by a garrison of 3400, composed of Free French fighters and a battalion of Jewish volunteers, which sits like a thorn in the side of the German advance, then the English will be stuck in a trap.

Bürger's machine-gun platoon pushes its way down onto the low, long hill. Out of the sandy haze, tongues of tracer fire reach lazily but lethally towards them.

'The spaghetti-eaters are coming from the north,' bellows Oberleutnant Krause, the company commander. 'Make sure we don't fail to make connection!'

The men have reached the first ring of barbed wire.

Private Hermes applies his wirecutters.

The wire comes apart with a metallic clink.

The first men squirm through the hole, and then the machine-gunners on the far side start on them. The enemy fire is coming from small strongpoints on the corners of the defences and covers the entire terrain. Mass-production slaughter.

'Take cover!' yells Feldwebel Bürger.

At last the Italian artillery joins in and turns its fire on the enemy.

The explosions are marked by smoke and cascades of sand.

The night turns light and bloody.

'Watch out!' Hermes calls out as loudly as he dare. Shadows appear and disappear again, nearer each time: French sappers hauling mines into the wire.

A German can't help sneezing; the French drop their mines and hurl themselves to the ground, open fire.

But Bürger and his men had them in their sights before the incident, and the struggle is bloody but brief.

Then Bürger's platoon gets underway, moves quickly across the sand, squirms for a while, then gets to its feet again, hurries onward. They take the pins out of their hand grenades as they run, throw them before they reach the concrete gun emplacement.

The platoon is greeted with massive defensive fire from rapid-fire Oerlikon cannon.

'This is the friggin' end,' oaths one.

'Bürger's platoon will move together... now!' yells the Feldwebel.

They move to their feet, exposing themselves to the enemy fire.

The screams of wounded men to Hermes' left and right. A severed head rolls at his feet like a football. Five or six of his mates have had it, but within a minute or two the attackers have got under the barrels of the rapid-fire cannon and are placing an explosive charge in the bunker wall.

The first Frenchmen come stumbling out with their hands in the air.

Bürger jabs a thumb to the rear.

A thick mass of Frenchmen are pouring out of the main fortress ahead, obviously moving in for a counter-attack. They disappear in the darkness, stumbling through the stink of cordite, make swift progress forward and seem about to cut the German machine-gun platoon off from the rest of the battalion.

A dispatch-runner rushes up to the Feldwebel. 'Order from Battalion HQ!' he pants even before he arrives. 'Return to starting-point!'

'My arse and overboard!' growls Bürger. 'All for friggin' nothing.' He waves to his men to retreat. 'Follow me! We'll have to go through the narrow wadi!'

They don't get far.

Suddenly tall, rangy figures rise out of the landscape. African Spahis.

They fight with long bayonets.

Private Hermes feels a savage blow in his back which nails him to the sand like an iron fist. Crawling on all fours, he tries to continue his escape, but soon he slips into unconsciousness, a night of nothingness.

The desert fortress repels the assault with a hail of death

from hundreds of guns. Shells and bullets rain over the German battalion as it floods back to its own lines. Young Paul Hermes is forgotten in the confusion, and left lying in the sand.

A half-hour later, the Spahis carry him back to the fort's hospital along with their own wounded.

When Hermes comes to a few hours later, he finds himself looking into the pretty face of a young girl who is bending over him; the eyes he sees are dark and big, and they belong to the daughter of a French captain attached to the garrison of Bir Hacheim.

'*J'appelle le médicin*,' she tells him.

The eighteen-year-old German, who has scarcely had time to realise that this war is blood and shit, stares after her as if he has seen an apparition as she calls the doctor from the next ward.

'Hello. Ritchie here,' says the commander of the British 8th Army as he learns that General Koenig, the commander of Bir Hacheim, is on the telephone line. 'How are things with you? Have you shown Jerry where to go?'

'Everything is fine,' answers the general, who after the war will be commander-in-chief of the French occupation forces in Germany. "The Germans took two forward machine-gun emplacements, but they withdrew again after a while. We have ammunition for another four days.'

'Hold on,' Ritchie calls down the line. 'Wait until we have the Desert Fox in the trap. We'll send you 20,000 rounds of anti-aircraft ammunition through the northern corridor. You may have to fight to keep the access free.'

'We'll do that,' the French officer says crisply. 'But the German Stukas will come when it is light.'

'Okay general,' the Englishman answers coolly. 'I'll send out the Royal Air Force. Good luck!'

Two days have passed since Rommels' most recent offensive started, and his forces are still battering uselessly at the gates of the Bir Hacheim. The main thrust of the German armies, which is already behind enemy lines, is seriously threatened with disaster.

On June 1st, the Desert Fox is told that Bir Hacheim cannot be taken.

'Come on – get in the vehicle,' Rommel tells his aides. 'I'll go to the place and take a look for myself.'

It is his style of command. But lethal fire greets him from the mouths of 1200 guns; he has to wait until Kesselring's Stukas can be brought into the battle.

22 aircraft break through the anti-aircraft curtain, circle over the fortress. Their Jericho-sirens howl over the besieged French. One plane dives, releases its bomb load very low. One wing is torn off by the force of the plane's own bombs. The Stuka drops like a stone and explodes on impact.

The other aircraft leave substantial holes in the fortress's defences, but very quickly thc Spitfires appear and move determinedly in for the kill.

Dog-fights over the fortress.

Before Rommel's eyes, the Spitfires shoot down one Stuka after another. The Ju 87s float like weary butterflies to earth.

Losses: nine Stukas.

A few hours later, Field Marshal Kesselring lands in his personal He 111.

'Rommel,' he says angrily. 'This can't go on. You'll have to take this goddamned hole with land forces.'

As if the Desert Fox hadn't already tried that!

He gets all the artillery he can together in an attempt to blast his way through the network of concrete turrets and bunkers. But when the attack gets under way, it grinds to a bloody halt just like every other one has.

The burst of machine-gun and tracer fire criss-cross the sand inexorably, and the attackers find themselves pinned down yet again. Faced with the death-defying courage of the defenders, Rommel is bleeding to death.

On the morning of June 8th, dawn brings thick mist as artillery and sappers prepare for another attack over the flat, coverless terrain. German sappers have cleared a corridor through the mine field, but before guns can be brought through to threaten the defences, the French regroup and pin down the gunners.

The two infantry companies promised get nowhere, and Rommel, who watches the assault from a foxhole fifty metres from his command post, sends them back.

The Desert Fox decides to send in Special Unit 288 under Oberst Menton, a commando group that had been put together for a special mission in Iraq.

Again the sappers clear a path through the mines, but every time one explodes and kills a few Germans, the French spot the attack direction and cut the assault group to pieces.

Nevertheless, their position is becoming more and more desperate.

General Koenig radios for help.

The British commander sends fighter-bombers that shoot rockets at anything on the ground that moves.

But the German attack is gradually gaining ground - despite the fact that in the space of a few minutes the French shoot up eleven German panzers.

By the evening, the German sappers have pushed forward to within 500 metres of the main fort. Mountain troops - who instead of fighting in the snows of Russia were sent to North Africa, of all places - overwhelm a network of trenches defended by Jewish volunteers.

The rest will be dealt with the next day by the Stukas.

At last they roar towards the fortress.

Bir Hacheim's skies are turned into a blanket of flame.

By the evening of June 10th, the German assault force has penetrated deep inside the enemy's defensive system and is fighting from bunker to bunker. In the process they take a prisoner who betrays a secret plan: while English tanks move towards the fortress, the place's defenders will break out of Bir Hacheim under cover of darkness.

The informant can even tell them where the corridor goes through the mine field.

While the garrison is making its preparations for the breakout, German artillery and anti-tank guns are moving into position to cut off their route to safety.

The fleeing French will run straight into the barrels of the German guns.

Shortly after midnight, the armoured spearhead of the breakout starts up engines.

The defenders use up their last smoke bombs. But the skies are suddenly alive with white and green flares, throwing a deadly, clear light over the terrain and showing the German guns and observers their targets: a long column of vehicles.

Bitter fighting in the corridor through the mines, finally man against man.

Quarter was given - but not taken.

By the time daylight comes, Bir Hacheim has fallen.

Anyone who can still walk tries to escape.

In the hospital wards, the German conquerors find 500 wounded, plus one doctor and some orderlies.

Only later do they realise that half of the garrison actually succeeded in breaking through to the rescuing English tanks.

But the southern cornerstone of the British defensive line has fallen, and so Rommel's last offensive can roll onwards. On June 21st, the Desert Fox takes the bloodily disputed port of Tobruk; in the process, he takes more than 32,000 prisoners and is promoted to Field Marshal. His next objectives are El Alamein, Alexandria, the Nile Estuary and Cairo.

Rommel is 100 kilometres west of Alexandria. The mass of his panzers is so battered as to be no longer combatworthy. The German-Italian air forces in the desert are hopelessly outnumbered.

JG 27, the desert fighter squadron, is a sort of travelling circus. Constantly threatened by fuel shortages, it always maintains its base as close as possible to the front line. When the pilots return from their ceaseless combat missions, they are threatened not only by hepatitis, malaria and hordes of flies, but also by British sabotage units that operate behind the lines, constantly attacking the improvised airstrips. Nevertheless, the pilots produce combat kills like they were going out of fashion.

Field Marshal Kesselring appears, unannounced, fresh from his headquarters in Rome, for an inspection. As is his custom, he watches a fighter flight landing. A young man wearing white tennis shoes and white socks clambers down from the cockpit, recognises the C-in-C South, goes up to him and says, 'I report to the Field Marshal twelve kills by my flight.'

'And how many are yours, Marseille?'

'All, Field Marshal.'

Kesselring offers him his hand, then sits down and stares wordlessly into the sand. The report has completely robbed him of the power of speech.

The propaganda machine has long since raised twenty-two-year-old Hans-Joachim Marseille, the 'unequalled virtuoso among the fighter pilots' (Adolf Galland) to the status of a popular idol with its vulgar description of him as the 'star of Africa'. The sharp, good-looking young Berliner came from a Hugenot family of French protestant descent, and if there had been no St Bartholomew's massacre would have probably been fighting on the other side.

Marseille was the son of a general, and this was probably the only reason that he wasn't transferred to the infantry at a very early date, for his early flying career was a catalogue of disasters and offences against 'good order and discipline in the air': he carried out mock attacks on farmworkers, landed on autobahns, once fired a burst of machine-gun fire in a neat line in front of his commander's tent as a kind of morning greeting. The then ensign was shot down four times during the French campaign, but achieved seven air victories himself. He was transferred to the desert and managed to ditch one aircraft even during the flight over. Even when he got there, he seemed to end up putting one plane after another in the sand.

When flying back from the front he would play at attacking the other Messerschmitts – provided he had enough fuel. Afterwards he would sit in his tent, talk with no one, and play with a new tactical concept that didn't give a hoot for the rules laid down at flying school. His aim was not to come at his opponent out of the sun and from altitude, but from any position.

Marseille quickly moved from theory to practice: during air battles he would fly with the landing flaps out, to cut his speed. He would open fire while climbing, while diving, while banking, even from an upside-down position. The progress of his suicide runs could be followed from the ground by watching the vapour trails that his 'Yellow 14', long known to friend and foe alike, traced crazily through the air. This untrammelled individualist, swinging between the military hall of fame and the court martial, became the fighter pilot whom experts on both sides see as the most successful of the Second World War.

Hans-Joachim Marseille became the smiling hero who collected love-letters by the bucketful and yet who was also a flat contradiction of hard-headed militarism. His fellow pilots, who were supposed to cover his flank, were dubbed 'the flying statisticians'. They had been given the job of confirming the victories chalked up by the Luftwaffe's youngest Hauptmann, and the statistics rapidly became unreal – 60, 70 and on to 100 aerial victories. On the path to his tent stood a sign with the message: 'To the best fighter squadron in the world'.

Marseille goes back into combat again and again. He

expects at least two kills per mission these days. On September 1st between 8.00 and 8.39 he shoots down two Curtises and two Spitfires, and in the second mission late that afternoon, in a space of ten minutes between Alam El Halfa, he downs eight Curtises, and in a third mission between 17.47 and 17.53 five more. The propaganda reports went through the German press under the colourful caption: 'One Man's Private Battle', and Marseille was awarded the Knight's Cross with diamonds.

'I immediately sensed the powerful effect of Marseille's charm and natural talent for leadership,' his general reported. 'We talked together well into the night. At the end of our talk, I mentioned the fact that I needed to fulfil an important call of nature before I had my nightcap and went to bed. Marseille immediately acquired a small spade and said, "Go straight ahead for sixty paces when you get out of the tent, then twenty paces to the right, and use the spade, Herr General." I obediently followed his instructions. In the morning when I awoke I left my tent to use the spade again. I was astonished to find that there were now signs showing the way. The last sign had an arrow point downwards with the notice: "At this point on September 22nd, the General of Fighter Forces answered the call of nature."'

During the month of September 1942, Hauptmann Marseille won 57 victories in the air. His last battle lasted ten minutes. Then he flew a mission without making contact with the enemy. 'At 11.22 the formation turned to begin its flight back to Fuka,' writes Karl-Ludwig Opitz in his description of this unique fighter ace's last moments. 'Marseille was flying a brand-new Me 109F, also marked with the yellow number 14. At 11.32 Marseille called up on the radio, "Elbe One! I have smoke coming out of the crate and I can hardly see!"'

Feldwebel Poettgen and Marseille's other comrades flew in close to 'Yellow 14' and Poettgen gave Marseille some information to correct his course. 'Just hold more to the right. Keep it up.'

'I can't see anything!' Marseille yelled, coughed. His ME 109F was smoking badly.

'Just three minutes to go to Alamein!' Poettgen told him.

When they got there, they would be beyond the British positions and Marseille would be able to bale out.

'I'll have to get out here!' Marseille panted into the radio mike.

The small white mosque of Sidi Abd El Rahman was already in sight. And now Marseille put his Messerschmitt into a flip. Feldwebel Poettgen left the formation and curved off to the left. He saw the cockpit cover fly away from 'Yellow 14'. Marseille fell from the cockpit, hit a piece of the superstructure and dropped like a stone. Poettgen saw him hit the ground and lie still.

The English author and World War Two fighter pilot Edward H. Sims writes in his book *Great Enemies*: 'His comrades suffered terribly from the shock, and his death affected the entire Luftwaffe in North Africa, so convinced had it become of his invincibility. His list of successes in North Africa included 101 Curtis Tomahawks and Kittyhawks, 30 Hurricanes, 16 Spitfires and 4 bombers. Thus with the exception of four aircraft, his kill total was all fighters. Higher kill totals would only be attained in the East, but Marseille's achievement would never be equalled by any other fighter pilot in action against the Western powers, even though he died more than two-and-a-half years before the end of the war. And his achievement of downing 17 aircraft in one day was exceeded only by one other German (Hauptmann Emil Lang shot down 18 Russian aircraft in one day on the Russian front).

'Today we can say that Marseille attained mastery of the swift surprise attack and of an almost scientific perfection in gunnery on the move – and to an extent that was very rarely achieved in aerial combat afterwards.'

The 'star of Africa' met his end on his 83rd mission, after 158 kills, on 30th September, and within three weeks Erwin Rommel's star was also on the wane. The machine of victory was simply refusing to work. On October 23rd, General Bernard Montgomery, a puritan who doesn't drink or smoke, and whose first act with his troops is to make himself ridiculous by a talk on VD, begins a counter-offensive.

'During the moonlit night of 23rd October 1942 at 21.40, 1200 guns of the British 8th Army open up the offensive on the Alamein Front,' wrote Janusz Piekalkiewicz in his book *Air War*. 'The German-Italian air forces have 129 bombers, 65 Stukas, 55 fighter-bombers and 123 fighters. Montgomery, on the other side, has 1500 aircraft – of which 1,200 are stationed in Egypt or Palestine. Within two-and-a-half hours, more than 80 tons of bomb are dropped on Rommel's route of advance and the planned German counter-attacks foiled.'

Honig's Company, twice decimated and brought back up to strength, is back on the retreat, with repaired Italian vehicles and some British vehicles captured in the previous months' fighting.

Corporal Giraff enthusiastically eats warm canned sardines in oil, because hepatitis is just as good as a nice limb wound to get you sent home. Then he grills a scorpion with his cigarette-lighter, and Corporal Prinz watches approvingly.

Little Muggelbauer is no longer with them. He had a harmless bullet wound - except that combined with it was a dose of tetanus. They needed no grave digging for Corporal Korbetzki: he stepped on a mine.

Honig's company is soon overtaken. The Hauptmann is killed. Corporal Giraff will never eat any more sardines: a direct hit. A few men escape onto a vehicle belonging to another company, including Corporal Prinz. Flesh wound in the upper thigh, bullet lodged in the chest.

Somewhere his comrades dump him at a field dressing station. He has pink foam on his lips. His rib cage is burning as if he was being tortured with hot coals. A few orderlies are working like madmen. Bandages are running out, no more morphine.

Outside there is the boom of the artillery. The little tent shakes from the shells landing close by. When the explosions stop, you can hear the wounded men screaming - and that's when you wish the fighting would start up again.

After a short bout of unconsciousness, Prinz comes to his senses again and sees the orderlies bringing in Italian red wine mixed with anti-neuralgia tablets, instead of an anaesthetic.

'Drink, you lot!' they shout. 'Drink whatever you can get down you!'

The corporal watches everything, wide awake, including the way the junior MO knocks men unconscious with a little hammer if they haven't already fainted from the pain.

Two other men in front of him. Then it is his turn. But he never gets that far.

Soldiers wearing flat helmets and with machine guns slung around their necks push their way into the tent, grin, nod, and go back outside.

Before an English MO administers a morphine injection twenty minutes later, Prinz, the beer baron, understands through his haze that for him the war is over.

For the rest of the Afrika Korps it goes on. 'The skeletons of German soldiers can be found all over the desert,' writes Hans Gert von Esebeck. 'Many generals and commanders lie next to their men under a pile of rocks, above which the wind sings its pale mourning and the sand is heaped. It was like a miracle, the way the desert suddenly came to life again. Vehicles appeared, British trucks, German guns, American tanks, with a handful of German soldiers, burned brown by the sun, worn down by the strains of the last weeks, a crazy bunch with their officers and their Marshal, a bunch who turned everything on its head, turned to face the enemy, held him up, hurt him and then disappeared back into the void . . .'

On November 13th the British recapture Tobruk, on the 17th Derna and on November 20th Benghazi. On the 7th November, British and American troops land in Morocco and Algeria from a fleet of 500 ships in 'Operation Torch' and thus stab Rommel in the back. The Desert Fox had always warned his Italian and German superiors that without a long-term solution to the supply problem Panzer Army Africa was doomed.

'The sins for which Berlin and Rome were responsible,' writes Hans Gert von Esebeck, 'were not just the serious errors for which the Army Group in Africa had to pay the price. They also involved an inability to realise – or a lack of desire to realise – that when Germany took on a highly-industrialised and rich world in a long war, she must inevitably lose.'

Half Time - And a Glimpse of Armageddon

As in 1942 the Second World War approached its halfway point, there were unmistakable signs that, despite the constant opening up of new theatres of war, the German homeland would soon also be turned into a battlefield. The rush of 'lightning victories' was over. Anyone who could read between the lines was aware that the military position was far worse than the official version would admit.

Setbacks and casualties could no longer be hidden. In the daily newspapers, even the obituary notices were uniform. Special bureaux were established in the local *Gau* offices of the Nazi Party which ensured that all war obituaries would be alike and therefore harmless. And so there was the monotonous repetition of the fact that so-and-so had fallen for 'folk, Führer and fatherland', while mothers and other surviving relatives were without exception 'in deep, yet proud mourning'. And yet it was those very sanitised individuals who were beginning to curse the dictator who had brought this suffering upon them and their families.

They were just the vanguard - most Germans were still held in suspicion by the brainwashing techniques of the Reich Radio and the Goebbels-controlled press.

'Perhaps 1942 is the last year of the war in which Germans felt no self pity - in which they were still calm and composed, even though happiness had long since left their calculations,' states Wolfgang Paul in his book *The Home Front War*. 'They did not know the full extent of what Hitler had brought upon them. They still did not have to excuse their ignorance of horrific, secret projects, but neither were they capable of releasing themselves from an entanglement that had dragged them willy-nilly into one of the most perilous undertakings in the history of the world.

'Most of them had still not given up the war for lost. They hoped for some favourable conclusion to the war that had already meant so much sacrifice for them.

'This hope was brave and foolish, and the sceptics among them preferred to keep their mouths shut rather than be denounced as 'defeatists' and risk the death penalty. Or they would plunge themselves blindly into the pleasures of the flesh, to buy themselves a few hours free of fear and worry. With the turning-point at the front the slogan began to appear: "Enjoy the war – the peace will be terrible."'

The American journalist John Gunther, who lived in Germany right up until Hitler's declaration of war on the USA, wrote; 'One thing really surprises me. The night clubs, the bars and wine shops are filled to overflowing. The streets are blacked out, yet inside the bars and cafés the lights are dazzling. People no longer care about saving money. The night life of Cologne is more impressive than Montmartre.'

Nevertheless, the writing on the wall is becoming so clear that few can overlook it. Indications, be they great or small, comic or tragic, all point to the fact that the Wehrmacht has conquered its way to a standstill and that the tide is turning. The Agriculture Ministry, for instance, recommended that bread no longer be put in bread bins, since it first had to dry out after purchase. In April '42, the food rations were cut: in future the average consumer was permitted only 200 grams of meat, 206 grams of fat and 2000 grams of bread. Inns and restaurants were instructed to only serve one-pot stews based on Wehrmacht recipes for two days in the week. Women and girls were only permitted a cigarette allowance between the ages of 25 and 55; anyone who exceeded this age only got her share of nicotine if she had a husband or son serving at the front. The introduction of tobacco rationing was the first public admission of the great cigarette shortage. The rural population which had not, in the past, enjoyed tobacco in large numbers, now used cigarettes as articles of barter.

From now on, annual vacations had to be officially entered on an individual's clothing coupon, to prevent civilian members of the 'folk community' from taking their ease twice in the same year. To save paper, it was officially suggested that people use the reverse of the original letter as a copy of any answering communications. There were now 1000 shoe exchanges in the Reich, and death duties had been abolished for the heirs of those killed in action. The Wehrmacht High Command stipulated that the last surviving son of any family that had already lost several members in action would be withdrawn from the front line and made to serve as a soldier only in the Home Reserve Army. The state had also established a special 'Racial-Hygienic Marriage Bureau' in Leipzig for maimed and crippled war casualties and for war blinded men.

The air raid warnings howled in the city streets with increasing frequency as the year wore on. The main cost to the civilian population was still a good night's sleep, but as early as November 1941 the Potsdamer Station in Berlin had been destroyed by fire during a raid, and the new British 1800 kilo bomb had been given its bloody première on a big apartment block in the Pariser Platz.

A hundred dead were buried under the ruins of the shattered building.

It was to be expected that the British would seize the chance presented by the transfer of almost all the Luftwaffe units previously engaged in the Battle of Britain to the Russian front. The RAF was quick to exploit its opportunity; the Luftwaffe was now on the defensive. Attackers and defenders alike continued to explore their technical and military possibilities, and each innovation turned up the screw of horror a notch more.

The German civilian population still had no notion of what it would face once the Americans became involved in the air war. President Roosevelt had just been granted a credit of 17.5 billion dollars for the construction of 148,000 aircraft – for the first two years of the war alone. And the German anti-aircraft batteries and night fighters could hardly cope with the English bombing raids.

'When the Luftwaffe High Command was still considering it could hold the British in check with fighters alone,' writes Franz Kurowski in his book *The Air War over Germany*, 'they were still thinking in terms of the sporadic bombing by the British during 1939/40. The existing forces of fighters and night fighters had been able to match the British when the raids were on that limited scale. But in comparison with England, Germany presented a large and vulnerable target, and there was no chance that Germany's fighters could achieve the kind of miracle that the RAF's aces had produced over the fields of Southern England during the Battle of Britain. It was simply not possible to cover every part of Germany that could be reached by enemy aircraft with enough flak and fighters to provide real protection from the enemy's bombs. The RAF, who knew this only too well, created a system of clever feint flights that drew the German defences and ensured worry-free flights into the Reich for the real bombing forces.

'Thus the number of British raids increased considerably after the withdrawal of German aircraft from the English Channel. While German fighters were battling in the skies over Crete and North Africa, in the East and South-East, while German Stukas were screaming in to the attack on the Russian Fleet at anchor in the Bay of Kronstadt and German bombers were finding their targets in the endless plains of Russia, the Royal Air Force had only one aim in mind: to fly to Germany, to attack Germany, and to hit the lifelines of the German people.'

British bombers flew into the Reich in greater and greater numbers to attack German cities, but these were still more for reasons of prestige and propaganda than systematic destruction. And, just as the Germans had over England, the British paid for their pleasure with high losses, even though the numbers cited in the Wehrmacht communiqués were notoriously exaggerated.

Navigation was often left to chance; the weather forecasts were a lottery with plenty of losers. Half-trained crews were thrown into the battle, shot each other up by accident, were responsible for mass collisions in mid-air and for collisions on take-off and landing. Also, the German long-distance night fighters proved a very effective weapon: they attacked their opponents during difficult night take-offs over their own bases, while they were at their most vulnerable.

But the British soon caught up. The new 'Gee' navigational aid was being given operational tests, and the armaments industry was starting to supply the first four-engined bombers, including the Lancaster, which was equipped with Rolls Royce Merlin engines that gave it an airspeed of 335 kilometres and could carry 6.25 tons of bombs up to 2600 kilometres.

The first two squadrons of this type of aircraft had been ready for active service. And if the Lancaster was the most successful bomber yet produced, the Stirling, also a four-engined aircraft, proved to be downright indestructible. 'In a collision with a German night fighter at this time,' writes Alastair Revie in his history of Bomber Command, 'a Stirling of 75th Squadron had four feet sliced off her right wing, a great hole torn in her tail, and a part of the tailplane ripped away. The aircraft flew on, dropped her bombs on the target, and five hours later landed safely at her home base.'

Lord Cherwell, scientific adviser to the British government, wrote a memorandum during this period in which he stated that one ton of bombs made 100-200 human beings homeless; this cold-blooded calculation continued to work out that the average life-expectancy of a bomber crew could not exceed fourteen missions. And, in fact, in the coming years it was statistically proved that every tenth mission would be one-way – but in the meantime, each bomber crew would have dropped 40 tons of bombs and this made around 60,000 Germans homeless. 22 million Germans lived in 58 cities and towns within the operational reach of the British bombers.

It was an invitation to a dance of death, but first the RAF had to attempt to break through the increasingly effective German defensive screen, the 'West Wall in the Sky', as the night fighter chief Oberst Joseph Kammhuber dubbed his forces' efforts.

'These defences had already proved their effectiveness,' states Eric Taylor in his book *The Thousand-Bomber Raid on Cologne*. 'In short, the system worked by giving each night fighter certain distinct areas of airspace, in which it would engage enemy aircraft in individual combat when British bombers approached en masse. Some 700 fighters worked hand in hand with a chain of 1500 radar stations and six regiments of searchlight units. The concept for this defensive system had been dreamed up by Oberst Joseph Kammhuber. The night visitors would be exposed to the attentions of his night fighters and flak batteries by thousands of searchlights probing the darkness for bombers. In order that his own aircraft were not subjected to attack from their own guns, their own sections of airspace were protected either by flak alone or by other fighters. This system proved to be highly effective, to such an extent that by the end of 1941 it was becoming increasingly difficult for the RAF's planes to enter the brightly-lit skies over Northern Germany without risking punishment for their boldness.

'In the autumn of 1941, Kammhuber, who had meanwhile been promoted to general, added to his searchlight screen with the introduction of a new radio-location instrument codenamed *Würzburg*, which could not only ascertain an attacker's direction and distance with great accuracy, but could even estimate his altitude. The fighters of the German Luftwaffe thus reached the peak of their operational efficiency just when it was most urgently needed.'

The British losses became intolerable; the 'sky bed' – as Kammhuber's defensive system was nicknamed on the German side – was a death bed so far as many enemy aircrews were concerned. The RAF quickly realised that the new *Würzburg* equipment was at the heart of the German air defence network. In order to render a weapon ineffective, one must first understand it. This forced the RAF to plan one of those insane operations which, if it failed, would simply disappear from the record, but if it succeeded would reap heroes and decorations aplenty. The mission was given the cover name 'Operation Biting'.

As a first step, a *Würzburg* installation was located on the French coast, atop some cliffs near the village of Bruneval, twenty kilometres north-west of Le Havre. The daredevil Spitfire pilot Tony Hill flew low over the radar station and returned from his near-suicide mission with some crucial photographs. The radar expert Professor R.V. Jones found differences from previous German radar installations in the enlargements. From the air, *Würzburg* looked like a huge, overgrown electric bowl-fire.

The British asked the French Resistance for as much information as possible about Bruneval and its environs, about the way the installation was housed and guarded, and for the architectural plans of the requisitioned villa in which the crew who operated the radar system had their quarters.

London decided to seize the German radar installation by a surprise attack and to 'kidnap' the 'huge bowl-fire' and take it back to England. I.D. Frost, a twenty-four-year-old major in the Parachute Regiment, was ordered to take 119 men, including radar experts, and to jump into Bruneval; he was then to bring the apparatus, if possible with living members of its crew, back to England.

'On the evening of February 27th 1942, twelve Whitley bombers set off from the airfield at Thruxton,' reports Janusz Piekalkiewicz. 'Twelve soldiers were crouched in each plane complete with their parachutes, and as the flight got under way they began to blacken their faces with greasepaint. Major Frost jumped first. Not a shot was fired; the Englishmen surrounded the radar installation and stormed into the isolated villa.

'The entire operation ran like clockwork, the result of endless, minutely detailed practise on a totally authentic model; plus the luck that followed Frost and his men. The Germans tried vainly to blow up the *Würzburg* apparatus. Their explosives and the fuses were, however, stored separately for safety reasons, and they failed to get them together in time. The Germans' own guard detail was in the middle of a night exercise and before it could take part in the action they had to swap the blanks in their weapons for real bullets.

'Meanwhile, the specialists had photographed the *Würzburg* and were in the process of taking the equipment to pieces. In their excitement, they sawed some parts up. It was only when they reached England that they realised the entire apparatus could be taken apart easily by hand. After they had fought their way through to the beach, they had a few minutes to wait in apprehension until the boats came. They had to leave behind a dead paratrooper and seven others who could not get to the beach in time.

'The most important result of the mission: the electromagnetic core of the machine, plus the frequency-selection parts, and several prisoners . . . Now Jones was able not only to work out which frequencies the apparatus operated on, but also he made the important discovery that once one frequency had been put out of action by jamming, it could not be switched onto another.'

It was just the right welcome present for Air Marshal Arthur T. Harris, previously in charge of the RAF Delegation in Washington, who was nominated overnight as new commander of Bomber Command and who walked into his headquarters with the words; 'Let us put an end to war – by bombing the life out the Germans.'

This experienced officer, with his small eyes, his big moustache, his high forehead, slightly protuberant ears, and a brow permanently knitted in pedantic exasperation, had made a name for himself in several colonial wars during the thirties by his ruthless use of bombers against rebels in Iraq and India.

'As soon as he took up his command,' says Janusz Piekalkiewicz, 'Harris emphasised that the only international convention to which he and his officers felt themselves bound was an agreement dating from the Franco-Prussian War of 1870/71 which forbade the dropping of explosives from gas-filled airships. And, in fact, this limitation was strictly adhered to by Bomber Command throughout the Second World War.'

When the new commander-in-chief had established himself at his headquarters in the woods near High Wycombe in Buckinghamshire, he stated; 'Perhaps there will come a day when every bomb can be scientifically aimed, but until we have reached that stage, we shall send over floods of bombers that will demolish Schickelgruber's houses and demoralise his workers.'

'Harris was the right man at the right time,' writes Alastair Revie. 'Yet again, the British had shown their tendency to muddle through somehow, in order to then – when it is almost too late – produce a leader out of a hat as if by magic . . . In any case, the will to fight on was intensified by having someone "at the top" who personified that determination.'

Harris's appointment meant the opening up of a new front – over Germany, Hitler's home front, and the first city to be put through the fire was Lübeck, with its mediaeval half-timbered buildings. On the night of March 18th 1942, the old Hanseatic city was attacked by 230 bombers, whose experienced crews dropped their bombs with expert precision. The beginners who followed them only need to glimpse the fires, which were visible from 80 kilometres away, to find their way to the target – and drop 144 tons of incendiary bombs and 160 tons of explosive bombs. Thirteen bombers were lost, including five through navigational errors.

Lübeck was the first German city to be 'coventryfied'. 2000 homes were destroyed. Cement works, canning factories, warehouses and the railway station were damaged. The Gothic city hall and the Marienkirche church, which dated back to the 12th century, were also reduced to ruins during the course of that night.

'Harris had taken an awesome responsibility on to himself,' comments Alastair Revie. 'But his plan to work with "carpet bombing" seemed to give the results Britain needed. At any rate, the raid on Lübeck was reckoned a success – especially in terms of prestige and propaganda. It showed the German people some of the horrors that other people had suffered from their own Luftwaffe. And for the first time in this war, an attack by Bomber Command on a German city had unleashed a sense of shock not just in the immediate locality but in the highest quarters in Berlin. Goebbels broke off from his tirades about the million starving Russians and screamed hungrily for revenge. Hitler was enraged, and immediately instructed the Luftwaffe to carry out a series of heavy raids – as early as that same April – on similar cities in England (all the ones that were included in Baedeker's guide), starting with Canterbury, Exeter, Norwich and York. 90 bombers had to be withdrawn from Sicily for this purpose. These raids had to be stopped quite soon afterwards, though the British cities concerned had been seriously damaged. When the German bombers had dropped some 2000 tons of bombs, it was decided that they were more urgently required on the Eastern Front and in the Mediterranean.'

The new commander-in-chief of Bomber Command, who will earn the nickname 'Bomber Harris' – and even 'Butcher Harris' – described the raid on Lübeck as 'just a sample' of what he intended. In his first attempt at 'area bombing', he had lost fewer planes than expected; he staged a further series of raids between April 24th and April 27th, in which 468 bombers dropped 442 tons of explosives and 359 tons of incendiaries in the course of four night attacks on residential areas of the city of Rostock. 60% of the old city burned out; 204 lay dead beneath the ruins, 89 seriously injured civilians had to be hospitalised, and 100,000 out of 123,000 inhabitants, most of whom had become homeless, had to be evacuated. And Bomber Command had once again lost only twelve bombers.

Bomber Harris found no opposition when he maintained that his mass bomber raids were the only effective antidote to Kammhuber's 'West Wall in the Sky'.

It was the old principle on which the success of Woolworth had been founded: it's all a matter of quantity. The only question was how the new Air Marshal was going to get the quantity as, buoyed up by the successful raids on Lübeck and Rostock, he suggested to Prime Minister Churchill that they attack a German city – Hamburg or Cologne – with a force of more than 1000 aircraft. So far as the British political leader was concerned, Harris's plan for 'Operation Millennium' – so called in mocking reference to the 'Thousand-Year Reich' – were pushing at an open door.

'And where will you get your thousand bombers?' asked the Prime Minister.

'I shall have to scrounge them,' answered Bomber Harris solemnly.

It was a near-impossible undertaking. Quite differently from Germany, in Britain not all aircraft were gathered under the same command in the same service, the RAF. The coastguard service and the navy had their own aircraft and were disinclined to use them for anything but their own purposes, the guarding of the coastline and the protection of convoys. Churchill was forced to intervene personally. Despite his involvement, the navy, for example, withdrew permission at the last moment for Harris to borrow 250 of its planes for his 'Millennium' raid.

Nevertheless the Air Marshal got his way. To attain his magical total, he combed the flying schools and transport squadrons, 'confiscated' half-trained pilots, brought veterans back into service, stole aircraft whose paint was hardly dry and had not yet completed the statutory number of air trials. According to his own calculations, one aircraft in ten would fail to return. With 1046 aircraft in his makeshift armada, that made a total of 104 anticipated losses.

A high price, but even if the lives of 104 crews were involved, war also is decided according to the law of supply and demand. The boss of Bomber Command had his vision of Cologne in flames and a crippling blow to the German air defence effort as the results of his conjuring up 1000 bombers.

High Wycombe's pessimistic estimates had to be revised upwards even before the raid started, for with all those flying cuckoos landing at 52 separate airfields there were a considerable number of collisions and cases of damage to landing gear.

A further element of risk was the weather. There were no such things as meteorological satellites, and the information gathered by special weather flights was often out of date by the time the aircraft landed. Of necessity, most weather forecasts were guesses. Bad weather and cloud cover was forecast for Germany on the day of the raid, although better weather was said to be approaching south of the Ruhr Area.

Air Marshal Harris had to act; he could not hold his borrowed armada together for much longer. On May 31st at 12.10, he issued the coded order for 'Millennium'. The aircraft were armed and refuelled. By 18.00 they were all cleared for take-off. It was now that the squadron commanders concerned were told their target: the industrial city of Cologne and its residential areas, easily seen in the moonlight and instantly identifiable from the twin spires of its cathedral, with a population of some 700,000.

The first part of this greatest air raid in this most brutal of wars was a feint: fifty fighter-bombers thoroughly confused the 'Sky bed' over Belgium, Holland, Northern France and Germany, including the Mosquito, 'the wooden wonder', which was being exposed to the enemy for the first time. This most interesting aircraft of the war had been a still-born child that no one wanted, because none of the experts believed that it would be possible to build a long-distance bomber - also usable as reconnaissance plane, pathfinder and night fighter - which could outrun enemy fighters. The aircraft designer and maker Geoffrey de Havilland built just such a plane behind the bureaucrats' backs at his own expense, and came up with an exceptionally light and manoeuvrable bomber that could attain an airspeed of 640 kilometres per hour. He showed it to Air Marshal Harris, who was delighted - and the German night fighters, who found themselves chasing a phantom built of wood, were despairing.

Shortly after midnight, the sirens began to howl in Cologne. It was the city's 295th air raid warning of the war, and the 115th bomb attack. Since enemy aircraft had previously only inflicted slight damage, many of the city's inhabitants simply turned over and went back to sleep, before the first bombs began to go off and sent them scurrying down to their air raid shelters in the cellars.

Everything happened with lightning speed. The duel between the flak and the British bombers was lit by the burning rows of streets below. The first wave of enemy bombers, 100 Wellingtons, was only armed with incendiary canisters. The raid began at 0.55. It was planned to last 90 minutes, during which 2000 tons of high-explosive and incendiary bombs would 'pulverise' the ancient Roman City and stronghold of carnival and fun.

The railway station in Mülheim was on fire; flames were pouring from the post office in Braunsfeld. The separate fires were sucked toward each other until they merged into a huge sea of flame that consumed the entire old city, and moved on into the suburbs. Water mains burst, fire fighting teams had to watch in horror as entire rows of streets burned like matchwood. Finally they were forced to put together a kilometre-long water pipeline from the Rhine to their firefighting equipment, but it was immediately torn apart by the collapse of a tenement block halfway between the river and the main fire.

Human beings suffocated in the cellars, were crushed by bursting walls. Children wandered in a daze through the burning streets, looking for their mothers. An air raid warden stumbled over a boot which still contained a foot; when they dug for the rest of the corpse, they found that it had been 'pulverised'. A clerk found his wife lying dead on the pavement with her brains spread over the slabs of stone.

All the telephone lines were cut. The southern spire of the St Gereon Church, founded in the fourth century by the Roman Empress Helena, was on fire. The bells fell to the ground with a huge clang. Pastor Brenner tried to find some volunteers to help save the north tower. He appealed to the firefighters. A local Nazi boss dismissed him with the words; 'Ach, what do we need with churches?' Teenagers climbed up a rope to the top of the tower, hauled up buckets of water and prevented the flames from spreading, even though the façades all around were on fire.

Air Vice-Marshal J.E.A. Baldwin, who accompanied the attack in a Stirling bomber, reports: 'The sky was full of aircraft on their way to Cologne. I could make out Wellingtons, Hampdens, a Whitley and some other Stirlings. Shortly before we arrived over the city, we deviated for a minute to locate the most suitable approach. During the manoeuvre I could clearly see the two spires of the cathedral, which were visible above the area of fire. Then we approached to drop our bombs, accompanied to starboard by a Wellington and astern by another Stirling. As we turned away, we flew around the flak curtain and eight minutes after dropping our bombs were on course for home. We looked back once more. The fires were like rising suns against the dark background. The further we flew from Cologne, the stronger this impression became. When the thin beams of the anti-aircraft searchlights became visible, it seemed to us as if we were leaving behind us a huge copy of the Japanese flag. Some nine minutes' flying time from the coast, we turned once more briefly, to take a last look. A vast volcano seemed to have become active in the distance.'

The third wave attacked. 5000 individual fires joined to make up 2000 great balls of fire. Almost 20,000 homes were destroyed. Plus 2135 workshops and 106 industrial plants. 'Millennium' was the beginning of the genocide from the air. Pure terror was now the aim of the air war, in this first night that this dance of death was celebrated it cost 469 dead and

5027 injured as well as a large number of irreplacable cultural treasures. Some 50,000 human beings were made homeless.

'Now the raid moved towards a crescendo,' writes Eric Taylor, who spoke to both English bomber crews and German eyewitnesses present at the destruction of Cologne. 'A flood of humanity poured onto the daylight-bright streets. Women carried tiny children hanging on their arms half asleep. Old people stumbled from their homes with bags and blankets draped around themselves. Determined, swift and silent, the mass of humanity moved forward, their faces showing boundless terror. And then, as quickly as it had filled, the street was empty.

'The skies were filled with lights of all kinds: Searchlight beams, flares, exploding shells, blazing aircraft, and millions on millions of gleaming sparks that floated up from the hundreds of fires all over the city. "It was a terrible sight. And somehow it had something of the grandeur of the twilight of the gods," a woman said later. A building worker who was going past some ruined stables, looked inside and saw a writhing mass of seriously-injured men and horses.

'In Cologne they still tell the story of how a Luftwaffe private was rescued from his girlfriend's house in the Luxemburg Strasse, where he was buried under the rubble. Two men from a rescue squad had dug their way through the rubble to him. But they could not get him out, because his right arm was stuck under a wall from the elbow down, with the whole weight of the house resting on it. A doctor crawled through the tunnel with his bag of instruments, reached the trapped man and amputated his forearm by the light of torch. They brought the unconscious man to the surface, with the stump still covered in dust and rubble.'

Total war in the air had begun, and soon the kind of horrific scenes that had been witnessed in Cologne were to become common almost all over Germany. Churchill congratulated Bomber Harris, who wrote in his memoirs: 'The most decisive of war weapons had finally been used on a massive scale.'

Of the 1046 British bombers, 868 had reached the target. 40 were shot down, 45 seriously damaged, of which twelve broke up on landing. The historian R.C. Mowat writes that 'by the use of terror as a weapon of war, a chapter of barbarism was begun which has never been exceeded in the history of the world, be it by the massacres of Genghis Khan or the destruction of Magdeburg in the Thirty Years' War.'

Goebbels launched unequalled tirades of hatred. The Reich Marshal, who at first had fed Hitler wrong information regarding losses among the civilian population of Cologne, ended up at daggers drawn with the dictator.

From London the BBC broadcast a message to the shattered people of Cologne: 'We are really not filled with glee at the devastation and terror we have had to inflict on Germany. We even experience sincere sympathy for the women and children who are being made to pay for the stupidity of those who brought Hitler to power and have kept him there.

'We are sorry for them. But when we remember Warsaw, Rotterdam, Coventry and Belgrade and imagine how the women, and even the children of Cologne applauded the Luftwaffe's actions, then we harden our hearts. For German women, and even children, should have been sufficiently alert to recognise an evil and put it aside. The women and children of the whole of the rest of Europe stand in the foremost front line of the struggle of justice against injustice.

'We are not motivated by the lust for revenge when we say that the events of last night in Cologne will be repeated elsewhere in Germany, if this means that the suffering of human beings in the countries occupied by Germany from Russia to France can be reduced by this.

'In this case, the end justifies the means. And our end is to bring the martyrdom of humanity to an end as swiftly as possible and to force the German people to experience the truth of the saying: "He who lives by the sword, shall die by the sword".'

Churchill told the House of Commons on June 2nd: 'I can say that as the year goes on, Germany's cities, ports and her centres of war industry will be subjected to a test unequalled in the experience of any other country.'

Dr Josef Goebbels replied over Radio Luxembourg: 'Mr Churchill is invited to continue his attacks with all the fury at his disposal. Time will show who can hold out the longest in this kind of warfare.'

The RAF accepted his cynical invitation. By June 1942, the British had already equalled the amount of damage done by the Luftwaffe. Within a short time after this, the British bomber offensive had begun to show real effects. Squadrons of fighters had to be withdrawn from the East, where they were urgently needed, and pressed into service defending the homeland. Every bomb that fell on Germany served Stalin, who had earlier openly called the English 'cowards'.

The aerial battle over Germany escalated further. The crews who carried out the work of destruction were pushed just as hard by Bomber Harris as their German counterparts had been by Göring in the autumn and winter of 1940 over England - though with the important difference that they were fighting, not for Hitler, but against him.

Bomber Command had few real survivors. For most of them, as Alastair Revie says, it was a matter of '- crashed, incinerated, torn to pieces, drowned, or - if they were lucky - taken prisoner. From a statistical point of view, their death was inevitable. They lived on borrowed time. They wiped the names of their comrades who never came back from the blackboard in the ops room and "drank one for his hide" - knowing that one day the ritual would be applied to them. They were given a few medals and promoted fast, until the day when the letter of condolence would go out to their relatives. Gradually such a fate became inevitable, and everyone would feel a shiver down their spine more often each time. Life increasingly consisted just of eating, drinking, flying and sweating - with fear or whatever. You could do what you liked, but one day it would be your turn. No one, not even the boys who had enjoyed incredible luck so far, bothered to deny it or resist the cold truth, which was that once you'd flown 18 missions, you'd flown one too many . . .

In the screaming headlines that announced the thousand-bomber raid on Cologne and inaugurated a new and grisly chapter in the history of war, the world lost sight of another event which was just as grimly important for Germany's home front as the holocaust on the Rhine. The US Brigadier-General Ira C. Eaker reported his establishment of the first American Bomber HQ in Europe. He arrived in Britain with six staff officers - who would soon be followed by hundreds and thousands of bomber crews - and set up his HQ in a girls' boarding school a few kilometres from High Wycombe.

The first American four-engined bombers to go into action in Europe take off, not from England, but from Egypt. 13 Liberators of the 9th US Air Fleet attack the Romanian oilfields at Ploesti. The oil derricks are covered by thick cloud and the flying fortresses are unable to get back to Egypt because of a shortage of fuel. Six of them crashland in Turkey, where they are interned.

The dress rehearsal had been a failure, but the old theatrical superstition that this means success for the main performance will be justified a thousandfold – and terribly – over Germany in the months and years to come.

The silent prayers at the mass graves of men and women and children tormented, mutilated, burned, crushed and blown apart in their own homes give way to the vulgar blare of the 'Russian fanfare', announcing new victories in the East. Special reports from the East are back again, fortissimo and unceasing. The moving motif from Franz Liszt's *Les Préludes* is misused to stoke up popular determination to 'hold on'. The people of Germany are being asked to prepare for years more of a war that in the opinion of most German commanders is now unwinnable.

The Russians are the first to break the winter stalemate in the spring of 1942. Their attempt to retake Kharkov ends in disaster, but even the Nazi dictator is forced to wait impatiently for the beginning of his summer offensive, forced to admit that with decimated, poorly armed men and no fuel he cannot hope to mount an effective attack.

Herbert Michaelis describes the situation as of March 30th 1942: 'Most of the 162 divisions on active service in the East are reckoned to be usable for defensive purposes at best. Only eight were certified as fully combatworthy for the coming offensive, three of these after reinforcement, and 47 were reckoned capable of limited offensive action. The 16 panzer divisions had a total of only 140 tanks fit for active service – less than the nominal strength of a single panzer division. Nothing could serve to illustrate the full extent of loss and waste during the first year of the war in Russia more vividly. The re-arming of the Army of the East faced great technical difficulties, especially in the case of the panzers. In the Luftwaffe's case, there was a noticeable shortage of experienced crews, as well as bombers and transport aircraft. The damage and the shortages were not quickly remedied. The fuel shortage continued. The confinement of the projected offensive to one section of the front and the postponement of its beginning until the summer of 1942 were both dictated by the reinforcement and supply situations. To strengthen the front – in the cases of Army Group North and Centre, 85 divisions had 2000 miles of front to defend! – four armies raised in satellite states had to be put into action.'

On June 28th, eleven days later than planned, the German summer offensive begins, on the same day as in the Ukraine south of Kharkov the defensive battle against the Soviets ends. 239,306 Russian soldiers are taken prisoner. The Soviets have lost 1249 tanks and 2026 guns and now have to defend themselves against a breakthrough in the area of Kursk, moving towards Bryansk. By July 8th, the Russians have been pushed back in the whole area between the Don and the Donets. Even before this, they had lost 170,000 prisoners, 300 tanks and 1400 guns to General von Manstein's counter-offensive on the Kerch Peninsula. On July 1st, Sebastopol fell, and by the 4th the entire Crimea was in German hands.

On August 3rd, German units reached the Kuban. On 21st, the German flag was raised on Mount Elbrus, the highest peak of the Caucasus. Millions of Germans see it flying at 180,000 feet two thousand miles away, and yet the soldiers who carry out this deed of heroism are already asking what is happening to their families at home. After Mannheim, Rostock, Lübeck and Cologne, the English – who in 1942 alone drop ten times as many bombs on the Reich as the Luftwaffe ever dropped on the British Isles – bomb (with a varying degree of success) Osnabrück, Mainz, Kassel, Nuremburg, Stuttgart, Munich and other cities with high-explosive and incendiary bombs totalling between 246 and 1450 tons.

It is true that rations can be increased from time to time – such as just before Christmas, for example – but the average weight of mineworkers, who receive the highest rations of all civilians, has decreased from 70.1 kilograms to 53.9. Skilled workers are still giving their all for the same wages they received in 1928; they receive 80.2 pfennigs an hour, and their female colleagues only 52.3 pfennigs. The first Hitler Youth boys are decorated for their bravery in air raids, and the new MG 42 can fire 1000 rounds a minute – except that anyone serving in the Army of the East will ask themselves where they're supposed to get that quantity of ammunition from. Six million forced labourers and five million prisoners-of-war are working for an armaments industry that is eating up 68% of the national income.

The advances in Russia continue. The Führer untrammelled commander of the German Wehrmacht, is in the process of ignoring his generals and repeating all the mistakes of the previous year – only more so. As if there was no prospect of a winter in 1942/43; as if the supply lines were not twice as long as they had been in the previous winter, which the army had survived only after the most terrible sacrifices. As early as August 1942, the German casualties in the summer offensive totalled 336,000 dead, more than 1.2 million wounded, and some 80,000 posted missing; a total of a million and a half soldiers, including 47,966 officers.

The Wehrmacht is spread between the Arctic Ocean and the Caucasus; bomber squadrons attached to the Luftwaffe and U-boats operate from bases in the north of Norway, inflicting devastating losses on the Murmansk convoys carrying Allied supplies to Soviet Russia. Every other freighter – loaded with American tanks and aircraft and in the custody of British sailors – ends up at the bottom of the icy sea.

A typical example is convoy PQ 17, one of the greatest catastrophes suffered by the Royal Navy in World War Two. Acting on a false report that the *Tirpitz* has broken out of harbour, the Admiralty orders the warships escorting the convoy back to port and leaves 36 cargo ships and four trawlers alone. German reconnaissance planes at first lose touch, but on July 4th a lone aircraft breaks through the cloud cover and sinks the first of the freighters. Then torpedo planes attack; finally Ju 88s and Heinekel 111s, get their turn. Split apart by the force of the German attack, the merchant ships try to escape by zigzagging, and some hit pack ice. The route through the Arctic Ocean becames a death-zone.

'Not a successful convoy,' Commodore Dowling reported to the Admiralty. 'This opinion has become one of the most celebrated British understatements,' writes Günter Karweina in his book *Convoy PQ 17*. 'Of the 35 freighters that left Iceland for the Soviet Union on June 27th 1942, only eleven reached their port of destination, Archangel. Two were forced to turn back shortly after leaving Iceland because of structural damage, 22 were sunk. Besides them, the rescue ship *Zaarfaran* and the naval tanker *Aldersdale* were also lost.'

'Along with the ships of PQ 17 were also lost: 3350 trucks and jeeps, 430 panzers, 210 aircraft, 99,316 tons of spares, food, armour plating, munitions etc.'

And the advance in the East continues. On October 3rd, the German forces operating in the Eastern Caucasus force their way south of the Terek and enter Alagir, thus cutting the

Russians' main line of communication in the Central Mountain Range – but on July 12th Stalin had already given the order that the Stalingrad front was to be held at all costs against his Nazi counterpart's furious efforts.

In his speech of November 8th 1942 – in memory of the 1923 coup attempt in Munich – Hitler says: 'I intend to reach the Volga, and at a certain point. Coincidentally, it bears the name of Stalin himself. But don't tell yourselves that this was my only reason for wanting to go there . . . for, in fact, it is a very important place. There, to be specific, we can cut off a waterway that carries 30 million tons of traffic . . . there is a gigantic centre for trade and exchange. I wanted to take it, and – as you can see – we're true to our word: we've got it!'

Ten days later, the Red Army moves onto the offensive against Stalingrad.

On November 25th an operation begins to supply the German 6th Army in Stalingrad from the air. Instead of the 950 tons daily promised by the Reich Marshal, he is able to supply only 300 tons, even though he throws all his resources into the struggle.

The 6th Army, – 300,000 strong at the beginning of the offensive – is now sitting in the jaws of a trap, threatened by cold, starvation and an overwhelming Soviet superiority.

Chronology

1940

25.6.40 Armistice in France.

19.7.40 Hitler's speech to the Reichstag with 'peace offer' to England.

21.7.40 The Commander-in-Chief of the Army receives orders from Hitler to prepare an operational plan for the Eastern Campaign.

30.7.40 A special Defence Economy Staff for England is created.

31.7.40 Hitler names September 15th as the date for 'Operation Sea Lion'.

1.8.40 Order no. 17: Hitler instructs the Wehrmacht to conduct intensified air and sea war against England.

13.8.40 'Eagle Day', the disastrous beginning to the air offensive against Britain, involves 2875 bombers, 3116 Stukas, 702 fighters and 227 fighter-bombers (the statistic is increased by the fact that many aircraft went into action more than once).

15.8.40 Bombers from Air Fleets 2, 3 and 5 fly 2119 missions against targets in Southern England.

25.8.40 The British Bomber Command attacks Berlin with 81 aircraft with minimal success.

3.9.40 Hitler names 21.9. as the new date for 'Operation Sea Lion'.

5/6.9.40 Heavy night raids on London by German bombers.

7.9.40 The 'Blitz' begins, a 65-day bombardment of British cities, portrayed by the Nazi propaganda machine as a revenge operation.

15.9.40 The 'Battle of Britain' day, in which 56 German and 26 British aircraft are shot down.

18.9.40 The Italian offensive against Egypt grinds to a halt at Sidi El Barrani.

12.10.40	Hitler postpones 'Operation Sea Lion' until the beginning of 1941, and thus consigns it to the waste-paper basket.
28.10.40	Beginning of the Italian invasion of Greece from Albania.
5.11.40	Franklin Delano Roosevelt is elected President of the United States for the third time by an overwhelming majority.
12.11.40	Hitler issues Order no. 18: the preparation of an attack on the Greek mainland from Bulgaria.
14/15.11.40	449 German aircraft attack Coventry. Prime Minister Churchill was warned of the raid in time by the 'Enigma' but decided not to warn the city; it suffers 554 dead and 865 seriously injured.
29.11.40	First war game to test 'Operation Barbarossa' led by General Paulus, later the defender of Stalingrad.
1/31.12.40	German U-boats report the sinking 39 Allied merchant ships with a total net tonnage of 229,500 NRT.

1941

29.1.41	Anglo-American General Staff talks regarding joint operations in the case of American entry into the war.
31.1.41	Troop assembly plan for 'Operation Barbarossa' completed.
12.2.41	General Erwin Rommel arrives in North Africa.
24.3.41	The German Afrika Korps captures El Agheila.
26/29.3.41	Naval battle at Matapan. The British sink two Italian heavy cruisers, two destroyers and damage the battleship *Vittorio Veneto*.
2.4.41	Rommel takes Agedabia and begins his offensive.
4.4.41	The Afrika Korps takes Benghazi.
6.4.41	Beginning of the campaigns against Yugoslavia and Greece.
11.4.41	Rommel's troops enter the port of Bardia.
17.4.41	Churchill gives permission for the evacuation of British troops from Greece.
30.4.41	The second German assault on Tobruk fails.

15/17.5.41 British thrust towards Solum fails.

18.5.41 The heavy cruiser *Prinz Eugen* and the battleship *Bismarck* break out of port in 'Operation Rheinübung'.

20/31.5.41 Victorious course of the airborne operation against Crete; German casualties: 4000 dead and missing, 2580 wounded; 151 Ju 52s are shot down.

24.5.41 The British battleship *Hood* is sunk by the *Bismarck*.

27.5.41 Sinking of the crippled *Bismarck* after a desperate battle.
The German Afrika Korps recaptures the Halfiya Pass on the Egyptian-Libyan border.

13.6.41 The Soviet newsagency TASS denies reports of German troops massing on the German-Soviet Demarcation Line.

22.6.41 Start of 'Operation Barbarossa', without declaration of war. Air raids on Kiev, Kovno, Sebastopol, Shitomir, Murmansk, Odessa and other cities. The advance continues at a rate of up to 100 kilometres per day.

2/20.10.41 Double battle at Vyasma and Bryansk.

3.10.41 Hitler declares as he initiates the Winter Aid Fund that 'this enemy has already been broken and will never rise again'.

15/17.11.41 The muddy season in Russia is prematurely brought to an end by the onset of freezing temperatures. Hitler begins the second phase of the battle for Moscow.

18.11.41 Beginning of the British counter-offensive in North Africa aiming at relief of Tobruk.

5.12.41 Final failure of the German attack on Moscow.

6.12.41 Soviet General Zhukov begins his counter-offensive, using winter-hardened Siberian troops.

7.12.41 The Japanese attack Pearl Harbor.
Rommel lifts his siege of Tobruk and withdraws to the Gazala Line.

8.12.41 Hitler allows a withdrawal to west of Moscow on defensive grounds.

11.12.41 Germany and Italy declare war on the USA.

23.12.41 The German Afrika Korps evacuates Benghazi.

1942

9.1.42 Soviet offensive on the Valdai Heights, in the course of which six German divisions are surrounded in Demyansk and have to be supplied from the air.

21.1.42 Rommel begins his counter-attack for the reconquest of Cyrenaica.

7.2.42 The Afrika Korps' counter-offensive comes to a halt west of Tobruk.

12.2.42 'Operation Cerberus': the *Scharnhorst*, *Prinz Eugen* and *Gneisenau*, with an escort of other German naval vessels, make a dash through the Channel under the protection of a German air operation.

14.4.42 The British and the Americans agree to a landing in French North Africa.

18.4.42 End of the winter battles in Russia with arrival of the mud.

21.5.42 Hitler postpones the invasion of Malta indefinitely.

10.6.42 Panzer Army Africa captures the fort at Bir Hacheim

21.6.42 Tobruk falls: Rommel is promoted to Field Marshal

25.6.42 General Auchinleck is appointed Allied Commander-in-Chief in the Middle East.

28.6.42 Beginning of 'Case Blue', the 1942 German summe offensive in the East, which leads to the conquest o huge areas of Southern Russia and ends in th catastrophe of Stalingrad.

3.7.42 After three days, Rommel gives up his attempt t break through the British defences at El Alamei and goes on the defensive.

13.8.42 General Alexander replaces General Auchinleck a British commander in the Middle East. Gener Montgomery takes over the British 8th Army.

31.8.42 Rommel begins his last offensive, which he is force to abandon three days later.

15/16/10.42 1000 British bombers attack Cologne.

23.10.42 General Montgomery sets in motion the Britis counter-attack at El Alamein that spells the end f Rommel.